2008
Yearbook of
Astronomy

2008
Yearbook of
Astronomy

edited by
Patrick Moore

co-editor
John Mason

MACMILLAN

First published 2007 by Macmillan
an imprint of Pan Macmillan Ltd
Pan Macmillan, 20 New Wharf Road, London N1 9RR
Basingstoke and Oxford
Associated companies throughout the world
www.panmacmillan.com

ISBN 978-0-230-70066-6

9 8 7 6 5 4 3 2 1

A CIP catalogue record for this book is available from
the British Library.

Typeset by Rowland Phototypesetting Ltd,
Bury St Edmunds, Suffolk
Printed and bound in Great Britain by
Mackays of Chatham, Chatham, Kent

Visit **www.panmacmillan.com** to read more about all
our books and to buy them. You will also find features,
author interviews and news of any author events, and
you can sign up for e-newsletters so that you're always
first to hear about our new releases.

Contents

Part III
Miscellaneous

Editors' Foreword

The *2008 Yearbook* follows the long-established pattern. The articles section includes contributions both from our regular authors and from some very welcome newcomers. As usual, we have done our best to give you a wide range, both of subject and of technical level. For example, Martin Mobberley looks back at one of the highlights of early 2007: the great comet C/2006 P1 (McNaught), which was truly spectacular; Fred Watson examines one of the most important events in the entire history of astronomy, the invention of the telescope in 1608; and Iain Nicolson explores a great conundrum of modern cosmology: dark energy and the accelerating universe. As always, Gordon Taylor has provided the material for the monthly notes, and John Isles and Bob Argyle have provided the information on variable stars and double stars respectively.

PATRICK MOORE
JOHN MASON
Selsey, August 2007

Preface

New readers will find that all the information in this *Yearbook* is given in diagrammatic or descriptive form; the positions of the planets may easily be found from the specially designed star charts, while the monthly notes describe the movements of the planets and give details of other astronomical phenomena visible in both the Northern and the Southern Hemispheres. Two sets of star charts are provided. The **Northern Charts** (pp. 17 to 41) are designed for use at latitude 52°N, but may be used without alteration throughout the British Isles, and (except in the case of eclipses and occultations) in other countries of similar northerly latitude. The **Southern Charts** (pp. 43 to 67) are drawn for latitude 35°S, and are suitable for use in South Africa, Australia and New Zealand, and other locations in approximately the same southerly latitude. The reader who needs more detailed information will find *Norton's Star Atlas* an invaluable guide, while more precise positions of the planets and their satellites, together with predictions of occultations, meteor showers and periodic comets, may be found in the *Handbook* of the British Astronomical Association. Readers will also find details of forthcoming events given in the American monthly magazine *Sky & Telescope* and the British periodicals *The Sky at Night*, *Astronomy Now* and *Astronomy and Space*.

Important note

The times given on the star charts and in the Monthly Notes are generally given as local times, using the 24-hour clock, the day beginning at midnight. All the dates, and the times of a few events (e.g. eclipses), are given in Greenwich Mean Time (GMT), which is related to local time by the formula

Local Mean Time = GMT − west longitude

In practice, small differences in longitude are ignored, and the observer will use local clock time, which will be the appropriate Standard (or Zone) Time. As the formula indicates, places in west longitude will have a Standard Time slow on GMT, while places in east longitude will have a Standard Time fast on GMT. As examples we have:

Standard Time in

New Zealand	GMT + 12 hours
Victoria, NSW	GMT + 10 hours
Western Australia	GMT + 8 hours
South Africa	GMT + 2 hours
British Isles	GMT
Eastern ST	GMT − 5 hours
Central ST	GMT − 6 hours, etc.

If Summer Time is in use, the clocks will have been advanced by one hour, and this hour must be subtracted from the clock time to give Standard Time.

Part I

Monthly Charts and Astronomical Phenomena

Notes on the Star Charts

The stars, together with the Sun, Moon and planets, seem to be set on the surface of the celestial sphere, which appears to rotate about the Earth from east to west. Since it is impossible to represent a curved surface accurately on a plane, any kind of star map is bound to contain some form of distortion.

Most of the monthly star charts that appear in the various journals and some national newspapers are drawn in circular form. This is perfectly accurate, but it can make the charts awkward to use. For the star charts in this volume, we have preferred to give two hemispherical maps for each month of the year, one showing the northern aspect of the sky and the other showing the southern aspect. Two sets of monthly charts are provided, one for observers in the Northern Hemisphere and one for those in the Southern Hemisphere.

Unfortunately, the constellations near the overhead point (the zenith) on these hemispherical charts can be rather distorted. This would be a serious drawback for precision charts, but what we have done is to give maps that are best suited to star recognition. We have also refrained from putting in too many stars, so that the main patterns stand out clearly. To help observers with any distortions near the zenith, and the lack of overlap between the charts of each pair, we have also included two circular maps, one showing all the constellations in the northern half of the sky, and one those in the southern half. Incidentally, there is a curious illusion that stars at an altitude of 60° or more are actually overhead, and beginners may often feel that they are leaning over backwards in trying to see them.

The charts show all stars down to the fourth magnitude, together with a number of fainter stars that are necessary to define the shapes of constellations. There is no standard system for representing the outlines of the constellations, and triangles and other simple figures have been used to give outlines that are easy to trace with the naked eye. The names of the constellations are given, together with the proper names of the brighter stars. The apparent magnitudes of the stars are indicated roughly by using different sizes of dot, the larger dots representing the brighter stars.

The two sets of star charts – one each for Northern and Southern Hemisphere observers – are similar in design. At each opening there is a single circular chart that shows all the constellations in that hemisphere of the sky. (These two charts are centred on the North and South Celestial Poles respectively.) Then there are twelve double-page spreads, showing the northern and southern aspects for each month of the year for observers in that hemisphere. In the **Northern Charts** (drawn for latitude 52°N) the left-hand chart of each spread shows the northern half of the sky (lettered 1N, 2N, 3N ... 12N), and the corresponding right-hand chart shows the southern half of the sky (lettered 1S, 2S, 3S ... 12S). The arrangement and lettering of the charts is exactly the same for the **Southern Charts** (drawn for latitude 35°S).

Because the sidereal day is shorter than the solar day, the stars appear to rise and set about four minutes earlier each day, and this amounts to two hours in a month. Hence the twelve pairs of charts in each set are sufficient to give the appearance of the sky throughout the day at intervals of two hours, or at the same time of night at monthly intervals throughout the year. For example, charts 1N and 1S here are drawn for 23 hours on 6 January. The view will also be the same on 6 October at 05 hours; 6 November at 03 hours; 6 December at 01 hours and 6 February at 21 hours. The actual range of dates and times when the stars on the charts are visible is indicated on each page. Each pair of charts is numbered in bold type, and the number to be used for any given month and time may be found from the following table:

Local Time	18h	20h	22h	0h	2h	4h	6h
January	11	12	1	2	3	4	5
February	12	1	2	3	4	5	6
March	1	2	3	4	5	6	7
April	2	3	4	5	6	7	8
May	3	4	5	6	7	8	9
June	4	5	6	7	8	9	10
July	5	6	7	8	9	10	11
August	6	7	8	9	10	11	12
September	7	8	9	10	11	12	1

Local Time	18h	20h	22h	0h	2h	4h	6h
October	8	9	10	11	12	1	2
November	9	10	11	12	1	2	3
December	10	11	12	1	2	3	4

On these charts, the ecliptic is drawn as a broken line on which longitude is marked every 10°. The positions of the planets are then easily found by reference to the table on p. 74. It will be noticed that on the **Southern Charts** the ecliptic may reach an altitude in excess of 62.5° on the star charts showing the northern aspect (5N to 9N). The continuations of the broken line will be found on the corresponding charts for the southern aspect (5S, 6S, 8S and 9S).

Northern Star Charts

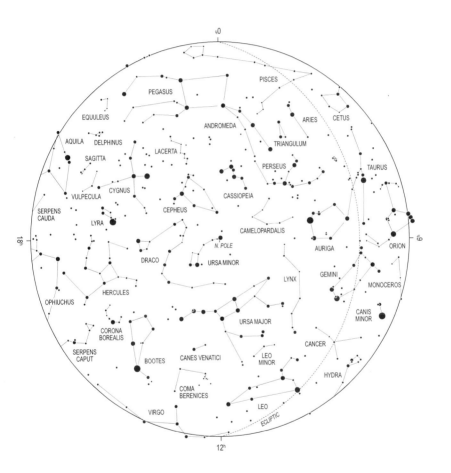

Northern Hemisphere

Note that the markers at 0^h, 6^h, 12^h and 18^h
indicate hours of Right Ascension.

1N

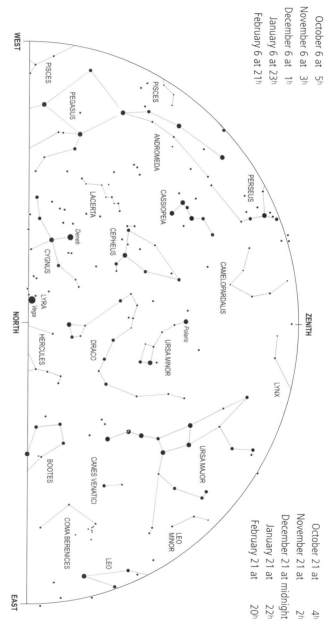

October 6 at 5h
November 6 at 3h
December 6 at 1h
January 6 at 23h
February 6 at 21h

WEST

PISCES

PEGASUS

PISCES

ANDROMEDA

LACERTA

CASSIOPEIA

PERSEUS

CEPHEUS

Deneb

CYGNUS

CAMELOPARDALIS

LYRA

Vega

NORTH

Polaris

HERCULES

DRACO

URSA MINOR

ZENITH

LYNX

BOOTES

CANES VENATICI

URSA MAJOR

COMA BERENICES

LEO MINOR

LEO

EAST

October 21 at 4h
November 21 at 2h
December 21 at midnight
January 21 at 22h
February 21 at 20h

1S

October 21 at 4h
November 21 at 2h
December 21 at midnight
January 21 at 22h
February 21 at 20h

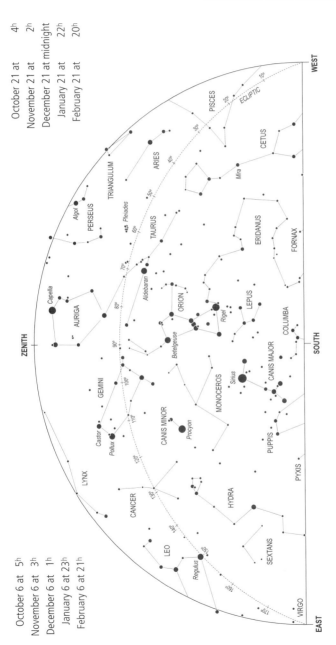

October 6 at 5h
November 6 at 3h
December 6 at 1h
January 6 at 23h
February 6 at 21h

2N

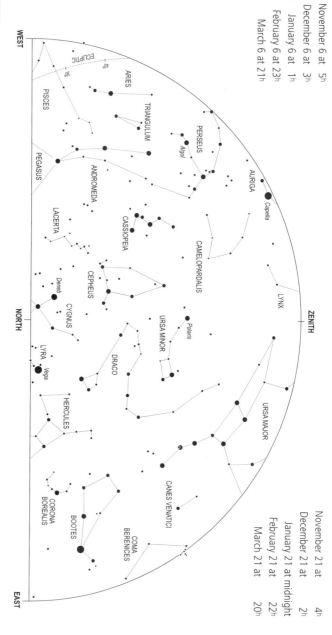

November 6 at 5h
December 6 at 3h
January 6 at 1h
February 6 at 23h
March 6 at 21h

November 21 at 4h
December 21 at 2h
January 21 at midnight
February 21 at 22h
March 21 at 20h

2S

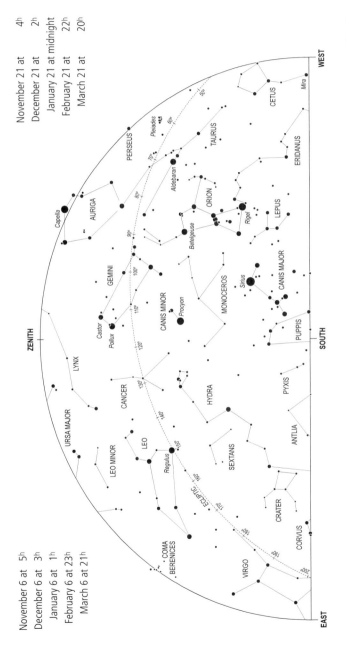

WEST

ZENITH

SOUTH

EAST

CETUS
Mira
PERSEUS
Pleiades
TAURUS
ERIDANUS
Aldebaran
ORION
AURIGA
Capella
Rigel
LEPUS
Betelgeuse
GEMINI
CANIS MAJOR
Sirius
MONOCEROS
CANIS MINOR
Procyon
Castor
Pollux
PUPPIS
LYNX
CANCER
HYDRA
PYXIS
URSA MAJOR
LEO MINOR
LEO
Regulus
ANTLIA
SEXTANS
COMA BERENICES
CRATER
ECLIPTIC
VIRGO
CORVUS

50°
60°
70°
80°
90°
100°
110°
120°
130°
140°
150°
160°
170°
180°
190°
200°

3N

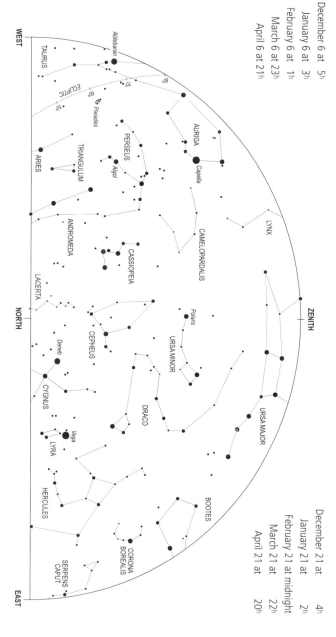

December 6 at 5h
January 6 at 3h
February 6 at 1h
March 6 at 23h
April 6 at 21h

December 21 at 4h
January 21 at 2h
February 21 at midnight
March 21 at 22h
April 21 at 20h

WEST

TAURUS
Aldebaran
ECLIPTIC
Pleiades
PERSEUS
AURIGA
Capella
TRIANGULUM
Algol
ARIES
LYNX
ANDROMEDA
CAMELOPARDALIS
CASSIOPEIA
LACERTA
ZENITH
NORTH
CEPHEUS
Polaris
URSA MINOR
Deneb
URSA MAJOR
CYGNUS
DRACO
Vega
LYRA
BOOTES
HERCULES
CORONA BOREALIS
SERPENS CAPUT
EAST

3S

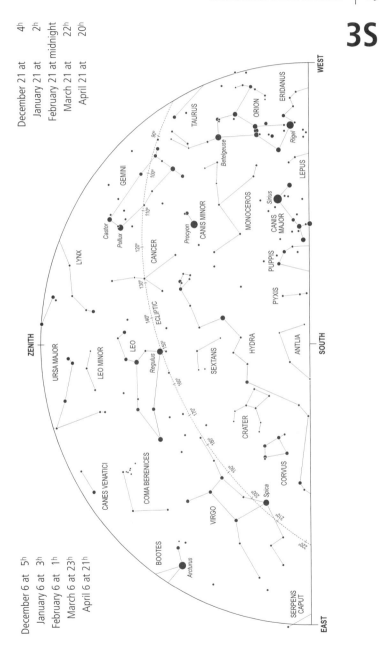

December 21 at   4ʰ
January 21 at   2ʰ
February 21 at midnight
March 21 at   22ʰ
April 21 at   20ʰ

December 6 at   5ʰ
January 6 at   3ʰ
February 6 at   1ʰ
March 6 at 23ʰ
April 6 at 21ʰ

4N

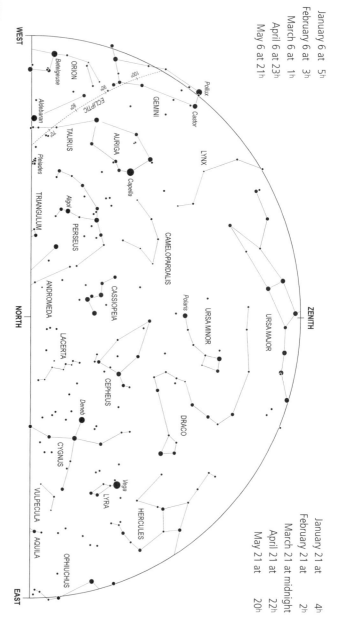

January 6 at 5h
February 6 at 3h
March 6 at 1h
April 6 at 23h
May 6 at 21h

January 21 at 4h
February 21 at 2h
March 21 at midnight
April 21 at 22h
May 21 at 20h

WEST

ORION
Betelgeuse
GEMINI
Pollux
Castor
Aldebaran
TAURUS
AURIGA
LYNX
Pleiades
Capella
ECLIPTIC
Algol
PERSEUS
TRIANGULUM
CAMELOPARDALIS
ANDROMEDA
CASSIOPEIA
Polaris
URSA MINOR
URSA MAJOR
ZENITH
LACERTA
CEPHEUS
DRACO
Deneb
CYGNUS
Vega
LYRA
HERCULES
VULPECULA
AQUILA
OPHIUCHUS

NORTH

EAST

4S

January 21 at 4ʰ
February 21 at 2ʰ
March 21 at midnight
April 21 at 22ʰ
May 21 at 20ʰ

January 6 at 5ʰ
February 6 at 3ʰ
March 6 at 1ʰ
April 6 at 23ʰ
May 6 at 21ʰ

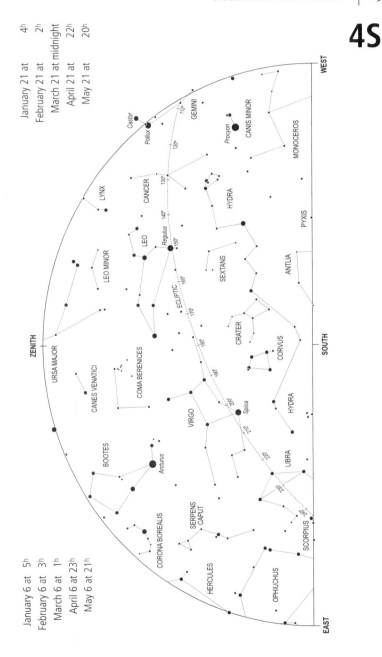

WEST

ZENITH

SOUTH

EAST

Castor
Pollux
GEMINI
Procyon
CANIS MINOR
MONOCEROS
LYNX
CANCER
HYDRA
PYXIS
LEO
LEO MINOR
Regulus
ECLIPTIC
SEXTANS
ANTLIA
URSA MAJOR
CANES VENATICI
COMA BERENICES
CRATER
CORVUS
HYDRA
BOOTES
Arcturus
VIRGO
Spica
LIBRA
CORONA BOREALIS
SERPENS CAPUT
SCORPIUS
HERCULES
OPHIUCHUS

110°
120°
130°
140°
150°
160°
170°
180°
190°
200°
210°
220°
230°
240°

5N

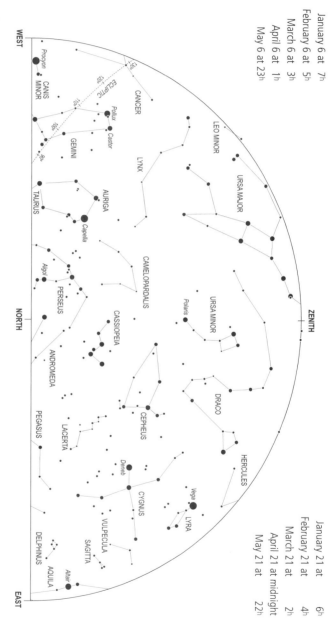

January 6 at 7h
February 6 at 5h
March 6 at 3h
April 6 at 1h
May 6 at 23h

January 21 at 6h
February 21 at 4h
March 21 at 2h
April 21 at midnight
May 21 at 22h

5S

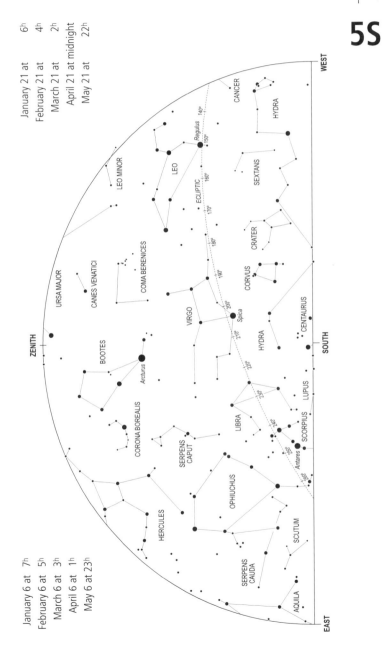

WEST

ZENITH

SOUTH

EAST

CANCER
HYDRA
LEO MINOR
LEO
Regulus
ECLIPTIC
SEXTANS
CANES VENATICI
COMA BERENICES
URSA MAJOR
CRATER
CORVUS
VIRGO
Spica
HYDRA
CENTAURUS
BOOTES
Arcturus
CORONA BOREALIS
LIBRA
LUPUS
SERPENS CAPUT
SCORPIUS
Antares
OPHIUCHUS
HERCULES
SCUTUM
SERPENS CAUDA
AQUILA

140°
150°
160°
170°
180°
190°
200°
210°
220°
230°
240°
250°
260°

6N

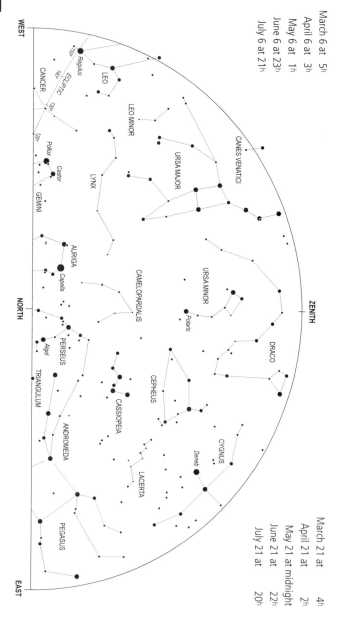

March 6 at 5h
April 6 at 3h
May 6 at 1h
June 6 at 23h
July 6 at 21h

WEST

NORTH

EAST

ZENITH

March 21 at 4h
April 21 at 2h
May 21 at midnight
June 21 at 22h
July 21 at 20h

CANCER
ECLIPTIC
Regulus
LEO
LEO MINOR
Pollux
Castor
GEMINI
LYNX
URSA MAJOR
CANES VENATICI
AURIGA
Capella
CAMELOPARDALIS
URSA MINOR
Polaris
DRACO
PERSEUS
Algol
CEPHEUS
TRIANGULUM
CASSIOPEIA
ANDROMEDA
CYGNUS
Deneb
LACERTA
PEGASUS

6S

March 21 at 4ʰ
April 21 at 2ʰ
May 21 at midnight
June 21 at 22ʰ
July 21 at 20ʰ

March 6 at 5ʰ
April 6 at 3ʰ
May 6 at 1ʰ
June 6 at 23ʰ
July 6 at 21ʰ

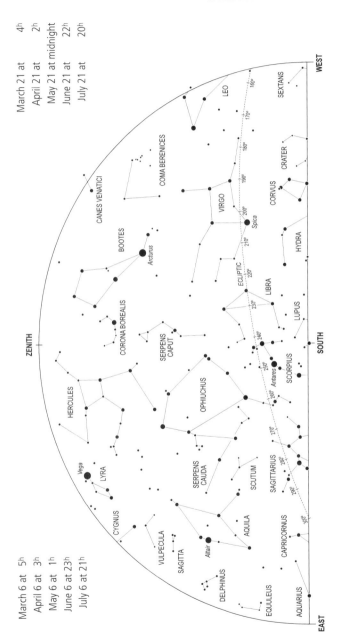

ZENITH

WEST

SOUTH

EAST

LEO
SEXTANS
COMA BERENICES
CRATER
CANES VENATICI
CORVUS
VIRGO
Spica
BOOTES
Arcturus
HYDRA
ECLIPTIC
LIBRA
CORONA BOREALIS
LUPUS
SERPENS CAPUT
SCORPIUS
Antares
HERCULES
OPHIUCHUS
Vega
LYRA
SERPENS CAUDA
SCUTUM
SAGITTARIUS
CYGNUS
VULPECULA
AQUILA
SAGITTA
Altair
CAPRICORNUS
DELPHINUS
EQUULEUS
AQUARIUS

7N

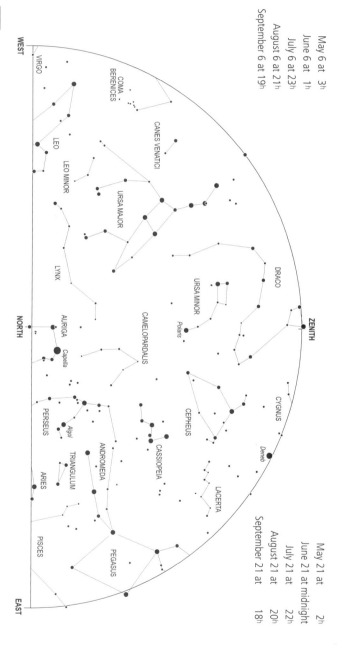

May 6 at 3h
June 6 at 1h
July 6 at 23h
August 6 at 21h
September 6 at 19h

WEST

VIRGO

COMA BERENICES

CANES VENATICI

LEO

LEO MINOR

URSA MAJOR

DRACO

LYNX

URSA MINOR

Polaris

ZENITH

CYGNUS

AURIGA

CAMELOPARDALIS

NORTH

Capella

Deneb

PERSEUS

Algol

CEPHEUS

TRIANGULUM

ANDROMEDA

CASSIOPEIA

ARIES

LACERTA

PISCES

PEGASUS

EAST

May 21 at 2h
June 21 at midnight
July 21 at 22h
August 21 at 20h
September 21 at 18h

May 21 at 2ʰ
June 21 at midnight
July 21 at 22ʰ
August 21 at 20ʰ
September 21 at 18ʰ

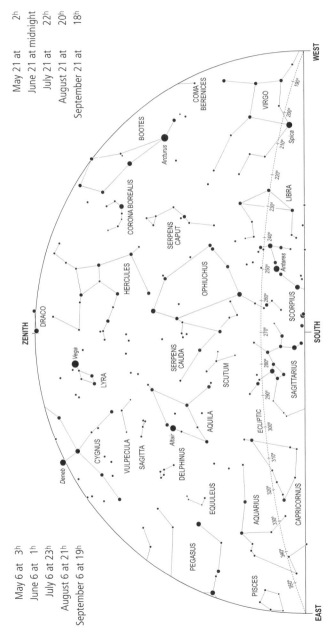

May 6 at 3ʰ
June 6 at 1ʰ
July 6 at 23ʰ
August 6 at 21ʰ
September 6 at 19ʰ

8N

July 6 at 1h
August 6 at 23h
September 6 at 21h
October 6 at 19h
November 6 at 17h

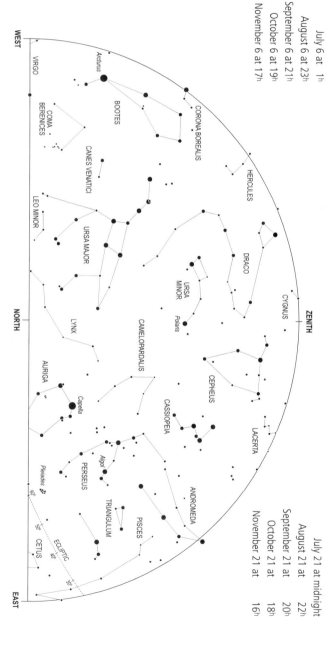

WEST

VIRGO

Arcturus

BOOTES

COMA
BERENICES

CORONA BOREALIS

CANES VENATICI

HERCULES

LEO MINOR

URSA MAJOR

DRACO

URSA
MINOR

Polaris

CYGNUS

ZENITH

NORTH

LYNX

CAMELOPARDALIS

CEPHEUS

AURIGA

Capella

CASSIOPEIA

LACERTA

Algol

PERSEUS

Pleiades

60°

50°

ECLIPTIC
40°

CETUS

30°

TRIANGULUM

ANDROMEDA

PISCES

EAST

July 21 at midnight
August 21 at 22h
September 21 at 20h
October 21 at 18h
November 21 at 16h

8S

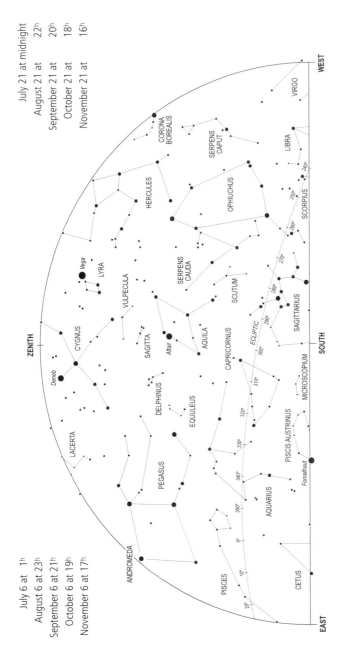

WEST

VIRGO

CORONA BOREALIS

SERPENS CAPUT

LIBRA

HERCULES

OPHIUCHUS

240°

250°

260°

SCORPIUS

ZENITH

Vega

LYRA

VULPECULA

SERPENS CAUDA

270°

CYGNUS

Deneb

SAGITTA

Altair

SCUTUM

280°

AQUILA

SAGITTARIUS

290°

ECLIPTIC

DELPHINUS

CAPRICORNUS

300°

SOUTH

LACERTA

EQUULEUS

310°

MICROSCOPIUM

PEGASUS

320°

330°

PISCIS AUSTRINUS

340°

Formalhaut

ANDROMEDA

350°

AQUARIUS

0°

PISCES

10°

CETUS

20°

EAST

9N

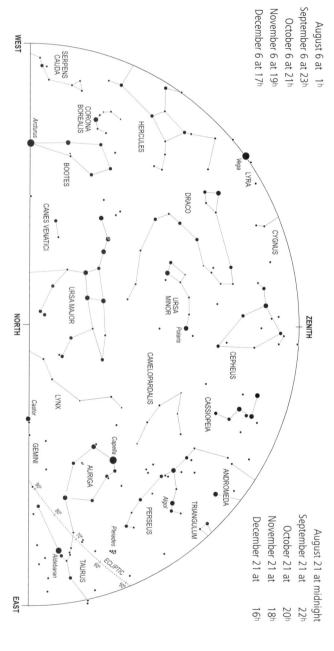

August 6 at 1h
September 6 at 23h
October 6 at 21h
November 6 at 19h
December 6 at 17h

August 21 at midnight
September 21 at 22h
October 21 at 20h
November 21 at 18h
December 21 at 16h

WEST

SERPENS
CAUDA

CORONA
BOREALIS

Arcturus

HERCULES

BOOTES

Vega

LYRA

CYGNUS

CANES VENATICI

DRACO

URSA
MINOR

Polaris

CEPHEUS

ZENITH

URSA MAJOR

NORTH

CAMELOPARDALIS

CASSIOPEIA

LYNX

Castor

GEMINI

Capella

AURIGA

ANDROMEDA

Algol

TRIANGULUM

PERSEUS

Pleiades

90°

80°

70°

Aldebaran

TAURUS

ECLIPTIC

50°

EAST

9S

August 21 at midnight
September 21 at 22ʰ
October 21 at 20ʰ
November 21 at 18ʰ
December 21 at 16ʰ

August 6 at 1ʰ
September 6 at 23ʰ
October 6 at 21ʰ
November 6 at 19ʰ
December 6 at 17ʰ

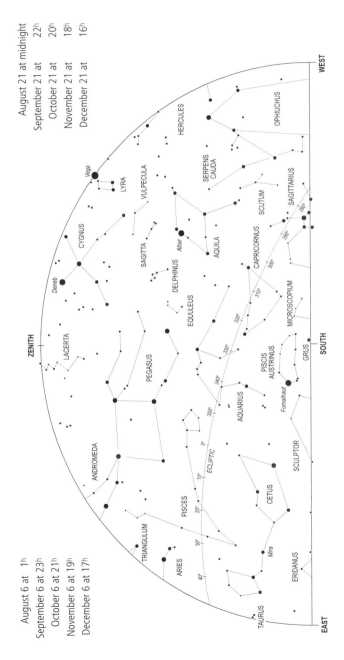

WEST

HERCULES

OPHIUCHUS

SERPENS CAUDA

Vega

LYRA

VULPECULA

CYGNUS

SCUTUM

SAGITTARIUS

Deneb

SAGITTA

Altair

AQUILA

CAPRICORNUS

280°

290°

300°

DELPHINUS

EQUULEUS

310°

MICROSCOPIUM

ZENITH

LACERTA

320°

PEGASUS

330°

PISCIS AUSTRINUS

GRUS

SOUTH

340°

AQUARIUS

Fomalhaut

350°

ANDROMEDA

0°

ECLIPTIC

10°

SCULPTOR

PISCES

20°

CETUS

TRIANGULUM

30°

Mira

40°

ARIES

ERIDANUS

TAURUS

EAST

10N

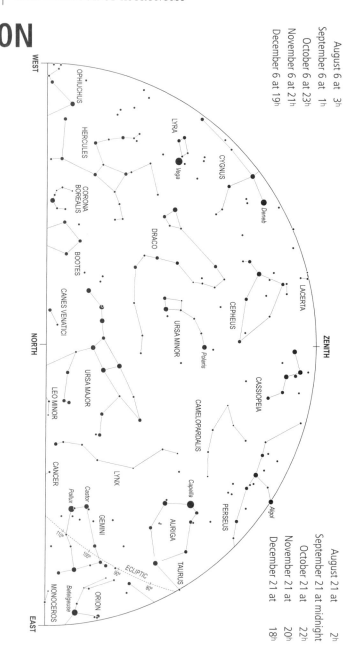

August 6 at 3h
September 6 at 1h
October 6 at 23h
November 6 at 21h
December 6 at 19h

August 21 at 2h
September 21 at midnight
October 21 at 22h
November 21 at 20h
December 21 at 18h

WEST

NORTH

EAST

ZENITH

OPHIUCHUS
HERCULES
LYRA
Vega
CYGNUS
Deneb
CORONA BOREALIS
BOOTES
DRACO
CEPHEUS
LACERTA
CANES VENATICI
URSA MINOR
Polaris
CASSIOPEIA
URSA MAJOR
LEO MINOR
CAMELOPARDALIS
PERSEUS
Algol
CANCER
LYNX
Capella
AURIGA
Pollux
Castor
GEMINI
TAURUS
ECLIPTIC
110°
100°
90°
80°
MONOCEROS
Betelgeuse
ORION

10S

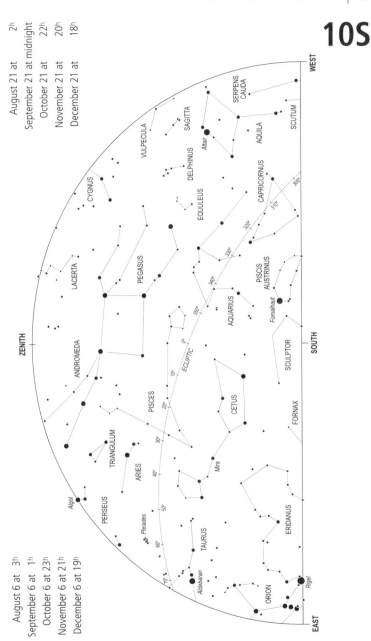

August 21 at 2ʰ
September 21 at midnight
October 21 at 22ʰ
November 21 at 20ʰ
December 21 at 18ʰ

August 6 at 3ʰ
September 6 at 1ʰ
October 6 at 23ʰ
November 6 at 21ʰ
December 6 at 19ʰ

WEST

ZENITH

SOUTH

EAST

SERPENS
CAUDA

SAGITTA

SCUTUM

VULPECULA

AQUILA

Altair

DELPHINUS

CYGNUS

CAPRICORNUS

EQUULEUS

300°

310°

320°

LACERTA

PEGASUS

330°

PISCIS
AUSTRINUS

340°

ANDROMEDA

AQUARIUS

Fomalhaut

350°

ECLIPTIC

0°

PISCES

SCULPTOR

10°

TRIANGULUM

20°

CETUS

FORNAX

ARIES

30°

Mira

PERSEUS

40°

Algol

Pleiades

50°

ERIDANUS

60°

TAURUS

ORION

70°

Aldebaran

Rigel

11N

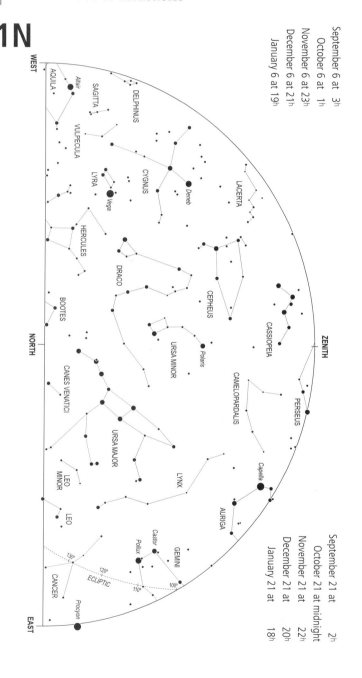

September 6 at 3ʰ
October 6 at 1ʰ
November 6 at 23ʰ
December 6 at 21ʰ
January 6 at 19ʰ

September 21 at 2ʰ
October 21 at midnight
November 21 at 22ʰ
December 21 at 20ʰ
January 21 at 18ʰ

WEST

AQUILA
Altair
SAGITTA
DELPHINUS
VULPECULA
LYRA
Vega
CYGNUS
Deneb
LACERTA
HERCULES
DRACO
CEPHEUS
CASSIOPEIA
BOOTES
URSA MINOR
Polaris
CAMELOPARDALIS
PERSEUS

NORTH

ZENITH

CANES VENATICI
URSA MAJOR
LYNX
Capella
LEO MINOR
LEO
AURIGA
Castor
Pollux
GEMINI
130°
120°
110°
100°
ECLIPTIC
CANCER
Procyon

EAST

11S

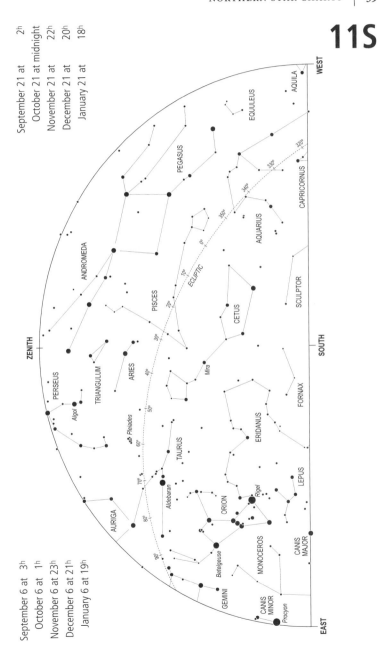

September 6 at   3ʰ
October 6 at   1ʰ
November 6 at 23ʰ
December 6 at 21ʰ
January 6 at 19ʰ

ZENITH

WEST

AQUILA

EQUULEUS

PEGASUS

ANDROMEDA

CAPRICORNUS

AQUARIUS

PISCES

ECLIPTIC

CETUS

SCULPTOR

SOUTH

Mira

PERSEUS

Algol

TRIANGULUM

ARIES

FORNAX

Pleiades

TAURUS

ERIDANUS

AURIGA

Aldebaran

ORION

Rigel

LEPUS

Betelgeuse

MONOCEROS

CANIS MAJOR

GEMINI

CANIS MINOR

Procyon

EAST

320°
330°
340°
350°
0°
10°
20°
30°
40°
50°
60°
70°
80°
90°

12N

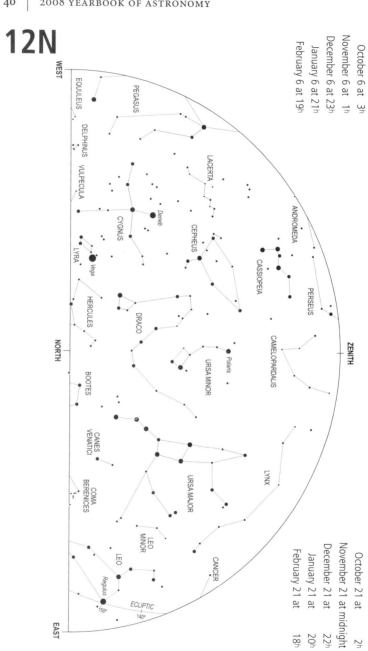

October 6 at 3h
November 6 at 1h
December 6 at 23h
January 6 at 21h
February 6 at 19h

October 21 at 2h
November 21 at midnight
December 21 at 22h
January 21 at 20h
February 21 at 18h

WEST

EQUULEUS
DELPHINUS
PEGASUS
VULPECULA
LACERTA
CYGNUS
Deneb
CEPHEUS
ANDROMEDA
CASSIOPEIA
PERSEUS
LYRA
Vega
HERCULES
DRACO
CAMELOPARDALIS
ZENITH
NORTH
Polaris
URSA MINOR
BOOTES
CANES VENATICI
URSA MAJOR
LYNX
COMA BERENICES
LEO MINOR
LEO
Regulus
CANCER
ECLIPTIC
150º
140º
EAST

12S

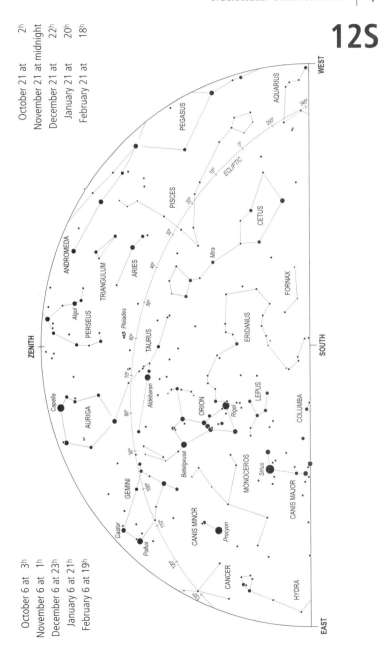

WEST

ZENITH

SOUTH

EAST

PEGASUS

AQUARIUS

PISCES

ECLIPTIC

CETUS

ANDROMEDA

TRIANGULUM

ARIES

Mira

FORNAX

Algol

PERSEUS

Pleiades

TAURUS

ERIDANUS

Capella

AURIGA

Aldebaran

ORION

Rigel

LEPUS

Betelgeuse

COLUMBA

GEMINI

MONOCEROS

Sirius

CANIS MAJOR

Castor

Pollux

CANIS MINOR

Procyon

CANCER

HYDRA

340°
350°
0°
10°
20°
30°
40°
50°
60°
70°
80°
90°
100°
110°
120°
130°

Southern Star Charts

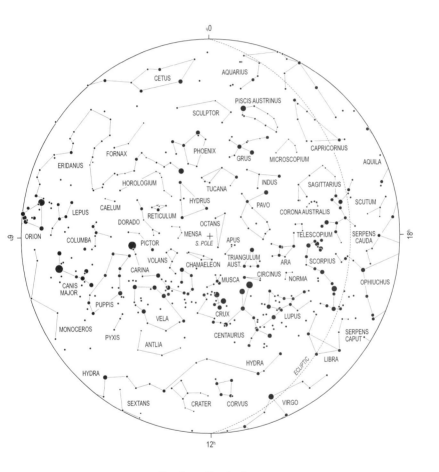

Southern Hemisphere

Note that the markers at 0ʰ, 6ʰ, 12ʰ and 18ʰ
indicate hours of Right Ascension.

1N

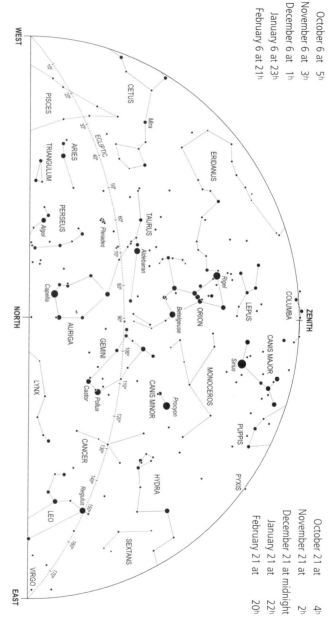

October 6 at 5ʰ
November 6 at 3ʰ
December 6 at 1ʰ
January 6 at 23ʰ
February 6 at 21ʰ

October 21 at 4ʰ
November 21 at 2ʰ
December 21 at midnight
January 21 at 22ʰ
February 21 at 20ʰ

1S

October 21 at 4ʰ
November 21 at 2ʰ
December 21 at midnight
January 21 at 22ʰ
February 21 at 20ʰ

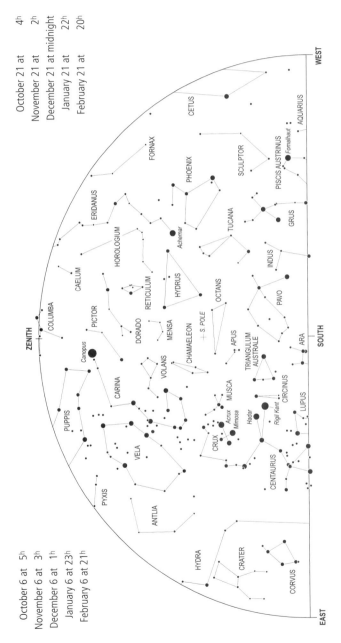

WEST

CETUS

AQUARIUS

Fomalhaut

PISCIS AUSTRINUS

SCULPTOR

PHOENIX

FORNAX

GRUS

TUCANA

ERIDANUS

Achernar

INDUS

HOROLOGIUM

HYDRUS

PAVO

CAELUM

RETICULUM

OCTANS

ZENITH

COLUMBA

PICTOR

DORADO

MENSA

S. POLE

APUS

ARA

SOUTH

Canopus

CARINA

CHAMAELEON

TRIANGULUM
AUSTRALE

CIRCINUS

PUPPIS

VOLANS

MUSCA

Acrux

Mimosa

Hadar

Rigil Kent

LUPUS

VELA

CRUX

CENTAURUS

PYXIS

ANTLIA

HYDRA

CRATER

CORVUS

EAST

October 6 at 5ʰ
November 6 at 3ʰ
December 6 at 1ʰ
January 6 at 23ʰ
February 6 at 21ʰ

2N

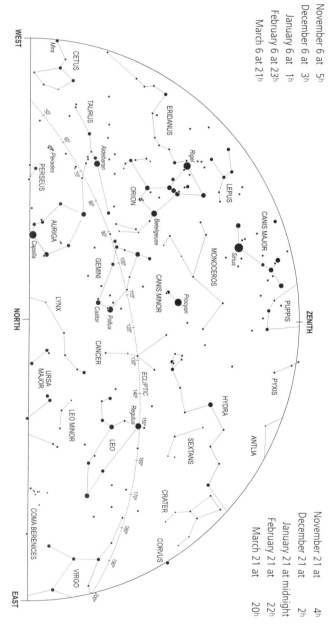

WEST

CETUS
Mira
TAURUS
ERIDANUS
Aldebaran
Rigel
Pleiades
PERSEUS
ORION
Betelgeuse
LEPUS
CANIS MAJOR
AURIGA
Capella
Sirius
GEMINI
MONOCEROS
ZENITH
Castor
Pollux
CANIS MINOR
Procyon
PUPPIS
LYNX
PYXIS
CANCER
URSA MAJOR
ECLIPTIC
HYDRA
ANTLIA
LEO MINOR
Regulus
SEXTANS
LEO
CRATER
COMA BERENICES
CORVUS
VIRGO

NORTH

EAST

50° 60° 70° 80° 90° 100° 110° 120° 130° 140° 150° 160° 170° 180° 190° 200°

2S

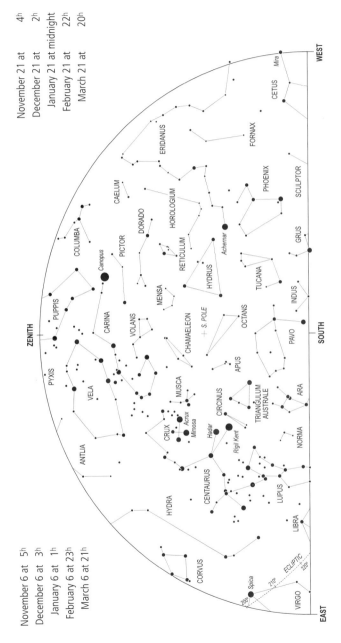

November 21 at 4ʰ
December 21 at 2ʰ
January 21 at midnight
February 21 at 22ʰ
March 21 at 20ʰ

November 6 at 5ʰ
December 6 at 3ʰ
January 6 at 1ʰ
February 6 at 23ʰ
March 6 at 21ʰ

WEST

ZENITH

SOUTH

EAST

Mira

CETUS

ERIDANUS

FORNAX

PHOENIX

SCULPTOR

CAELUM

DORADO

HOROLOGIUM

GRUS

PICTOR

RETICULUM

Achernar

COLUMBA

MENSA

HYDRUS

TUCANA

Canopus

INDUS

PUPPIS

CARINA

VOLANS

CHAMAELEON

+ S. POLE

OCTANS

PAVO

PYXIS

VELA

MUSCA

APUS

ARA

ANTLIA

CRUX

Acrux

Mimosa

CIRCINUS

TRIANGULUM
AUSTRALE

Hadar

Rigil Kent

NORMA

HYDRA

CENTAURUS

LUPUS

LIBRA

CORVUS

Spica

ECLIPTIC

210°

200°

VIRGO

3N

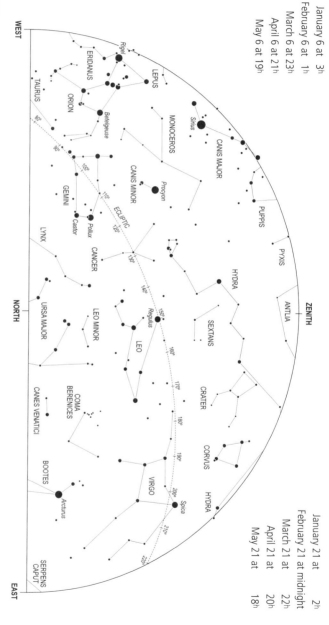

January 6 at 3h
February 6 at 1h
March 6 at 23h
April 6 at 21h
May 6 at 19h

WEST

ERIDANUS
Rigel
LEPUS
TAURUS
ORION
Betelgeuse
MONOCEROS
Sirius
CANIS MAJOR
80°
90°
CANIS MINOR
GEMINI
Procyon
PUPPIS
100°
Castor
Pollux
110°
ECLIPTIC
120°
LYNX
CANCER
130°
PYXIS
ANTLIA
ZENITH
140°
HYDRA
URSA MAJOR
LEO MINOR
150°
Regulus
SEXTANS
180°
LEO
CRATER
170°
COMA
BERENICES
180°
CANES VENATICI
190°
CORVUS
BOOTES
VIRGO
200°
Arcturus
Spica
HYDRA
210°
220°
SERPENS
CAPUT

NORTH

EAST

January 21 at   2h
February 21 at midnight
March 21 at 22h
April 21 at 20h
May 21 at 18h

3S

January 21 at 2h
February 21 at midnight
March 21 at 22h
April 21 at 20h
May 21 at 18h

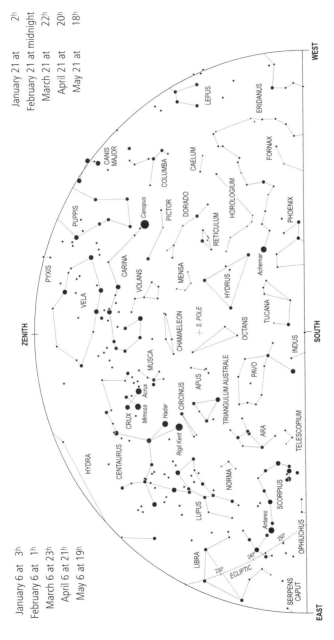

ZENITH

WEST

SOUTH

EAST

January 6 at 3h
February 6 at 1h
March 6 at 23h
April 6 at 21h
May 6 at 19h

LEPUS
ERIDANUS
CANIS MAJOR
COLUMBA
CAELUM
FORNAX
Canopus
PICTOR
DORADO
PHOENIX
PUPPIS
HOROLOGIUM
RETICULUM
Achernar
PYXIS
CARINA
VOLANS
MENSA
HYDRUS
VELA
CHAMAELEON
S. POLE
TUCANA
OCTANS
INDUS
MUSCA
Acrux
CRUX
Mimosa
Hadar
CIRCINUS
APUS
TRIANGULUM AUSTRALE
PAVO
Rigil Kent
ARA
CENTAURUS
TELESCOPIUM
HYDRA
NORMA
SCORPIUS
LUPUS
Antares
250°
LIBRA
240°
OPHIUCHUS
230°
ECLIPTIC
SERPENS CAPUT

4N

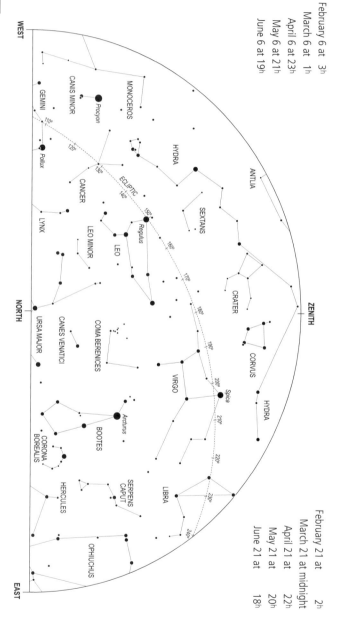

February 6 at 3ʰ
March 6 at 1ʰ
April 6 at 23ʰ
May 6 at 21ʰ
June 6 at 19ʰ

February 21 at 2ʰ
March 21 at midnight
April 21 at 22ʰ
May 21 at 20ʰ
June 21 at 18ʰ

4S

February 21 at 2ʰ
March 21 at midnight
April 21 at 22ʰ
May 21 at 20ʰ
June 21 at 18ʰ

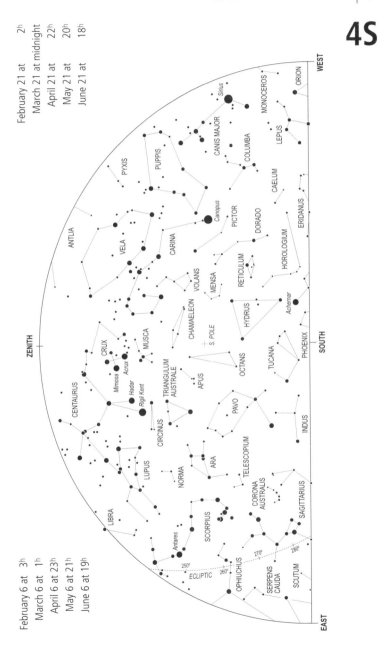

WEST

ORION
MONOCEROS
Sirius
LEPUS
CANIS MAJOR
COLUMBA
CAELUM
PUPPIS
PYXIS
ERIDANUS
Canopus
PICTOR
DORADO
HOROLOGIUM
ANTLIA
CARINA
VELA
RETICULUM
Achernar
VOLANS
MENSA
CHAMAELEON
HYDRUS
PHOENIX
ZENITH
MUSCA
S. POLE
SOUTH
CRUX
Acrux
OCTANS
TUCANA
Mimosa
Hadar
TRIANGULUM AUSTRALE
APUS
Rigil Kent
CENTAURUS
PAVO
INDUS
CIRCINUS
ARA
LUPUS
TELESCOPIUM
NORMA
LIBRA
CORONA AUSTRALIS
SAGITTARIUS
SCORPIUS
Antares
OPHIUCHUS
ECLIPTIC 250° 260° 270° 260°
SERPENS CAUDA
SCUTUM

EAST

February 6 at 3ʰ
March 6 at 1ʰ
April 6 at 23ʰ
May 6 at 21ʰ
June 6 at 19ʰ

5N

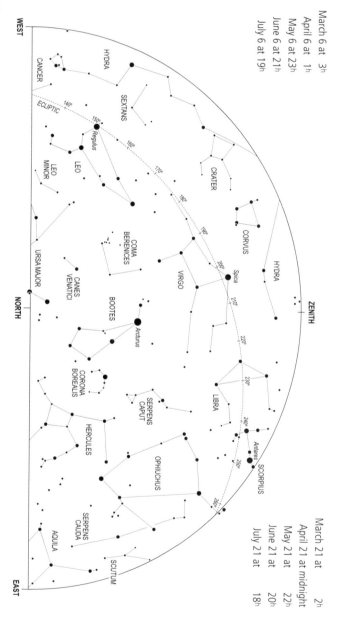

March 6 at 3h
April 6 at 1h
May 6 at 23h
June 6 at 21h
July 6 at 19h

March 21 at 2h
April 21 at midnight
May 21 at 22h
June 21 at 20h
July 21 at 18h

WEST

NORTH

EAST

ZENITH

CANCER
HYDRA
SEXTANS
ECLIPTIC 140°
150°
Regulus
LEO MINOR
LEO
160°
170°
CRATER
180°
CORVUS
190°
COMA BERENICES
200°
Spica
HYDRA
URSA MAJOR
CANES VENATICI
VIRGO
210°
BOOTES
Arcturus
220°
CORONA BOREALIS
SERPENS CAPUT
LIBRA
230°
240°
HERCULES
250°
Antares
SCORPIUS
OPHIUCHUS
260°
SERPENS CAUDA
AQUILA
SCUTUM

5S

March 21 at 2ʰ
April 21 at midnight
May 21 at 22ʰ
June 21 at 20ʰ
July 21 at 18ʰ

March 6 at 3ʰ
April 6 at 1ʰ
May 6 at 23ʰ
June 6 at 21ʰ
July 6 at 19ʰ

WEST

EAST

ZENITH

SOUTH

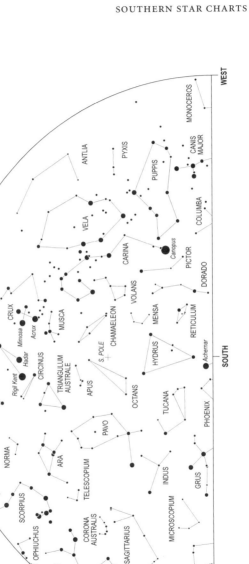

MONOCEROS
CANIS MAJOR
PUPPIS
ANTLIA
PYXIS
COLUMBA
VELA
HYDRA
CARINA
Canopus
PICTOR
DORADO
CENTAURUS
CRUX
Mimosa
Acrux
MUSCA
VOLANS
CHAMAELEON
MENSA
RETICULUM
Achernar
Hadar
CIRCINUS
S. POLE
HYDRUS
Rigil Kent
TRIANGULUM AUSTRALE
APUS
OCTANS
LUPUS
NORMA
ARA
PAVO
TUCANA
PHOENIX
TELESCOPIUM
INDUS
GRUS
SCORPIUS
OPHIUCHUS
CORONA AUSTRALIS
SAGITTARIUS
MICROSCOPIUM
270°
280°
290°
300°
310°
ECLIPTIC
CAPRICORNUS

6N

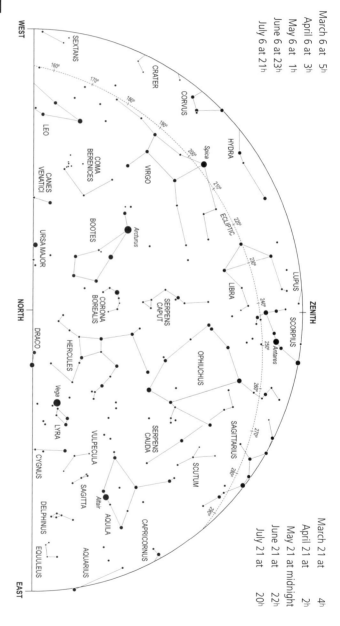

March 6 at 5h
April 6 at 3h
May 6 at 1h
June 6 at 23h
July 6 at 21h

March 21 at 4h
April 21 at 2h
May 21 at midnight
June 21 at 22h
July 21 at 20h

WEST

SEXTANS

CRATER

CORVUS

HYDRA

LEO

COMA BERENICES

VIRGO

Spica

CANES VENATICI

ECLIPTIC

LUPUS

URSA MAJOR

BOOTES

Arcturus

LIBRA

ZENITH

SCORPIUS

Antares

CORONA BOREALIS

SERPENS CAPUT

OPHIUCHUS

NORTH

DRACO

HERCULES

Vega

SERPENS CAUDA

SAGITTARIUS

LYRA

VULPECULA

SCUTUM

CYGNUS

SAGITTA

Altair

AQUILA

CAPRICORNUS

DELPHINUS

EQUULEUS

AQUARIUS

EAST

160° 170° 180° 190° 200° 210° 220° 230° 240° 250° 260° 270° 280° 290°

6S

March 21 at 4ʰ
April 21 at 2ʰ
May 21 at midnight
June 21 at 22ʰ
July 21 at 20ʰ

March 6 at 5ʰ
April 6 at 3ʰ
May 6 at 1ʰ
June 6 at 23ʰ
July 6 at 21ʰ

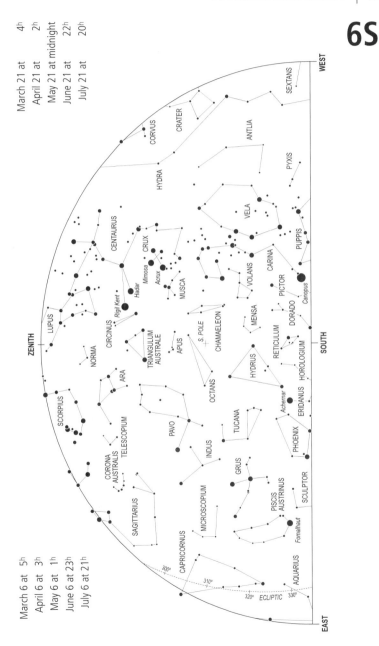

WEST

SEXTANS

CORVUS

CRATER

ANTLIA

HYDRA

PYXIS

VELA

PUPPIS

CENTAURUS

CRUX

Mimosa

Acrux

MUSCA

CARINA

VOLANS

Canopus

PICTOR

DORADO

Hadar

Rigil Kent

ZENITH

LUPUS

CIRCINUS

TRIANGULUM AUSTRALE

APUS

S. POLE

CHAMAELEON

MENSA

RETICULUM

HOROLOGIUM

NORMA

ARA

OCTANS

HYDRUS

Achernar

ERIDANUS

SOUTH

SCORPIUS

TELESCOPIUM

PAVO

TUCANA

PHOENIX

CORONA AUSTRALIS

INDUS

GRUS

SAGITTARIUS

MICROSCOPIUM

PISCIS AUSTRINUS

SCULPTOR

Fomalhaut

CAPRICORNUS

AQUARIUS

300°

310°

320° ECLIPTIC 330°

EAST

7N

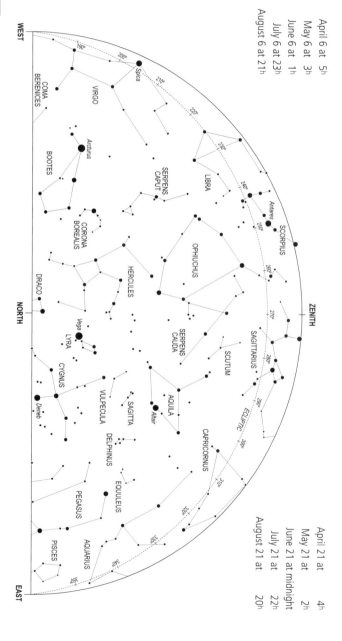

April 6 at 5h
May 6 at 3h
June 6 at 1h
July 6 at 23h
August 6 at 21h

WEST

COMA BERENICES
VIRGO
Spica
190°
200°
210°
220°
230°
Arcturus
BOOTES
SERPENS CAPUT
LIBRA
240°
Antares
250°
SCORPIUS
CORONA BOREALIS
OPHIUCHUS
260°
DRACO
HERCULES
270°
ZENITH
Vega
LYRA
SERPENS CAUDA
SAGITTARIUS
280°
CYGNUS
SCUTUM
290°
Deneb
VULPECULA
AQUILA
Altair
SAGITTA
ECLIPTIC
300°
DELPHINUS
CAPRICORNUS
EQUULEUS
310°
320°
PEGASUS
330°
AQUARIUS
340°
PISCES
350°

NORTH

EAST

April 21 at 4h
May 21 at 2h
June 21 at midnight
July 21 at 22h
August 21 at 20h

April 21 at 4ʰ
May 21 at 2ʰ
June 21 at midnight
July 21 at 22ʰ
August 21 at 20ʰ

April 6 at 5ʰ
May 6 at 3ʰ
June 6 at 1ʰ
July 6 at 23ʰ
August 6 at 21ʰ

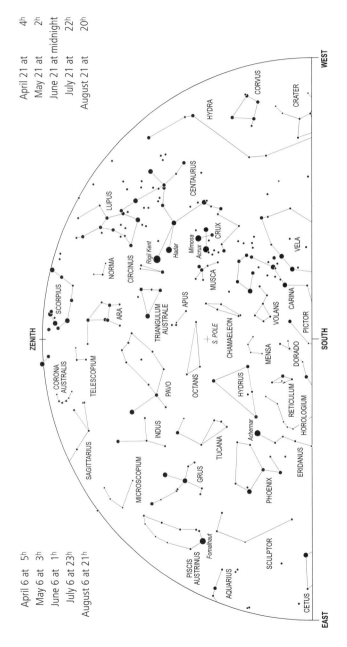

WEST

CORVUS

CRATER

HYDRA

CENTAURUS

LUPUS

Mimosa
Acrux
CRUX

VELA

Rigil Kent
Hadar

NORMA

CIRCINUS

MUSCA

SCORPIUS

ARA

APUS

CARINA

ZENITH

TRIANGULUM
AUSTRALE

VOLANS

PICTOR

CORONA
AUSTRALIS

TELESCOPIUM

S. POLE

CHAMAELEON

MENSA

DORADO

SOUTH

PAVO

OCTANS

HYDRUS

RETICULUM

SAGITTARIUS

INDUS

TUCANA

Achernar

HOROLOGIUM

MICROSCOPIUM

GRUS

PHOENIX

ERIDANUS

Fomalhaut

SCULPTOR

PISCIS
AUSTRINUS

AQUARIUS

CETUS

EAST

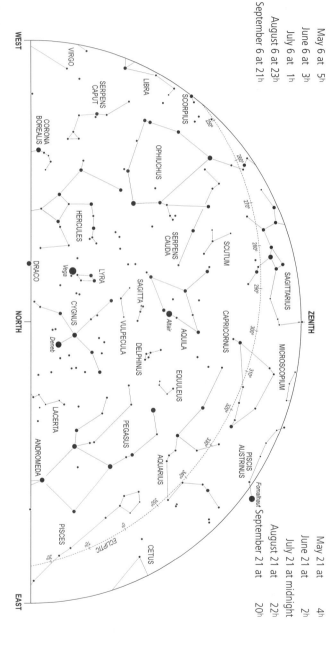

May 6 at 5h
June 6 at 3h
July 6 at 1h
August 6 at 23h
September 6 at 21h

WEST

VIRGO
LIBRA
SERPENS CAPUT
SCORPIUS
CORONA BOREALIS
OPHIUCHUS
HERCULES
SERPENS CAUDA
SCUTUM
SAGITTARIUS
DRACO
Vega
LYRA
SAGITTA
CYGNUS
Altair
AQUILA
CAPRICORNUS
Deneb
VULPECULA
DELPHINUS
MICROSCOPIUM
EQUULEUS
ZENITH
LACERTA
PEGASUS
AQUARIUS
PISCIS AUSTRINUS
ANDROMEDA
Fomalhaut
PISCES
ECLIPTIC
CETUS

250°
260°
270°
280°
290°
300°
310°
320°
330°
340°
350°
0°
10°
20°

NORTH

EAST

May 21 at 4h
June 21 at 2h
July 21 at midnight
August 21 at 22h
September 21 at 20h

May 21 at 4ʰ
June 21 at 2ʰ
July 21 at midnight
August 21 at 22ʰ
September 21 at 20ʰ

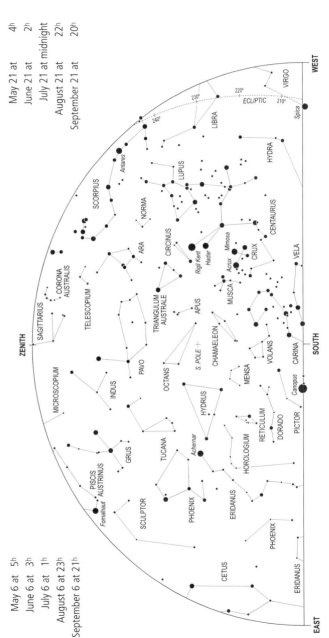

WEST

VIRGO

ECLIPTIC

230° 220° 210° Spica

240°

Antares

LIBRA

HYDRA

SCORPIUS

LUPUS

NORMA

CENTAURUS

ARA

CIRCINUS

Mimosa

VELA

CORONA
AUSTRALIS

Rigil Kent

Hadar

Acrux

CRUX

SAGITTARIUS

TELESCOPIUM

TRIANGULUM
AUSTRALE

APUS

MUSCA

ZENITH

PAVO

OCTANS

S. POLE +

CHAMAELEON

CARINA

SOUTH

MICROSCOPIUM

INDUS

HYDRUS

VOLANS

Canopus

MENSA

RETICULUM

PICTOR

TUCANA

Achernar

DORADO

GRUS

HOROLOGIUM

PISCIS
AUSTRINUS

Fomalhaut

SCULPTOR

PHOENIX

ERIDANUS

PHOENIX

CETUS

ERIDANUS

EAST

May 6 at 5ʰ
June 6 at 3ʰ
July 6 at 1ʰ
August 6 at 23ʰ
September 6 at 21ʰ

9N

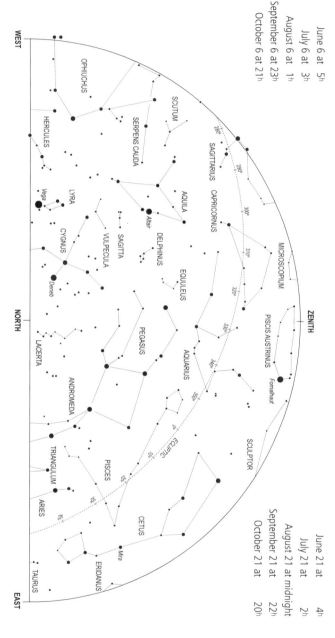

June 6 at 5h
July 6 at 3h
August 6 at 1h
September 6 at 23h
October 6 at 21h

WEST

OPHIUCHUS

SCUTUM

HERCULES

SERPENS CAUDA

SAGITTARIUS

AQUILA

CAPRICORNUS

MICROSCOPIUM

ZENITH

280°

290°

300°

310°

320°

Vega

LYRA

Altair

DELPHINUS

CYGNUS

VULPECULA

SAGITTA

EQUULEUS

Deneb

330°

PISCIS AUSTRINUS

340°

Fomalhaut

NORTH

PEGASUS

AQUARIUS

350°

LACERTA

ANDROMEDA

0°

SCULPTOR

TRIANGULUM

PISCES

ECLIPTIC

10°

20°

ARIES

30°

CETUS

40°

Mira

TAURUS

ERIDANUS

EAST

June 21 at 4h
July 21 at 2h
August 21 at midnight
September 21 at 22h
October 21 at 20h

9S

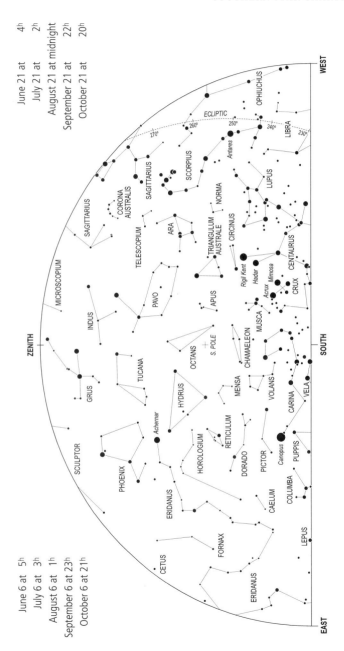

June 21 at 4ʰ
July 21 at 2ʰ
August 21 at midnight
September 21 at 22ʰ
October 21 at 20ʰ

June 6 at 5ʰ
July 6 at 3ʰ
August 6 at 1ʰ
September 6 at 23ʰ
October 6 at 21ʰ

WEST

EAST

ZENITH

SOUTH

OPHIUCHUS

ECLIPTIC
270° 260° 250° 240° 230°
LIBRA

Antares

SCORPIUS

SAGITTARIUS

CORONA
AUSTRALIS

NORMA

LUPUS

TRIANGULUM
AUSTRALE

CIRCINUS

CENTAURUS

ARA

Rigil Kent
Hadar
Mimosa
Acrux

CRUX

TELESCOPIUM

SAGITTARIUS

MICROSCOPIUM

PAVO

APUS

MUSCA

CHAMAELEON

INDUS

OCTANS

S. POLE

MENSA

VOLANS

TUCANA

HYDRUS

RETICULUM

CARINA

VELA

GRUS

Achernar

DORADO

PICTOR

Canopus

PUPPIS

SCULPTOR

PHOENIX

HOROLOGIUM

CAELUM

COLUMBA

ERIDANUS

FORNAX

LEPUS

CETUS

ERIDANUS

10N

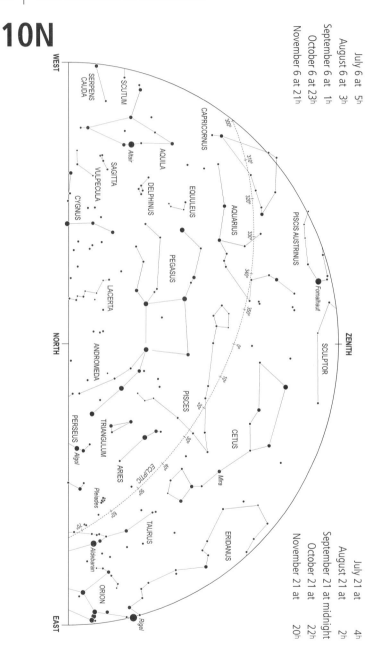

July 6 at 5h
August 6 at 3h
September 6 at 1h
October 6 at 23h
November 6 at 21h

July 21 at 4h
August 21 at 2h
September 21 at midnight
October 21 at 22h
November 21 at 20h

WEST

SERPENS CAUDA
SCUTUM
CAPRICORNUS
Altair
AQUILA
SAGITTA
VULPECULA
DELPHINUS
EQUULEUS
AQUARIUS
CYGNUS
PEGASUS
LACERTA
ANDROMEDA
PISCIS AUSTRINUS
Fomalhaut
SCULPTOR
ZENITH
PISCES
CETUS
Mira
PERSEUS
Algol
TRIANGULUM
ARIES
ECLIPTIC
Pleiades
TAURUS
ERIDANUS
Aldebaran
ORION
Rigel

NORTH

EAST

10S

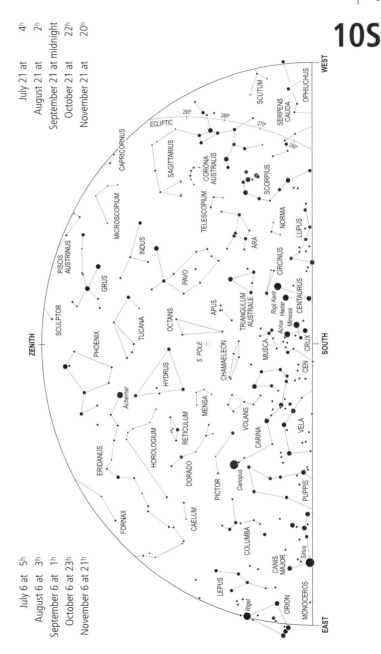

July 21 at 4ʰ
August 21 at 2ʰ
September 21 at midnight
October 21 at 22ʰ
November 21 at 20ʰ

July 6 at 5ʰ
August 6 at 3ʰ
September 6 at 1ʰ
October 6 at 23ʰ
November 6 at 21ʰ

WEST

OPHIUCHUS
SERPENS
CAUDA
SCUTUM

ECLIPTIC
290°
280°
270°
260°

CAPRICORNUS
SAGITTARIUS
CORONA
AUSTRALIS
SCORPIUS
TELESCOPIUM
NORMA
ARA
LUPUS
MICROSCOPIUM
CIRCINUS
INDUS
PAVO
Rigil Kent
CENTAURUS
PISCIS
AUSTRINUS
GRUS
TRIANGULUM
AUSTRALE
Acrux Hadar
Mimosa
CRUX
APUS
MUSCA
SCULPTOR
TUCANA
OCTANS
CHAMAELEON
CEN
ZENITH
PHOENIX
S. POLE
CEN
SOUTH
HYDRUS
Achernar
MENSA
VOLANS
VELA
RETICULUM
ERIDANUS
HOROLOGIUM
CARINA
DORADO
PICTOR
Canopus
PUPPIS
FORNAX
CAELUM
COLUMBA
Sirius
LEPUS
CANIS
MAJOR
Rigel
ORION
MONOCEROS
EAST

11N

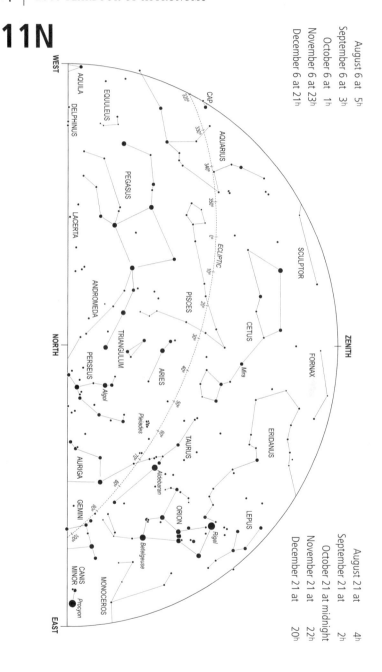

August 6 at 5h
September 6 at 3h
October 6 at 1h
November 6 at 23h
December 6 at 21h

August 21 at 4h
September 21 at 2h
October 21 at midnight
November 21 at 22h
December 21 at 20h

WEST

AQUILA
EQUULEUS
DELPHINUS
CAP
AQUARIUS
320°
330°
340°
350°
0°
ECLIPTIC
10°
PEGASUS
SCULPTOR
LACERTA
20°
PISCES
ZENITH
ANDROMEDA
CETUS
30°
FORNAX
NORTH
TRIANGULUM
Mira
40°
PERSEUS
ARIES
ERIDANUS
Algol
50°
Pleiades
60°
AURIGA
70°
TAURUS
Aldebaran
80°
GEMINI
90°
ORION
LEPUS
100°
Betelgeuse
Rigel
CANIS
MINOR
MONOCEROS
Procyon

EAST

11S

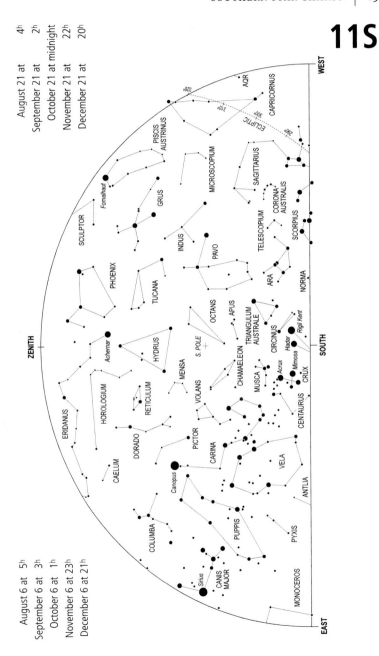

August 21 at 4ʰ
September 21 at 2ʰ
October 21 at midnight
November 21 at 22ʰ
December 21 at 20ʰ

August 6 at 5ʰ
September 6 at 3ʰ
October 6 at 1ʰ
November 6 at 23ʰ
December 6 at 21ʰ

WEST

ZENITH

SOUTH

EAST

AQR
CAPRICORNUS
320°
310°
300°
ECLIPTIC
290°
PISCIS AUSTRINUS
MICROSCOPIUM
SAGITTARIUS
CORONA AUSTRALIS
Fomalhaut
GRUS
SCULPTOR
INDUS
PAVO
TELESCOPIUM
SCORPIUS
ARA
NORMA
PHOENIX
TUCANA
OCTANS
APUS
TRIANGULUM AUSTRALE
CIRCINUS
Rigil Kent
Achernar
HYDRUS
MENSA
S. POLE
CHAMAELEON
MUSCA
Acrux
Hadar
Mimosa
CRUX
ERIDANUS
HOROLOGIUM
RETICULUM
VOLANS
CENTAURUS
CAELUM
DORADO
PICTOR
CARINA
VELA
ANTLIA
COLUMBA
PUPPIS
PYXIS
Canopus
Sirius
CANIS MAJOR
MONOCEROS

12N

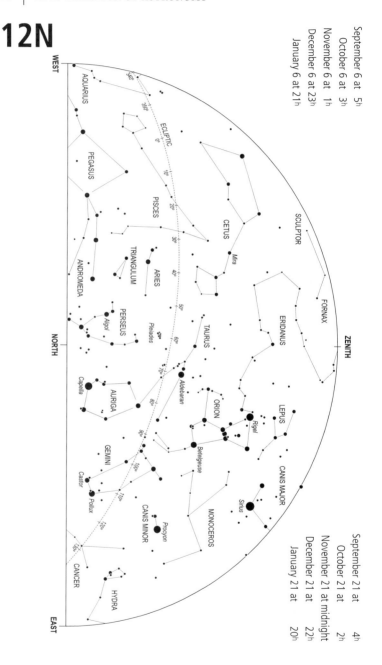

WEST

NORTH

EAST

ZENITH

AQUARIUS
PEGASUS
PISCES
ANDROMEDA
TRIANGULUM
ARIES
PERSEUS
Algol
Pleiades
CAPELLA
Capella
AURIGA
GEMINI
Castor
Pollux
CANCER
HYDRA
CETUS
Mira
TAURUS
Aldebaran
ORION
Betelgeuse
CANIS MINOR
Procyon
MONOCEROS
SCULPTOR
FORNAX
ERIDANUS
LEPUS
Rigel
CANIS MAJOR
Sirius

ECLIPTIC
0°
10°
20°
30°
40°
50°
60°
70°
80°
90°
10h
11h
12h
13h
340°
350°

12S

September 21 at 4ʰ
October 21 at 2ʰ
November 21 at midnight
December 21 at 22ʰ
January 21 at 20ʰ

WEST

ZENITH

SOUTH

EAST

September 6 at 5ʰ
October 6 at 3ʰ
November 6 at 1ʰ
December 6 at 23ʰ
January 6 at 21ʰ

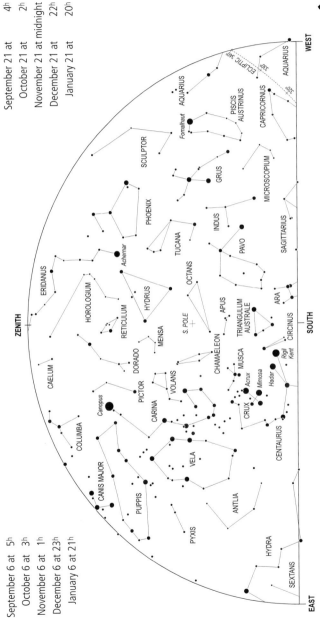

AQUARIUS
ECLIPTIC 340°
350°
AQUARIUS
PISCIS AUSTRINUS
CAPRICORNUS
Fomalhaut
320°
SCULPTOR
GRUS
MICROSCOPIUM
PHOENIX
INDUS
SAGITTARIUS
TUCANA
PAVO
Achernar
ERIDANUS
OCTANS
ARA
HOROLOGIUM
HYDRUS
APUS
RETICULUM
S. POLE
TRIANGULUM AUSTRALE
CIRCINUS
CAELUM
MENSA
CHAMAELEON
Rigil Kent
DORADO
MUSCA
Hadar
PICTOR
VOLANS
Acrux
Mimosa
Canopus
CARINA
CRUX
CENTAURUS
COLUMBA
VELA
CANIS MAJOR
ANTLIA
PUPPIS
PYXIS
HYDRA
SEXTANS

The Planets and the Ecliptic

The paths of the planets about the Sun all lie close to the plane of the ecliptic, which is marked for us in the sky by the apparent path of the Sun among the stars, and is shown on the star charts by a broken line. The Moon and naked-eye planets will always be found close to this line, never departing from it by more than about 7°. Thus the planets are most favourably placed for observation when the ecliptic is well displayed, and this means that it should be as high in the sky as possible. This avoids the difficulty of finding a clear horizon, and also overcomes the problem of atmospheric absorption, which greatly reduces the light of the stars. Thus a star at an altitude of 10° suffers a loss of 60 per cent of its light, which corresponds to a whole magnitude; at an altitude of only 4°, the loss may amount to two magnitudes.

The position of the ecliptic in the sky is therefore of great importance, and since it is tilted at about 23.5° to the Equator, it is only at certain times of the day or year that it is displayed to the best advantage. It will be realized that the Sun (and therefore the ecliptic) is at its highest in the sky at noon in midsummer, and at its lowest at noon in midwinter. Allowing for the daily motion of the sky, it follows that the ecliptic is highest at midnight in winter, at sunset in the spring, at noon in summer and at sunrise in the autumn. Hence these are the best times to see the planets. Thus, if Venus is an evening object in the western sky after sunset, it will be seen to best advantage if this occurs in the spring, when the ecliptic is high in the sky and slopes down steeply to the horizon. This means that the planet is not only higher in the sky, but will remain for a much longer period above the horizon. For similar reasons, a morning object will be seen at its best on autumn mornings before sunrise, when the ecliptic is high in the east. The outer planets, which can come to opposition (i.e. opposite the Sun), are best seen when opposition occurs in the winter months, when the ecliptic is high in the sky at midnight.

The seasons are reversed in the Southern Hemisphere, spring beginning at the September Equinox, when the Sun crosses the Equator on its way south, summer beginning at the December Solstice, when the

Sun is highest in the southern sky, and so on. Thus, the times when the ecliptic is highest in the sky, and therefore best placed for observing the planets, may be summarized as follows:

	Midnight	**Sunrise**	**Noon**	**Sunset**
Northern latitudes	December	September	June	March
Southern latitudes	June	March	December	September

In addition to the daily rotation of the celestial sphere from east to west, the planets have a motion of their own among the stars. The apparent movement is generally *direct*, i.e. to the east, in the direction of increasing longitude, but for a certain period (which depends on the distance of the planet) this apparent motion is reversed. With the outer planets this *retrograde* motion occurs about the time of opposition. Owing to the different inclination of the orbits of these planets, the actual effect is to cause the apparent path to form a loop, or sometimes an S-shaped curve. The same effect is present in the motion of the inferior planets, Mercury and Venus, but it is not so obvious, since it always occurs at the time of inferior conjunction.

The *inferior planets*, Mercury and Venus, move in smaller orbits than that of the Earth, and so are always seen near the Sun. They are most obvious at the times of greatest angular distance from the Sun (greatest elongation), which may reach 28° for Mercury, and 47° for Venus. They are seen as evening objects in the western sky after sunset (at eastern elongations) or as morning objects in the eastern sky before sunrise (at western elongations). The succession of phenomena, conjunctions and elongations always follows the same order, but the intervals between them are not equal. Thus, if either planet is moving round the far side of its orbit its motion will be to the east, in the same direction in which the Sun appears to be moving. It therefore takes much longer for the planet to overtake the Sun – that is, to come to superior conjunction – than it does when moving round to inferior conjunction, between Sun and Earth. The intervals given in the following table are average values; they remain fairly constant in the case of Venus, which travels in an almost circular orbit. In the case of Mercury, however, conditions vary widely because of the great eccentricity and inclination of the planet's orbit.

		Mercury	Venus
Inferior Conjunction	to Elongation West	22 days	72 days
Elongation West	to Superior Conjunction	36 days	220 days
Superior Conjunction	to Elongation East	35 days	220 days
Elongation East	to Inferior Conjunction	22 days	72 days

The greatest brilliancy of Venus always occurs about 36 days before or after inferior conjunction. This will be about a month after greatest eastern elongation (as an evening object), or a month before greatest western elongation (as a morning object). No such rule can be given for Mercury, because its distances from the Earth and the Sun can vary over a wide range.

Mercury is not likely to be seen unless a clear horizon is available. It is seldom as much as 10° above the horizon in the twilight sky in northern temperate latitudes, but this figure is often exceeded in the Southern Hemisphere. This favourable condition arises because the maximum elongation of 28° can occur only when the planet is at aphelion (furthest from the Sun), and it then lies well south of the Equator. Northern observers must be content with smaller elongations, which may be as little as 18° at perihelion (when closest to the Sun). In general, it may be said that the most favourable times for seeing Mercury as an evening object will be in spring, some days before greatest eastern elongation; in autumn, it may be seen as a morning object some days after greatest western elongation.

Venus is the brightest of the planets and may be seen on occasions in broad daylight. Like Mercury, it is alternately a morning and an evening object, and it will be highest in the sky when it is a morning object in autumn, or an evening object in spring. Venus is to be seen at its best as an evening object in northern latitudes when eastern elongation occurs in June. The planet is then well north of the Sun in the preceding spring months, and is a brilliant object in the evening sky over a long period. In the Southern Hemisphere a November elongation is best. For similar reasons, Venus gives a prolonged display as a morning object in the months following western elongation in October (in northern latitudes) or in June (in the Southern Hemisphere).

The *superior planets*, which travel in orbits larger than that of the Earth, differ from Mercury and Venus in that they can be seen opposite the Sun in the sky. The superior planets are morning objects after conjunction with the Sun, rising earlier each day until they come to opposition. They will then be nearest to the Earth (and therefore at their brightest), and will be on the meridian at midnight, due south in northern latitudes, but due north in the Southern Hemisphere. After opposition they are evening objects, setting earlier each evening until they set in the west with the Sun at the next conjunction. The difference in brightness from one opposition to another is most noticeable in the case of Mars, whose distance from Earth can vary considerably and rapidly. The other superior planets are at such great distances that there is very little change in brightness from one opposition to the next. The effect of altitude is, however, of some importance, for at a December opposition in northern latitudes the planets will be among the stars of Taurus or Gemini, and can then be at an altitude of more than 60° in southern England. At a summer opposition, when the planet is in Sagittarius, it may only rise to about 15° above the southern horizon, and so makes a less impressive appearance. In the Southern Hemisphere the reverse conditions apply, a June opposition being the best, with the planet in Sagittarius at an altitude that can reach 80° above the northern horizon for observers in South Africa.

Mars, whose orbit is appreciably eccentric, comes nearest to the Earth at oppositions at the end of August. It may then be brighter even than Jupiter, but rather low in the sky in Aquarius for northern observers, though very well placed for those in southern latitudes. These favourable oppositions occur every fifteen or seventeen years (e.g. in 1988, 2003 and 2018). In the Northern Hemisphere the planet is probably better seen at oppositions in the autumn or winter months, when it is higher in the sky – such as in 2005 when opposition was in early November. Oppositions of Mars occur at an average interval of 780 days, and during this time the planet makes a complete circuit of the sky.

Jupiter is always a bright planet, and comes to opposition a month later each year, having moved, roughly speaking, from one zodiacal constellation to the next.

Saturn moves much more slowly than Jupiter, and may remain in the same constellation for several years. The brightness of Saturn depends on the aspects of its rings, as well as on the distance from Earth and Sun. The Earth passed through the plane of Saturn's rings in 1995 and 1996, when they appeared edge-on; we saw them at maximum opening, and Saturn at its brightest, in 2002. The rings will next appear edge-on in 2009.

Uranus and *Neptune* are both visible with binoculars or a small telescope, but you will need a finder chart to help locate them (such as those reproduced in this *Yearbook* on pages 119 and 125). *Pluto* (now officially classified as a 'dwarf planet') is hardly likely to attract the attention of observers without adequate telescopes.

Phases of the Moon in 2008

	New Moon				First Quarter				Full Moon				Last Quarter		
	d	h	m		d	h	m		d	h	m		d	h	m
Jan	8	11	37	Jan	15	19	46	Jan	22	13	35	Jan	30	05	03
Feb	7	03	44	Feb	14	03	33	Feb	21	03	30	Feb	29	02	18
Mar	7	17	14	Mar	14	10	46	Mar	21	18	40	Mar	29	21	47
Apr	6	03	55	Apr	12	18	32	Apr	20	10	25	Apr	28	14	12
May	5	12	18	May	12	03	47	May	20	02	11	May	28	02	57
June	3	19	23	June	10	15	04	June	18	17	30	June	26	12	10
July	3	02	19	July	10	04	35	July	18	07	59	July	25	18	42
Aug	1	10	13	Aug	8	20	20	Aug	16	21	16	Aug	23	23	49
Aug	30	19	58	Sept	7	14	04	Sept	15	09	13	Sept	22	05	04
Sept	29	08	12	Oct	7	09	04	Oct	14	20	02	Oct	21	11	55
Oct	28	23	14	Nov	6	04	03	Nov	13	06	17	Nov	19	21	31
Nov	27	16	55	Dec	5	21	26	Dec	12	16	37	Dec	19	10	29
Dec	27	12	22												

All times are GMT

Longitudes of the Sun, Moon and Planets in 2008

Date		Sun °	Moon °	Venus °	Mars °	Jupiter °	Saturn °
January	6	285	257	248	88	274	158
	21	300	100	266	85	278	158
February	6	317	303	286	84	281	157
	21	332	150	304	87	284	155
March	6	346	324	321	91	286	154
	21	1	172	340	96	289	153
April	6	17	14	0	103	291	152
	21	31	218	18	110	292	152
May	6	46	53	37	118	292	152
	21	60	250	55	126	292	152
June	6	76	107	75	135	291	153
	21	90	295	93	144	290	154
July	6	104	144	112	153	288	155
	21	119	329	130	162	286	157
August	6	134	192	150	172	284	158
	21	148	19	168	181	283	160
September	6	164	236	188	191	283	162
	21	178	72	206	201	283	164
October	6	193	268	224	211	284	166
	21	208	112	243	221	285	168
November	6	224	312	262	233	288	169
	21	239	163	280	243	290	170
December	6	254	346	298	254	293	171
	21	269	198	315	265	296	172

Longitude of *Uranus*   350°   *Moon:* Longitude of ascending node
              Neptune   323°   Jan 1: 330°   Dec 31: 311°

Mercury moves so quickly among the stars that it is not possible to indicate its position on the star charts at convenient intervals. The monthly notes must be consulted for the best times at which the planet may be seen.

The positions of the other planets are given in the table on p. 74. This gives the apparent longitudes on dates that correspond to those of the star charts, and the position of the planet may at once be found near the ecliptic at the given longitude.

EXAMPLES

In southern latitudes two planets are seen in the evening about an hour after sunset, in the west-north-western sky early in July. Identify them.

The southern chart 5N shows longitudes 135° to 260° along the ecliptic. Reference to the table on p. 74 for 6 July gives the longitude of Mars as 153° and that of Saturn as 155°, Mars being lower down in the sky than Saturn, and also brighter than Saturn. Note the proximity to the star Regulus.

The positions of the Sun and Moon can be plotted on the star maps in the same manner as for the planets. The average daily motion of the Sun is 1°, and of the Moon 13°. For the Moon an indication of its position relative to the ecliptic may be obtained from a consideration of its longitude relative to that of the ascending node. The latter changes only slowly during the year, as will be seen from the values given on p. 74. Let us denote by d the difference in longitude between the Moon and its ascending node. Then if $d = 0°, 180°$ or $360°$, the Moon is on the ecliptic. If $d = 90°$ the Moon is 5° north of the ecliptic, and if $d = 270°$ the Moon is 5° south of the ecliptic.

On 6 May the Moon's longitude is given in the table on p. 74 as 53° and the longitude of the ascending node is found by interpolation to be about 324°. Thus $d = 89°$ and the Moon is about 5° north of the ecliptic. Its position may be plotted on northern star charts 1S, 2S, 11S and 12S, and on southern star charts 1N, 2N, 10N, 11N, and 12N.

Some Events in 2008

Jan   2   *Earth* at Perihelion
       8   New Moon
   22   *Mercury* at Greatest Eastern Elongation (19°)
   22   Full Moon

Feb   6   *Mercury* at Inferior Conjunction
     7   New Moon, Annular Eclipse of the Sun
   21   Full Moon, Total Eclipse of the Moon
   24   *Saturn* at Opposition in Leo

Mar 3   *Mercury* at Greatest Western Elongation (27°)
     7   New Moon
   20   Equinox (Spring Equinox in Northern Hemisphere)
   21   Full Moon

Apr   6   New Moon
   16   *Mercury* at Superior Conjunction
   20   Full Moon

May 5   New Moon
   14   *Mercury* at Greatest Eastern Elongation (22°)
   20   Full Moon

Jun   3   New Moon
     7   *Mercury* at Inferior Conjunction
     9   *Venus* at Superior Conjunction
   18   Full Moon
   20   *Pluto* at Opposition in Sagittarius
   20   Solstice (Summer Solstice in Northern Hemisphere)

Jul   1   *Mercury* at Greatest Western Elongation (22°)
     3   New Moon
     4   *Earth* at Aphelion

      9 *Jupiter* at Opposition in Sagittarius
     18 Full Moon
     29 *Mercury* at Superior Conjunction

Aug   1 New Moon, Total Eclipse of the Sun
     15 *Neptune* at Opposition in Capricornus
     16 Full Moon, Partial Eclipse of the Moon
     30 New Moon

Sep   4 *Saturn* in Conjunction with Sun
     11 *Mercury* at Greatest Eastern Elongation (27°)
     13 *Uranus* at Opposition in Aquarius
     15 Full Moon
     22 Equinox (Autumn Equinox in Northern Hemisphere)
     29 New Moon

Oct   6 *Mercury* at Inferior Conjunction
     14 Full Moon
     22 *Mercury* at Greatest Western Elongation (18°)
     28 New Moon

Nov 13 Full Moon
     25 *Mercury* at Superior Conjunction
     27 New Moon

Dec   5 *Mars* in Conjunction with Sun
     12 Full Moon
     21 Solstice (Winter Solstice in Northern Hemisphere)
     27 New Moon

Monthly Notes 2008

January

New Moon: 8 January   *Full Moon*: 22 January

EARTH is at perihelion (nearest to the Sun) on 2 January at a distance of 147 million kilometres (91.3 million miles).

MERCURY is at greatest eastern elongation on 22 January (19°) and is therefore visible as an evening object. Observers in the tropics are the most favourably placed, losing only a few days observing at the beginning and again at the end of the month. Those in northern temperate latitudes may expect to see it from the middle of the month almost to the end, whereas those in southern latitudes will start to see it a few days earlier and lose it a few days earlier. Mercury's magnitude fades during its period of visibility from −0.9 to +0.9 (+0.4 for those in the Southern Hemisphere). Mercury will be seen low above the western horizon at the end of evening civil twilight.

VENUS, magnitude −4.0, is a brilliant object, completely dominating the south-eastern sky before dawn, though for observers in the latitudes of the British Isles the duration of its period of visibility shortens noticeably during the month, and because of its southerly declination it is never at any great altitude.

MARS was at opposition in December last and is still a brilliant object in the evening sky as soon as darkness falls. It is moving retrograde in the constellation of Taurus until it reaches its second stationary point, in the Milky Way, at the end of the month, whereupon it resumes its direct motion. During the month its magnitude fades noticeably, from −1.5 to −0.6.

JUPITER, magnitude −1.9, is emerging from the morning twilight, becoming visible above the eastern horizon before dawn. Observers in the tropics and southern latitudes will be able to see the planet after the first week of the month, but because of its southern declination those

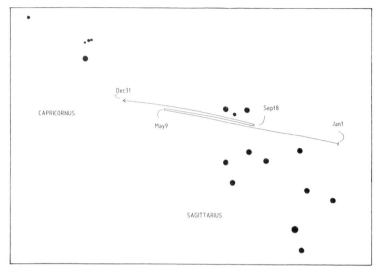

Figure 1. The path of Jupiter against the background stars of Sagittarius and Capricornus during 2008.

in the latitudes of the British Isles will not be able to detect it until the last few days of January. Then it may be seen very low above the south-eastern horizon about half an hour before sunrise. For these observers it will never be seen very high above the horizon, even when on the meridian, since Jupiter remains in Sagittarius throughout 2008, as will be seen from Figure 1, which shows the path of Jupiter among the stars during the year. Venus is two magnitudes brighter than Jupiter and is moving eastwards towards it; by the end of the month the two planets are less than 2° apart.

SATURN rises in mid-evening and will be found in Leo, nearly 10° east of Regulus. Although moving retrograde it will not move back as far as that star before resuming its direct motion in May. Saturn's magnitude is +0.4. Its movement among the stars throughout the year is shown in Figure 14, given with the notes for July.

The Moons of Mars. Tennyson wrote about 'the snowy poles of a moonless Mars'; he was only partially right. The polar caps are indeed icy, but there are two satellites, both discovered in 1877 by the

American observer Asaph Hall using the 66-centimetre Clark refractor at Washington; they were named Phobos and Deimos, after the attendants of the mythical God of War. They are somewhat irregular in shape: Phobos (Figure 2) has a longest diameter of 27 kilometres, Deimos only 15 kilometres. This makes them rather elusive telescopic objects, particularly as they are close to the planet. Phobos moves at only about 5,990 kilometres above the Martian surface, which is about the same as the distance between London and Aden; the orbital period of Phobos (7h 39m 27s) is much shorter than a Martian sol (Martian day). Deimos moves 20,100 kilometres above the surface, in a period of 29h 21m 16s.

The largest crater on Phobos, Stickney (the maiden name of Asaph

Figure 2. This image, taken by the High Resolution Stereo Camera on board ESA's Mars Express spacecraft, shows the Mars-facing side of the moon Phobos, taken from a distance of less than 200 kilometres on 22 August 2004. (Image courtesy of ESA/DLR/FU Berlin (G. Neukum).)

Hall's wife), is 9.6 kilometres across. Near it are some very unusual grooves and ridges. It was originally thought that these were formed at the time of the impact that produced Stickney, but it now seems that this is not so; more probably, the features were formed by debris thrown up from Mars during a crater-producing impact. It has even been calculated that the crater concerned was the 236-kilometre-diameter Lyot, at Martian latitude 50.7° N, longitude 330.7° W. This has not been proved, but it does seem likely.

Phobos is not in a stable orbit; it is spiralling slowly inwards, and will crash on to Mars in between 30 and 100 million years from now; Deimos, much further out, will not suffer a similar fate. In 1959 Iosif Shklovskii, a famous Russian astronomer, wrote a paper suggesting that Phobos and Deimos were not captured asteroids, as most people believed, but were artificial space stations, built by Martians for reasons of their own. This theory was not well received by the Soviet authorities. (When I asked Shklovskii about it, many years later, he told me that he had been making a joke!) When astronauts eventually go to Mars, as they probably will do before the end of the twenty-first century, the satellites may prove to be useful. It has been suggested that the pioneer travellers will go first to Deimos or Phobos and then make the final descent to Mars from there. Because the satellites have so weak a pull of gravity, 'landing' on them will really be in the nature of a docking operation.

Interestingly, in November 2007, NASA is sponsoring the First International Conference on the Exploration of Phobos and Deimos to consider all aspects of the science, robotic reconnaissance and human exploration of the two moons of Mars.

Is there any life on Mars? We do not yet know, but in the near future we have every hope of finding out, even though we are not likely to meet any of Iosif Shklovskii's satellite-building engineers.

This Month's Centenary. This month, on 21 January, sees the centenary of the birth of a great Danish astronomer, Bengt Georg Daniel Strømgren. His parents were Svante Strømgren, professor of astronomy at Copenhagen University, and his wife Hedwig (née Lindforss). Bengt was educated in Copenhagen, and in 1929 completed his doctoral degree at the University. One of his tutors was the great physicist Neils Bohr, and Strømgren went on to make valuable contributions to quantum theory.

After a spell as a lecturer, he was invited to Chicago by Otto Struve. When he returned home, Denmark had been occupied by the Germans, but Strømgren managed to initiate the building of a new observatory, the Brorfelde. After the liberation he spent over twenty years in the United States, and became Director of the Yerkes and McDonald Observatories. He was happily married; in 1967 he and his family went back to Denmark, and he died in Copenhagen in 1987.

He made many contributions to astrophysics, notably in connection with the chemical composition of the stars. He also discovered the so-called Strømgren Spheres – huge shells of ionized hydrogen around stars. He received a number of honours, including the Gold Medal of the Royal Astronomical Society, and an asteroid, 1846 Bengt, is named after him.

February

New Moon: 7 February   *Full Moon*: 21 February

MERCURY is at inferior conjunction on 6 February and reaches greatest western elongation on 3 March. During this period it is well south of the Sun and thus poorly placed for observation by those in northern temperate latitudes. However, the planet is well placed for observation by those in the Southern Hemisphere and in the tropics, and for observers in this part of the world this will be the most favourable morning apparition of the year. Figure 3 shows, for observers in latitude 35°S, the changes in azimuth (true bearing from the north through east, south and west) and altitude of Mercury on successive mornings when the Sun is 6° below the horizon. This condition is known as the beginning of morning civil twilight and in this latitude and at this time of year occurs about 25 minutes before sunrise. The changes in the brightness of the planet are indicated by the relative sizes of the circles marking Mercury's position at five-day intervals. It will be noticed that Mercury is at its brightest after it reaches greatest western elongation (27°) on 3 March. The diagram gives positions for a time at the beginning of morning civil twilight on the Greenwich meridian, on the stated date. Observers in different longitudes should note that the actual positions of Mercury in azimuth and altitude will differ slightly from those shown in the diagram. This change will be much greater still for the Moon, if it is shown, as its motion is about 0.5° per hour. Venus is approaching Mercury and passes just over 1° south of it on 26 February. For observers in the latitudes of the British Isles, Mercury remains too close to the Sun for observation throughout the month.

VENUS continues to be visible as a splendid object in the early-morning sky, magnitude −3.9, though for observers in the latitudes of the British Isles it will only be seen low above the south-eastern horizon for a short period, just before dawn.

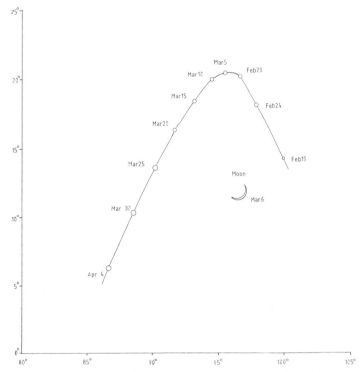

Figure 3. Morning apparition of Mercury, from latitude 35°S. The position of the crescent Moon is shown for 6 March as an aid to locating the planet. (Angular diameters of Mercury and the crescent Moon not to scale.)

MARS continues to be visible after darkness falls as an evening object in the southern and western skies. The planet is moving eastwards in Taurus, as will be seen by reference to the diagram given with the notes for March (Figure 5). During February its magnitude fades from −0.6 to +0.2.

JUPITER, magnitude −1.9, is visible in the eastern sky in the mornings, before dawn. Venus passes 0.6° north of Jupiter on the first day of February.

SATURN reaches opposition on 24 February and thus is visible throughout the hours of darkness. Its magnitude is +0.2 and its distance from the Earth at closest approach is 1,240 million kilometres (771 million miles).

Making the Most of Saturn! For British observers, Saturn is particularly well placed this month; it comes to opposition on the 24th and is well north of the celestial equator, with the rings still fairly open. However, this will not last. The rings are closing, and in 2009 will be edge-on, so that they will be seen as nothing more than a slender line of light – near the time of the ring-plane crossing, Saturn will be shorn of its beauty. This month the Cassini Division (between the A and B rings) is still very prominent, and the Encke Division (in the A ring) is by no means difficult, but you will notice a great difference next year.

Explorer 1. America's first artificial satellite, Explorer 1, was launched on 1 February 1958 – fifty years ago this month – and remained aloft until 31 March 1970, when it fell back into the upper atmosphere and burned away. Data transmission had stopped on 23 May 1958, when the batteries were exhausted.

Explorer 1 was built at the Jet Propulsion Laboratory, with scientific instrumentation designed by Dr James Van Allen (Figure 4) of Iowa University. It was sent up following the launch of the first two Soviet Sputniks, events that caused great alarm in the White House! The American rocket programme was floundering, and in desperation the officials handed over the mission to the team led by Wernher von Braun. It took von Braun only a few weeks to put Explorer 1 safely into orbit, with a perigee of 354 kilometres, an apogee of 2,515 kilometres and a period of 114.8 minutes. The total weight was 14 kilograms, of which the instruments accounted for 8.3 kilograms.

Explorer 1 was responsible for the discovery of the zones of intense radiation surrounding the Earth, now known as the Van Allen Belts. This was the first scientific discovery made by space-research methods.

This Month's Eclipses. There are two eclipses this month. To see the annular solar eclipse of 7 February, I am afraid you will have to travel far to the south, because the path of annularity starts in the South Pacific and ends in Antarctica. But the total eclipse of the Moon early on the 21st should be seen well – clouds permitting. Lunar eclipses are not important, but they are lovely to watch, particularly if varied colours show up. Of course, all sunlight reaching the eclipsed Moon

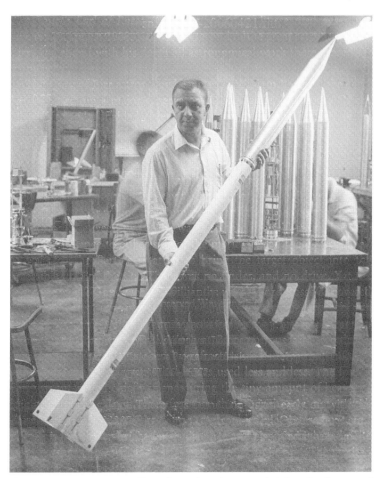

Figure 4. Dr James A. Van Allen, whose pioneering research led to the discovery of radiation belts surrounding the Earth. Van Allen played a key rôle in the US-Soviet space race of the 1950s and 60s. As a professor of physics at Iowa, he directed several graduate students in the assembly of data-gathering equipment for Explorer 1, the US's first satellite, launched in 1958. (Image courtesy of The University of Iowa Libraries.)

has to pass through the shell of atmosphere surrounding the Earth, so that everything depends upon the conditions in our upper air. Sometimes the full Moon remains bright; at other times it is obscure, and occasionally it's difficult to find even with a telescope. Totality lasts just 51 minutes, between 03.00 and 03.51 UT. The partial phase begins at 01.43 and ends at 05.09 UT.

At maximum eclipse this month, the entire disc of the Moon only just passes into the southern part of the umbra (the darker, central part of the Earth's shadow). Consequently, we may expect the southern part of the totally eclipsed Moon to remain rather bright. Watch this month – and have your camera at the ready.

February Anniversaries. Charles Pritchard was born on 29 February 1808 at Alberbury, Shropshire. He meant to enter the Anglican ministry, and held various teaching and clerical posts until 1870, when he became Professor of Astronomy at Oxford University. He was the first to use photography to measure stellar parallaxes, and in 1885 he completed a catalogue of the magnitudes of 2,784 stars. He died on 28 May 1893.

William Henry Pickering was born 150 years ago in Boston, Massachusetts, on 15 February 1858; he was the younger brother of Edward Charles Pickering, long-time Director of the Harvard College Observatory. William was concerned mainly with lunar and planetary research; for a time he joined Percival Lowell at Flagstaff, and paid special attention to Mars, proving that the dark areas were not sheets of water. In 1898 he discovered Phoebe, the ninth satellite of Saturn; this was the first satellite to be discovered photographically. Perhaps his best work was his photographic atlas of the Moon, published in 1903, in which each area of the surface was shown under several different conditions of illumination. Yet some of his ideas were strange: he believed that dark patches inside the crater Aristarchus moved around, and could be due to swarms of lunar insects or small animals! He died on 17 January 1938.

March

New Moon: 7 March   *Full Moon:* 21 March

Equinox: 20 March

Summer Time in the United Kingdom commences on 30 March.

MERCURY remains too close to the Sun for observation throughout the month for observers in the latitudes of the British Isles. For those in the tropics and the Southern Hemisphere it remains well placed for observation throughout the month, visible above the eastern horizon at the beginning of morning civil twilight (see Figure 3, given with the notes for February). During the month its magnitude brightens from +0.2 to −0.6. Mercury and Venus remain within a few degrees of each other throughout the month, though Venus is always the brighter planet of the two by at least a factor of twenty. At the beginning of the month Venus is about 2° east of Mercury, but this decreases gradually until Mercury overtakes Venus on 24 March, passing only 1° south of Venus, and ending the month 3° ahead.

VENUS continues to be visible as a brilliant object in the early-morning sky, magnitude −3.9. However, observers in northern temperate latitudes will find the planet coming to the end of its period of visibility: in particular, those as far north as the British Isles will have lost it in the glare of the rising Sun after the first week of the month.

MARS is no longer the conspicuous object it was in January: its magnitude fades from +0.2 to +0.8 during the month. In the middle of the month it will be crossing the meridian around the time of the end of civil twilight and remains visible in the evenings in the western sky until well after midnight, even by the end of the month. During the month it moves steadily eastwards from Taurus into Gemini, as will be seen from Figure 5.

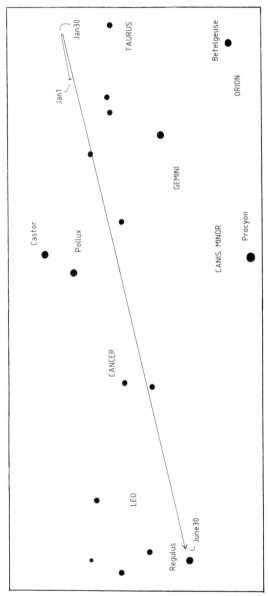

Figure 5. The path of Mars against the background stars of Taurus, Gemini, Cancer and Leo during the first six months of 2008.

JUPITER continues to be visible as a brilliant morning object in the eastern sky for an hour or two before dawn, magnitude −2.0. The path of Jupiter among the stars is shown in Figure 1, given with the notes for January.

SATURN, magnitude +0.3, becomes visible above the eastern horizon as soon as darkness falls and remains available for observation for the greater part of the night. Saturn remains in the constellation of Leo throughout the year.

The Non-identical Twins. The magnificent pattern of Orion is past his best, but his retinue remains on view, with Sirius flashing low in the south-west. (It is actually a pure white star; the flashing colours are caused by the Earth's unsteady atmosphere.) Look too for the twins Castor and Pollux in the constellation of Gemini, which are high up. In mythology they really were twins, but Pollux was immortal while Castor was not (the morals of the ancient Olympians were always questionable). When Castor was killed, Pollux pleaded to be allowed to share his immortality with his brother. His request was granted, and both boys were placed in the sky.

Even a casual glance will show that Pollux is the brighter of the two by about half a magnitude (1.15 against 1.58). It is also closer, 34 light years against 52 light years, so that the twins are in no way related. Castor is a good double; components magnitudes 1.9 and 2.9, separation 4.4 seconds of arc. This is a binary, period uncertain, but in excess of 400 years; each component is a spectroscopic binary. There is a much fainter member of the system, Castor C, made up of a pair of red dwarfs: it is an eclipsing binary and is therefore given a variable star designation, YY Geminiorum. All in all, therefore, Castor is made up of six stars, four bright and two dim.

Pollux is an orange K-type star, thirty-three times as luminous as the Sun. It has no stellar companion but it does have a large planet, considerably more massive than Jupiter, which we may be sure is a gas giant, even though we cannot observe it telescopically and have detected it by indirect means. Use binoculars to look at the twins in turn; the difference in colour is very obvious indeed.

The Ice Cliffs of Dione. Dione is one of Saturn's icy satellites; it has a diameter of 1,120 kilometres, and is rather denser than the other icy moons, so it must have a rocky core. The Voyager images showed 'wispy' markings on the disc, which were interpreted as being deposits of ice or frost. However, images from the Cassini orbiter, taken in 2006 and 2007 (Figure 6), showed that this was not so. The 'wisps' are actually towering, steep ice cliffs, produced by tectonic activity.

The cliffs meander through the smoother regions of the surface, hinting at some sort of icy vulcanism or resurfacing. According to planetary scientist William McKinnon, 'Dione is tectonically active – many cliffs are sharp and fresh-looking. Internal forces are ripping the satellite's surface apart ... the images confirm the rich variety of terrain, from the usual heavily cratered regions to a broad expanse of lightly cratered, smooth terrain.'

Figure 6. During a close flyby of Saturn's icy moon Dione, the Cassini spacecraft captured a set of images of the 'wispy terrain' which consists of bright ice cliffs created by tectonic fractures. The surface is also clearly very heavily cratered. (Image courtesy of NASA/JPL/ Space Science Institute.)

At magnitude 10.7, Dione is an easy telescopic object. It is about the same size as Tethys, but the two differ: Tethys lacks the tall cliffs and is less dense, so its globe contains much more ice than rock.

Tau Boötis. Boötes, the Herdsman, is prominent because it contains Arcturus, which is the brightest star in the Northern Hemisphere of the sky – marginally superior to Capella and Vega. Its magnitude is −0.05, and it is one of only four stars to exceed magnitude 0; the others are Sirius, Canopus and Alpha Centauri (assuming that you combine the two main components of Alpha Centauri). Arcturus is a lovely orange star, 37 light years away and 115 times as luminous as the Sun; the amount of heat received from Arcturus has been estimated as equal to that of a candle at a distance of 8 kilometres on a calm day!

However, Arcturus is by no means the only interesting feature of the Herdsman. For example, Epsilon Boötis (Izar) is a fine, easy double, while Zeta is a close binary whose components appear almost identical (magnitudes 4.5 and 4.6, separation 0.6 seconds of arc). But there is also Tau Boötis, near the 2.7-magnitude Eta (Seginus), to which astronomers using the Canada–France–Hawaii Telescope (CFHT) on Mauna Kea have been paying particular attention.

Tau – which has never been given the honour of a proper name – is of magnitude 4.5, adjoining its slightly brighter neighbour Upsilon (4.1). Tau is 50 light years away, of spectral type F7; it is almost three times as luminous as the Sun, and 1.4 times as massive. Its age has been given as a thousand million years, and it is weakly active. For some time it has been known that there is an attendant planet, at least 4.4 times as massive as Jupiter, orbiting the star every 3.3 days at a distance of about 7.3 million kilometres – so close-in that the planet must be a searingly hot gas giant (a so-called 'hot Jupiter'). What makes Tau so exceptional is that the star is rotating in step with the planet's orbit. The star's behaviour is similar to that of our Moon, which always keeps the same face pointed towards the Earth. It is unusual to find the larger body – in this case a star – being tidally locked by a smaller body.

The CFHT was used to make measurements of the star's rotation; the equator spins in 15 days, 18 per cent faster than at the poles. Such a differential rotation is crucial in the generation of a star's magnetic field. The CFHT observations showed that the star possesses a magnetic field just a little greater than our Sun's, but with a more complex structure. This is the first detection of a magnetic field around a star with a 'hot Jupiter' planet.

Boötes is not striking, apart from the presence of Arcturus, but it is easy to make out its shape (Figure 7). A few stars in the region of the 3.5-magnitude Beta (Nekkar) were once hived off to form a separate constellation, Quadrans Muralis (the Mural Quadrant); this did not survive the axe wielded by the International Astronomical Union, but at least we remember it because it has given its name to the Quadrantid meteor shower of early January.

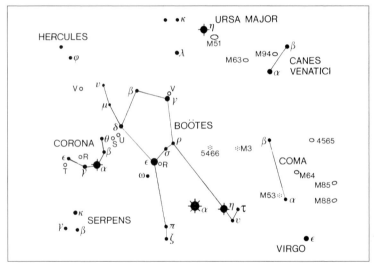

Figure 7. The principal stars of Boötes, the Herdsman. The star Tau Boötis, which has an attendant planet several times the mass of Jupiter, is to the right of the somewhat brighter Eta Boötis, which is in turn to the right of the brilliant Arcturus (Alpha Boötis), shown lower centre on this map.

April

MERCURY passes through superior conjunction on 16 April and remains too close to the Sun for observation until the last few days of the month, when it becomes visible low in the west-north-western sky at the end of evening civil twilight. During this short period its magnitude fades from −1.2 to −0.9. For observers in northern temperate latitudes this will be the most favourable evening apparition of the year. Figure 8 shows, for observers in latitude 52°N, the changes in azimuth (true bearing from the north through east, south and west) and altitude of Mercury on successive evenings when the Sun is 6° below the horizon. This condition is known as the end of evening civil twilight, and in this latitude and at this time of year occurs about 35 minutes after sunset. The changes in the brightness of the planet are indicated by the relative sizes of the circles marking Mercury's position at five-day intervals. It will be noticed that Mercury is at its brightest before it reaches greatest eastern elongation (22°) on 14 May. The diagram gives positions for a time at the end of evening civil twilight on the Greenwich meridian, on the stated date. Observers in different longitudes should note that the actual positions of Mercury in azimuth and altitude will differ slightly from those shown in the diagram. This change will be much greater still for the Moon, if it is shown, as its motion is about 0.5° per hour.

VENUS, magnitude −3.9, is already too close to the Sun for observation from the latitudes of the British Isles. Even further south it is coming to the end of its period of visibility, though those in southern latitudes will still be able to see it right through the month, low down above the eastern horizon shortly before sunrise.

MARS continues to move direct in the constellation of Gemini. Towards the end of the month it will be seen to the south of Castor and

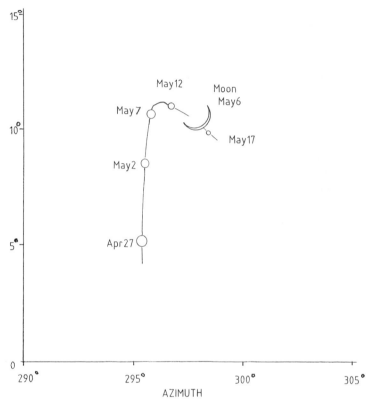

Figure 8. Evening apparition of Mercury, from latitude 52°N. The position of the crescent Moon is shown for 6 May as an aid to locating the planet. (Angular diameters of Mercury and the crescent Moon not to scale.)

Pollux. Mars is visible in the western sky in the evenings, its magnitude fading from +0.8 to +1.2.

JUPITER, magnitude −2.2, is slowly brightening though still three months from opposition. It remains visible as a bright object in the constellation of Sagittarius. The planet is now crossing the meridian before dawn, near overhead for those in low southern latitudes, but only at a low altitude for those in the latitudes of the British Isles.

SATURN continues to be visible as an evening object in Leo until after midnight. Its magnitude is +0.5.

Karl Luther and the Discovery of Kalypso. Asteroid No. 53 was discovered by the German astronomer Karl Luther 150 years ago, on 4 April 1858. It is hardly a striking object. It is a normal member of the Main Belt of asteroids; it moves round the Sun at a mean distance of 392 million kilometres in a period of 4.24 years, and its diameter is 115 kilometres. It is of type C (carbonaceous). It was named after the same deity as Calypso, one of Saturn's satellites (a Tethys co-orbital), so that to avoid any confusion it seems sensible to spell the asteroid's name with a K.

The mean opposition magnitude is 11.7, and the rotation period is around 27 hours. Obviously, an ordinary telescope will show it only as a point of light, and it has not been imaged by any spacecraft.

Karl Theodore Robert Luther worked at Düsseldorf, and was an enthusiastic asteroid hunter; he made his first discovery (of 17 Thetis) on 17 April 1852, and his last (288 Glauke) on 20 February 1890. Altogether he found twenty-four asteroids, of which his last is probably the most interesting. Glauke has the exceptionally slow rotation period of about 1,300 hours – almost two months – making it the slowest-rotating non-planetary object known in the Solar System. Its rotation is believed to be 'tumbling'. It is only about 32 kilometres in diameter, and at magnitude 13.2 is one of the faintest of Luther's asteroids. Karl Luther was born on 16 April 1822, and died on 15 February 1900.

The Crow and the Cup. This is a good time of the year to follow the long, sprawling constellation of Hydra, the Watersnake, which begins south of Cancer and meanders along in the southern sky until it ends south of Spica in Virgo. Now that Argo Navis has been broken up, Hydra is the largest constellation in the sky, covering 1,303 square degrees, but it has only one bright star, the reddish Alpha (Alphard), magnitude 2.0. Next come Gamma (3.0) and Zeta and Nu (each 3.1). The southernmost of the main stars, Beta (4.3), is at declination −34 degrees, so that as seen from Britain it is always very low down.

On the Watersnake's back there are two separate constellations, Corvus, the Crow, and Crater, the Cup (Figure 9). Despite their small size and lack of brilliant stars, both were included in Ptolemy's original list of forty-eight constellations, and both have mythological

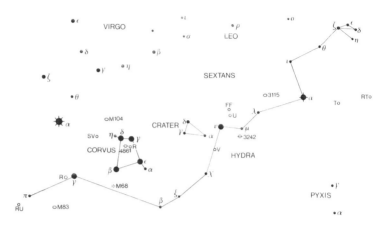

Figure 9. The principal stars of the long and meandering constellation Hydra, the Watersnake, together with the smaller neighbouring patterns of Crater, the Cup and Corvus, the Crow. Hydra represents the multiple-headed monster which lived in the Lernaean Marshes, until it was killed by Hercules. Its brightest star Alphard (Alpha Hydrae) is known as 'the Solitary One', because there are no other bright stars near to it.

associations. Crater is said to represent the goblet of the wine god Bacchus. Corvus has a more definite legend. When Apollo became enamoured of Coronis, mother of the great doctor Aesculapius, he sent a crow to watch her and report on her behaviour. The crow came back with a report that was decidedly unfavourable, but Apollo was apparently satisfied, and rewarded the bird with a place in the sky.

Corvus has four stars above the fourth magnitude; they are arranged in the shape of a quadrilateral, and this makes the constellation easy to find, particularly since it lies in a barren region. The four stars are:

Star	Proper Name	Magnitude	Spectral Type	Luminosity Sun = 1	Distance light years
Gamma	Minkar	2.6	B8	250	185
Betaz	Kraz	2.7	G5	600	290
Delta	Algorel	2.9	B9	60	117
Epsilon	—	3.0	K2	96	104

Curiously, Alpha Corvi (Alkhiba) is only of magnitude 4.0, a magnitude fainter than any of the stars making up the quadrilateral. Bayer's system seems to have gone badly wrong here.

The most interesting objects in Corvus are the Antennae galaxies NGC 4038 and 4039 (Figure 10). Their position is RA 12h 01.9m, Dec. −18° 53′. These are two galaxies in collision with each other. It is

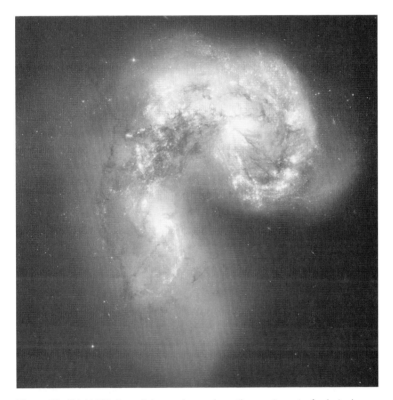

Figure 10. This Hubble Space Telescope image shows the merging pair of galaxies known as the Antennae galaxies. In the course of the collision, billions of stars will be formed. The two galaxies are dotted with brilliant star-forming regions surrounded by glowing hydrogen gas. The brightest and most compact of these starbirth regions are called super star clusters. The blobs to the left and right of image centre are the two cores of the original galaxies and consist mainly of old stars criss-crossed by filaments of dust. (Image courtesy of NASA, ESA, and the Hubble Heritage Team (STScI/AURA)-ESA/Hubble Collaboration with thanks to B. Whitmore (Space Telescope Science Institute).)

by no means a 'brief encounter' – it began around 500 million years ago. The individual stars seldom hit each other, but the interstellar gas and dust is colliding all the time, so that it is compressed and triggers a 'firestorm' of star formation. The apparent magnitudes are respectively 11 and 13.

Crater is very dim; its leaders, Delta (magnitude 3.7), Gamma (4.1) and Alpha or Alkes (also 4.1), form a triangle close to Nu Hydrae. There are various faint galaxies in Crater, but nothing of special interest to the user of a small telescope.

May

New Moon: 5 May   *Full Moon:* 20 May

MERCURY is at greatest eastern elongation (22°) on 14 May and, for observers in the tropics and in the Northern Hemisphere, continues to be visible low above the west-north-western horizon at the end of evening civil twilight, until just after the middle of the month. During this period its magnitude fades from −0.8 to +1.1. Observers should refer to the diagram given with the notes for April (Figure 8). For those in the Southern Hemisphere the visibility period only starts after the first week of the month and ends about ten days later.

VENUS is no longer visible from northern temperate latitudes, but can still be seen for the first three weeks of the month from the tropics and southern latitudes, low above the eastern horizon before sunrise. Its magnitude is −3.9.

MARS, its magnitude fading from +1.2 to +1.5 during the month, is still visible in the western sky in the evenings but by the end of the month is lost to view before midnight. Mars continues to move eastwards, passing from Gemini into Cancer early in the month. In the early hours of 23 May it will be seen passing in front of the open cluster Praesepe (the Beehive), M44.

JUPITER, magnitude −2.5, continues to be visible as a conspicuous object in the morning skies, in the east. On 9 May it reaches its first stationary point and then moves slowly retrograde in the constellation of Sagittarius.

SATURN, magnitude +0.7, reaches its second stationary point in Leo on 3 May and resumes its direct (eastward) motion. It is well placed for observation as soon as darkness falls. However, from the Southern Hemisphere it will be lost from view before midnight, though observers in northern latitudes will see it for a little longer.

The War God and the Beehive. During this month Mars, the planet of the God of War, passes in front of the open cluster M44 (NGC 2632), in Cancer. Mars is well below the first magnitude, so that its red light will not swamp the dim stars of the cluster.

M44, otherwise known as Praesepe, is an easy naked-eye object, and must have been known since very ancient times; Hipparchus included it as 'a cloudy star' in his catalogue drawn up around 139 BC, and in Ptolemy's catalogue of around AD 50 it was numbered 449. In 1609 Galileo, using his tiny telescope, recorded that 'the nebula called Praesepe contains not one star only, but a mass of more than 40 small ones. We have noted 36 besides the Aselli.' The Aselli, or 'Asses', are the stars that lie to either side of Praesepe – they are so named because an old name for the cluster itself was 'the Manger'. Asellus Australis (Delta Cancri) is the brighter of the two, at magnitude 3.9; it is of type K, and distinctly orange. Asellus Borealis (Gamma Cancri) is of type A; magnitude 4.7. Incidentally, Johann Bayer allocated Praesepe a Greek letter when compiling his star catalogue in 1503; the cluster was listed as Epsilon Cancri. (The only other cluster with a Greek letter is the far-southern globular, Omega Centauri.)

Praesepe is the most prominent open cluster in the Northern Hemisphere of the sky apart from the Pleiades and the Hyades in Taurus. Unlike the Pleiades, it contains no nebulosity, and there are few hot, white or bluish stars; the leaders are in general yellowish or orange, so that the cluster is obviously odd. Its age has been estimated at 730 million years. It is by no means closely packed; the true diameter is about 15 light years, and the total number of cluster stars is at least 200. It has retained its separate identity because it is several hundred light years away from the main plane of the Galaxy, and there are not many 'field stars' close enough to disrupt it gravitationally. The apparent diameter is 95 minutes of arc; the integrated magnitude is 3.7, and according to ESA's astrometric satellite Hipparcos the distance is 577 light years. It is known as the Beehive (I have never understood why in Ancient China it had the unattractive name of 'the Exhalation of Piled-up Corpses'!).

The cluster is centred at RA 08h 40.1m, Dec. +19° 59'. The cluster, together with Mars, will attract astrophotographers towards the end of this month.

Cancer's Other Bright Cluster. Praesepe is not the only notable open cluster in Cancer the Crab (Figure 11). There is also M67, near Alpha Cancri or Acubens (magnitude 4.2). The integrated magnitude of M67 is 6.1, so that it is not far below naked-eye visibility; binoculars show it well. Its position is RA 08h 50.4m, Dec. +11° 49'. The apparent diameter is 30 minutes of arc; its distance has been given as 2,700 light years.

M67 is one of the oldest of all known open clusters in our Galaxy. It owes its longevity to the fact that it lies in a sparsely populated area, well over 1,000 light years from the galactic plane; a reasonable estimate for its age is around 4,000 million years, more than 15 'cosmic years' – one cosmic year being the time taken by the Sun to complete one orbit around the centre of the Galaxy. M67 was not listed by Ptolemy, and seems to have been first seen around 1775 by Kohler.

Excluding the Pleiades and the two Magellanic Clouds, which must have been familiar in prehistoric times, the only nebular objects definitely recorded before the invention of the telescope were NGC869/884, the Sword Handle in Perseus; M44, Praesepe; M7, an open cluster in Scorpius; M31, the Andromeda Galaxy; and IC 2391,

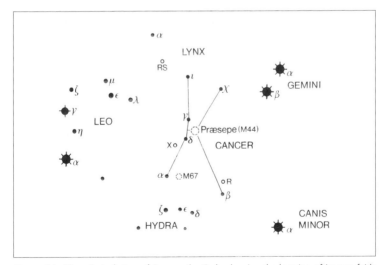

Figure 11. The principal stars of Cancer, the Crab, showing the location of its two fairly bright open clusters – M44, also known as Praesepe or the Beehive cluster (centre), and the slightly fainter and much older M67 (below centre).

the o Velorum cluster. Of these the first three were listed by Ptolemy, and the last two by the Arab astronomer Al-Sûfi in AD 964.

Not a great deal seems to be known about the discoverer of M67, Johann Gottfried Kohler, except that he lived in Dresden and was the first to record M59 and M60, both elliptical galaxies in Virgo, while hunting for comets. He described M59 and M60 as 'two very small nebulae, hardly visible in a 3-foot telescope, one above the other'. Charles Messier discovered them independently a few nights later (15 April 1779).

June

New Moon: 3 June   *Full Moon:* 18 June

Solstice: 20 June

MERCURY passes through inferior conjunction on 7 June, but then moves away from the Sun to reach greatest western elongation (22°) on 1 July. The long summer twilight precludes observation from northern temperate latitudes. Visibility conditions improve as one travels further south, and those in the tropics and in the Southern Hemisphere will be able to locate the planet low above the east-north-east horizon about half an hour before sunrise during the last few days of the month. During this period its magnitude brightens from +1.1 to +0.7.

VENUS passes through superior conjunction on 9 June and is therefore too close to the Sun for observation. Indeed, for a short while on that date no Earth-based instrument could detect it, since it is actually occulted by the Sun. It is interesting to note that at this particular conjunction it is exactly halfway between the only two transits of the planet that occur this century – in 2004 and 2012.

MARS has now faded to magnitude +1.6, but continues to be visible in the evenings in the western sky. Towards the end of June, Mars moves from Cancer into Leo. Observers will note that Mars is moving towards Saturn, coming to within 5° of that planet by the last day of the month, when it passes 0.8° north of Regulus.

JUPITER continues to be visible as a conspicuous object in the night sky, magnitude −2.7, as it approaches opposition early next month. Even observers in the British Isles will be able to see the planet in the south-eastern sky before midnight.

SATURN continues to be visible in the western sky in the evenings. Saturn's magnitude is +0.9 and therefore noticeably brighter than

Mars, which is moving eastwards towards it and will overtake it next month.

PLUTO reaches opposition on 20 June, in the constellation of Sagittarius, at a distance of 4,558 million kilometres (2,832 million miles). It is visible only with a moderate-sized telescope, since its magnitude is +14. In August 2006, the International Astronomical Union downgraded it from its status as a planet, preferring to call it a 'dwarf planet'.

Explosion in Siberia. A hundred years ago – to be precise, at 7.17 a.m. on 30 June 1908 – there was a violent explosion in the Tunguska region of Siberia, now known as the Krasnoyarsk Krai region of Russia. Something or other fell from the sky and devastated an area centred on latitude 60° 55′N, longitude 101° 57′E. Over a region 2,150 square kilometres in area, 80 million trees were blown flat (Figure 12), and

Figure 12. Some of the 80 million trees that were flattened over an area of 2,150 square kilometres by the blast in the remote Tunguska region of Siberia on 30 June 1908. Although the devastation was tremendous, the site was so remote that little was known about the impact of the explosion until scientific expeditions arrived to study it in 1927. (Image courtesy of Russian Academy of Sciences.)

the energy of the blast was later estimated as being equivalent to 20 megatons of TNT (over a thousand times more powerful than the bomb dropped on Hiroshima). Reindeer suffered badly, but nobody was killed because the region was so sparsely inhabited.

Because Tunguska is so remote, and because of the unsettled state of affairs in Imperial Russia at that time, world comment was surprisingly muted, even though the explosion was registered by seismic stations all over Europe and Asia. No scientific expeditions reached the site until 1927, when a team led by Leonid Kulik did so. However, some eyewitness reports have survived, and here are extracts from one of these, by a forester named S. Semenov:

> At breakfast-time I was sitting by the house at the Vanavara trading post [60 kilometres south of the explosion centre]. I suddenly saw that directly to the north, over Onkoul's Tunguska road, the sky split in two and fire appeared high and wide over the forest. The split in the sky grew larger, and the entire northern side was cleaved with fire. At that moment I became unbearably hot, as though my shirt was on fire; . . . I wanted to tear off my shirt and throw it down, but then the sky closed, and a strong thump sounded, and I was thrown several yards. I lost my senses for a moment, but then my wife ran out and helped me to the house. After that came noises, as though rocks were falling or cannons were firing; the earth shook. . . . When the sky opened up, hot winds raced between the houses. Later we saw that many windows had been shattered, and iron locks snapped.

It must have been terrifying, but at least there were no human casualties. It was calculated that if the impactor had struck 4 hours 47 minutes later, it would have wiped out the city of St Petersburg (a cynical politician is alleged to have regretted that it didn't, in view of the fact that the Bolshevik Revolution began there a few years later!). But what caused the explosion? Theories have not been lacking, and here are a few of them:

1. The impactor was a large meteoroid, which burst when around 10 kilometres above the Earth's surface. This is much the most probable explanation; such an airburst would explain the violence of the explosion, and the lack of a crater. A meteoroid around 20 metres in diameter would be adequate.

2. The impactor was a small asteroid, or a fragment of an asteroid. This is really the same thing as 1 above, because there seems to be little difference between a small asteroid and a large meteoroid, though it is usually assumed that an asteroid has a higher average density than a meteoroid.

3. The impactor was a small comet (F.J.W. Whipple, 1930). Since a comet is mainly ice and dust, it could have been completely vapourized, leaving no detectable traces. In 1978 the Slovak astronomer Lubor Kresak even suggested that a fragment of Encke's periodical comet was responsible, because this comet is the parent of the Beta Taurid meteor shower that – significantly? – peaks at the end of June.

4. The explosion was caused by the annihilation of a piece of antimatter coming from space – not impossible, but surely very, very unlikely.

5. The explosion was caused when a visiting spaceship crash-landed, and exploded – here, perhaps, it is kindest just to say 'No comment!'

Since then there has been only one other major impact: on 12 February 1947, again in a virtually uninhabited part of Siberia, about 430 kilometres north-east of Vladivostok. However, there is no mystery about it; the fall of meteorites (known as the Sikhote–Alin fall, Figure 13) was observed, and many craters, both large and small, were located. Another major fall may, of course, happen at any time.

Pluto at Opposition. Pluto reaches opposition on 20 June, but it is only of the fourteenth magnitude. No doubt astrologers and their kind will note the opposition date, blissfully ignoring the fact that Pluto is now known to be only one of numerous Kuiper Belt objects – and not even the largest of the swarm. If they feel inclined to take Pluto into consideration, they must also include Eris, Quaoar, Varuna, Sedna, Orcus . . . and so on. In the end their horoscopes will start to look a little complicated!

Figure 13. One of the most spectacular meteorite falls occurred on 12 February 1947, in the Sikhote-Alin mountains of eastern Russia. An eyewitness painted this impression of the bright meteor as it streaked across the sky, shedding sparks and leaving a trail of swirling smoke. After it disappeared over the horizon, great explosions thundered and echoed from the hills, so loud they were heard 100 kilometres away. (Image courtesy of NASA JSC (photo S79–29470).)

July

EARTH is at aphelion (furthest from the Sun) on 4 July at a distance of 152 million kilometres (94.5 million miles).

MERCURY is not suitably placed for observation by Northern Hemisphere observers, but for those near to and south of the equator the planet will continue to be visible in the early-morning skies for the first half of the month, low above the east-north-eastern horizon before dawn. During its period of visibility its magnitude brightens from +0.5 to −1.0. Thereafter Mercury will be too close to the Sun to be observable, as it reaches superior conjunction on 29 July.

VENUS, magnitude −3.9, becomes visible very early in the month, in the evenings, low above the western horizon after sunset for observers in the tropics: within a week its region of visibility has spread to include those in the Southern Hemisphere and as far north as Mediterranean latitudes. However, the long duration of summer twilight in the latitudes of the British Isles means that observers there will be lucky to see it at all before early in August.

MARS is still an evening object, magnitude +1.7, moving steadily eastwards in Leo throughout the month, passing less than 1° north of Regulus on 1 July and less than 1° south of Saturn on 10–11 July. Observers in the latitudes of the British Isles will not be so fortunate, as they will suffer from the long duration of summer twilight. They may be able to see it for the first week or so low above the western horizon after the end of evening civil twilight, but after that they will not be able to see it again this year. The path of Mars among the stars during the next few months is shown in Figure 14.

JUPITER, magnitude −2.7, is now at its brightest, since it is at opposition on 9 July and therefore available for observation throughout

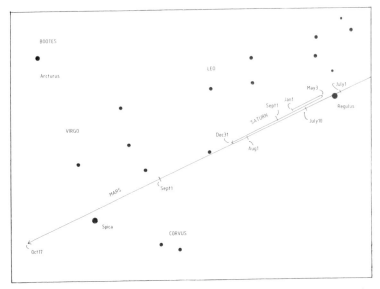

Figure 14. The path of Saturn against the background stars of Leo during 2008. Also shown (as the longer of the two lines) is the path of Mars against the stars of Leo and Virgo from July to October. The Red Planet is not suitably placed for observation during the last two months of the year as it passes through superior conjunction on 5 December.

the night wherever you are on our planet. It is a disappointing object for observers in high northern temperate latitudes because of its low altitude, even when on the meridian (for example, the maximum altitude as seen from southern England is only 16°, the same as the midwinter Sun). When closest to the Earth its distance is 623 million kilometres (387 million miles). The path of Jupiter among the stars is shown in Figure 1, given with the notes for January.

SATURN, magnitude +0.9, can still be seen in the western sky for several hours after sunset, for those in tropical and southern latitudes. Unfortunately, for observers in the latitudes of the British Isles it will soon get lost in the long summer evening twilight. The path of Saturn among the stars during the year is shown in Figure 14, which also shows Mars passing south of Saturn during this month.

The Loveliest Comet. A century and a half ago – during July 1858 – the most beautiful comet of all time was shining in the night sky. It had been discovered on 2 June by the Italian astronomer Giovanni Donati, it brightened steadily during June and July, and by September had risen to magnitude −1. It reached perihelion on 30 September, when it was 86.8 million kilometres from the Sun, came closest to Earth (about 75 million kilometres) on 9 October and remained a naked-eye object through to November. The last observation of it was made on 4 March 1859. Its period is about 2,000 years, so that, regretfully, it will not be seen in our time.

There have been brighter comets, but none so breathtakingly lovely. It had two straight ion tails, but what made it unique was the prominent dust tail that developed around the time of the closest approach to Earth, curved like a scimitar and extending for 60 degrees. Many drawings and engravings of it were made (Figure 15), and it was actually the first comet to be photographed; it was recorded by an English commercial photographer, W. Usherwood, who used a portrait camera the plate of which showed the comet's head together with a very faint image of a tail. On the following night a photograph was obtained from the Harvard College Observatory in America. No further comet photography took place until 1881. It is a great pity that Donati's Comet was seen before photography had been properly developed.

Many years ago I was talking to Madame Flammarion, second wife of the famous French astronomer Camille Flammarion. I happened to mention Donati's Comet, and her face lit up in a smile. 'Yes,' she said, 'that was the most beautiful thing I have ever seen in the sky. How I wish I could see it again!'

Giovanni Battista Donati was born in Pisa on 16 December 1862, and graduated from Pisa University. In 1852 he joined the staff of the Florence Observatory and became Director in 1864; he discovered six comets, including that of 1858, and was a pioneer of astronomical spectroscopy – he was in fact the first to obtain and analyse the spectrum of a comet. A lunar crater is named in his honour: 20.7°S, 5.2°E, in the area of Arzachel; diameter 35 kilometres. It is well formed, with a central peak, and adjoins a crater named after another famous comet hunter, Hervé Faye. Giovanni Donati died in Florence on 20 September 1873.

Figure 15. A contemporary engraving of a view of Donati's comet hanging over the city of Paris in October 1858. In addition to two narrow, straight ion tails, the comet developed a prominent dust tail, curved like a scimitar, around the time of closest approach to Earth, and it has been described as the most beautiful comet ever seen.

Less Familiar Star Names. July is not the best month for stargazing but it is the best time to find the red supergiant Antares, in Scorpius, low in the south. It is flanked by two stars just above the third magnitude, Tau and Sigma Scorpii. Tau has no individual name, but Sigma has: Alniyat.

Proper names of stars are generally used only for the brighter stars, plus a few special cases such as the long-period variable star Mira (Omicron Ceti). However, some star names are decidedly bizarre. Here are a few, selected at random:

Alpha Aquarii	Sadalmelik
Gamma Aquilae	Tarazed
Beta Carinae	Miaplacidus
Zeta Aurigae	Sadatoni
Eta Canis Majoris	Aludra
Gamma Cephei	Alrai
Zeta Ceti	Baten Kaitos
Alpha Crateris	Alkes
Gamma Cygni	Sadr
Delta Draconis	Tais
Delta Edidani	Theemini
Delta Geminorum	Wasat
Mu Leonis	Rassalas
Zeta Ophichuni	Han
Lambda Orionis	Haka
Beta Sagittaeii	Arkab
Theta Serpentis	Alya
Delta Ursae Minoris	Yilun
Iota Virginis	Syrma

There are many others. Note, incidentally, that some 'agencies' claim to be able to give stars names of your choosing (naturally on payment of money). Stars have not been named for many centuries, so have nothing to do with schemes of this sort. It is equivalent to pouring money into a particularly murky drain.

August

New Moon: 1 and 30 August   *Full Moon:* 16 August

MERCURY is moving eastwards, away from the Sun: it is also moving southwards in declination so that it will not be suitably placed for observation in northern temperate latitudes. Opportunities for seeing Mercury improve as the observer's latitude decreases, and those in the tropics and the Southern Hemisphere will be able to see the planet in the western evening sky after the first ten days of the month. For observers in southern latitudes this will be the most favourable evening apparition of the year. Figure 16 shows, for observers in latitude 35°S, the changes in azimuth (true bearing from the north through east, south and west) and altitude of Mercury on successive evenings when the Sun is 6° below the horizon. This condition is known as the end of evening civil twilight and in this latitude and at this time of year occurs about 25 minutes after sunset. The changes in the brightness of the planet are indicated by the relative sizes of the circles marking Mercury's position at five-day intervals. It will be noticed that Mercury is at its brightest before it reaches greatest eastern elongation (27°) on 11 September. The diagram gives positions for a time at the end of evening civil twilight on the Greenwich meridian, on the stated date. Observers in different longitudes should note that the actual positions of Mercury in azimuth and altitude will differ slightly from those shown in the diagram. This change will be much greater still for the Moon, if it is shown, as its motion is about 0.5° per hour. Mercury passes 1° north of Regulus on 10 August, but this will be a difficult observation to make as Regulus is two magnitudes fainter than Mercury.

VENUS, magnitude −3.9, is moving slowly out from the Sun and is visible low above the western horizon in the evenings after sunset. For observers in the latitudes of the British Isles there will be little chance of seeing the planet until after the first ten days of the month. Venus is in the same region of the sky as Mercury, passing within a degree of that

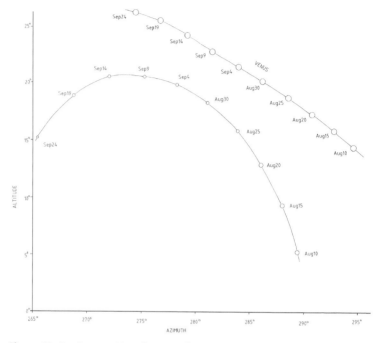

Figure 16. Evening apparition of Mercury, from latitude 35°S. The position of the brilliant planet Venus (above), which is also visible in the morning sky at the time, is shown at 5-day intervals for the period from 10 August to 24 September as an aid to locating Mercury. (Angular diameters of Mercury and Venus not to scale.)

planet on 21 August, as will be seen from Figure 16. Venus passes 1° north of Regulus on 5 August.

MARS will not be visible to observers in the latitudes of the British Isles, but those in low northern temperate latitudes and further south will still be able to see it low in the western sky in the evenings, magnitude +1.7. During the month Mars passes from Leo into Virgo.

JUPITER remains a brilliant object, visible during the greater part of the night from sunset to the early-morning twilight, magnitude −2.6.

SATURN, although no longer visible to those in high northern temperate latitudes, can still be seen by observers further south, low in the western sky, for a short while in the early evenings until the middle of the month. Its magnitude is +0.9.

NEPTUNE reaches opposition on 15 August, in the constellation of Capricornus. At opposition Neptune is 4,342 million kilometres (2,698 million miles) from the Earth. It is not visible to the naked eye since its magnitude is +7.8. Figure 17 shows the path of Neptune among the stars during the year. The two brightest stars are Gamma Capricorni (magnitude +3.7, RA 21h 40.6m, Dec. −16.6°) and Delta Capricorni (magnitude +2.9, RA 21h 47.6m, Dec. −16.1°). These two stars are shown on Northern Star Chart 8S and Southern Star Chart 8N, just below and to the left of '320'.

This Month's Eclipses. There are two eclipses this month, one of the Sun and one of the Moon, but only the lunar eclipse will be seen well from Britain.

The total solar eclipse of 1 August is not particularly promising. The track of totality begins in northern Canada at about 09.21 UT; the totality zone is 206 kilometres wide, and the Sun is completely hidden for 1m 30s. The track crosses North Greenland at about 9.30, and passes near the North Pole before reaching Russia at 10.10 UT; the track here is 232 kilometres wide, and the duration 2m 25s minutes. Not far inland, greatest eclipse yields 2m 27s of totality. The path then moves south-east, crossing into Mongolia and then China, where the eclipse ends at 11.21 UT. Best weather prospects are along the border of Mongolia and north-western China. Greenland might seem an attractive site, but the weather conditions there, even in August, are decidedly dubious!

Britain will see a partial eclipse. At Greenwich the maximum phase is timed for 09.18 UT, but only 22 per cent of the Sun is covered; from Edinburgh the eclipse is greatest at 09.17, with 35 per cent obscuration.

The partial lunar eclipse of 16 August will at least be visible from Britain in its entirety, clouds permitting. It begins at 19.35 and ends at 22.44 UT; at maximum obscuration just over 80 per cent of the surface is covered by the Earth's shadow. It cannot honestly be said that lunar eclipses are important, but they are interesting to watch and to photograph; with 80 per cent obscuration, we may reasonably hope to see some of the lovely colours so often striking during totality.

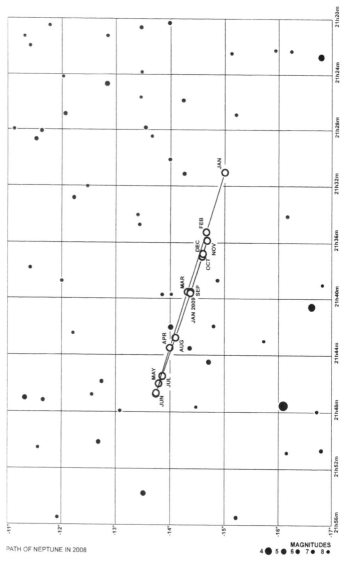

PATH OF NEPTUNE IN 2008

MAGNITUDES
4 ● 5 ● 6 ● 7 ● 8 ●

Figure 17. The path of Neptune against the stars of Capricornus during 2007. The two brightest stars, both shown at the lower left on the chart, are Gamma Capricorni (magnitude +3.7, RA 21h 40.6m, Dec. −16.6°) and Delta Capricorni (magnitude +2.9, RA 21h 47.6m, Dec. −16.1°).

The Fourth Earl of Rosse. The fourth Earl of Rosse died a century ago, on 30 August 1908. He was the second of the great astronomers of Birr Castle, and with his death all astronomical work there ceased for many years.

The story of Birr astronomy began with William Parsons, the third Earl, who set up a major observatory at the castle, in County Offaly, central Ireland. Unaided except by workers from the Birr estate, he built a 36-inch reflector and then, in 1845, a 72-inch telescope – the 'Leviathan' – which was far larger than any of its predecessors (William Herschel's biggest telescope had a main mirror only 49 inches in diameter). It was a strange instrument; nothing like it had ever been built before, and it is safe to say that nothing like it will ever be built again. The mirror was of speculum metal, and the tube was mounted at the bottom, between two stone walls, so that it could swing for only a limited distance to either side of the meridian and the observer had to wait for the Earth's rotation to bring the target object into the accessible area of the sky. There was no finder, and no drive. Yet the telescope worked, and worked brilliantly; with it Lord Rosse discovered the spiral forms of the objects we now know to be galaxies.

Lord Rosse died in 1867 and was succeeded by his son Laurence, who became the fourth Earl. Work at Birr continued, but gradually the 'Leviathan' was overtaken by refractors and more modern-type, glass-mirrored reflectors, so that it was used less and less. The fourth Earl was interested chiefly in measuring the tiny amount of heat sent to us from the Moon, and for this the 72-inch was not suited. Astronomical activity at Birr did not end suddenly; it petered out, and after the fourth Earl's death the great telescope was neglected. The mirror was sent to the Science Museum in London for safe keeping.

Today the scene is very different. The 'Leviathan' has been restored to its original glory, and is fully operational again for both display and research. Of course it is limited, and can never match a modern telescope of the same aperture, but it is unique. I am proud to say that I played a small part in its restoration, and should you be in that part of Ireland I strongly recommend that you pay it a visit. The grounds of Birr Castle are open to the public almost every day of the year.

The Star Clouds of Sagittarius. Given dark, clear skies, look this month for the star clouds in Sagittarius, very low down in the south. From the British Isles, they are never seen to advantage. From southerly latitudes they are a magnificent sight. They mask our view of the centre of the Galaxy, over 25,000 light years away.

Perseids. Finally, do not forget the Perseid meteors, which are produced by débris from Comet 109P/Swift-Tuttle. Stare upwards into a dark, clear sky any time between 1 and 18 August, and you will be very unlucky not to see a meteor or two. Unfortunately, the full Moon on 16 August will be a nuisance, but the early stages of the shower, and the rise to maximum, should be observable without too much interference from moonlight.

In most years the Perseids produce corrected zenithal hourly rates of about 80 meteors per hour at maximum, with rates at around half that level on the nights before and after the peak. It seems that the heightened Perseid activity that followed the parent comet's return to perihelion in 1992 has now subsided. However, the Perseids remain one of the most reliable meteor showers of the year.

September

New Moon: 29 September   *Full Moon:* 15 September

Equinox: 22 September

MERCURY continues to be observable in the evenings, though not for observers in northern temperate latitudes north of about 30°N. For observers further south it is a particularly favourable occasion since Mercury reaches aphelion on 3 September, only eight days before greatest eastern elongation (27°). Reference should be made to Figure 16, given with the notes for August, where it will be seen that the planet remains visible until about the beginning of the last week of September. During its period of visibility its magnitude fades from 0.0 to +1.1. Mercury, Venus and Mars are only a few degrees apart around 11 September (see below).

VENUS continues to be visible as an evening object, low above the western horizon after sunset. Its magnitude is −3.9. Observers in the latitudes of the British Isles will only be able to see it very low above the horizon, despite its increasing elongation from the Sun, as the planet moves rapidly southwards in declination.

MARS, magnitude +1.7, continues to be visible low above the western horizon after darkness has fallen, but only to observers in the tropics and in southern latitudes. An aid to locating Mars during the first three weeks of the month is the presence of the brighter planets Mercury (whose magnitude fades from 0.0 to +1.1 during this period) and Venus at magnitude −3.9. At the very beginning of the month Mars will be found about 4° above Mercury, while ten days later it will have moved to a position about 3° to the right of Mercury, only slightly increasing this separation during the following ten days. Venus is close by the other two planets and from 9 to 11 September all three are roughly in a straight line at the same altitude, with Mercury on the left and Venus on the right, Mars being much closer to Venus than to

Mercury. Note the presence of the thin waxing crescent Moon in the area around 1–2 September.

JUPITER, magnitude −2.4, continues to be visible as a conspicuous object in the western sky in the evenings. For observers in the latitudes of the British Isles it is lost to view well before midnight, though those further south are more fortunate. Jupiter reaches its second stationary point on 8 September and then resumes its direct motion.

SATURN passes through conjunction on 4 September and is therefore not available for observation at first. During the last week or ten days of the month it gradually becomes visible to observers in the tropics and further north, low above the eastern horizon before the morning twilight inhibits observation. Its magnitude is +0.9. Observers further south will have to wait until October before being able to glimpse the planet.

URANUS is at opposition on 13 September, in the constellation of Aquarius. It is then 2,856 million kilometres (1,775 million miles) from the Earth. Uranus is barely visible to the naked eye as its magnitude is +5.7, but it is readily located with only small optical aid. Figure 18 shows its path among the stars during the year. The brightest stars in the diagram are composed of the little group of stars Psi 1, Psi 2 and Psi 3 Aquarii and also Phi and Chi Aquarii. The positions of the brighter stars in the diagram are as follows:

Phi Aquarii (magnitude +4.2, RA 23h 14.8m, Dec. −6.0°)
Chi Aquarii (magnitude +5.1, RA 23h 17.2m, Dec. −7.9°)
Psi 1 Aquarii (magnitude +4.2, RA 23h 16.4m, Dec. −8.7°)
Psi 2 Aquarii (magnitude +4.4, RA 23h 18.4m, Dec. −9.1°)
Psi 3 Aquarii (magnitude +5.0, RA 23h 19.4m, Dec. −9.6°)

The stars Phi Aquarii and Psi 2 and Psi 3 are shown on Northern Star Chart 9S and Southern Star Chart 9N at a longitude of about 339°, just south of the celestial equator.

Does Anything Ever Happen on the Moon? Most textbooks will say 'no', apart from man-made activities, but long-term lunar observers disagree. Of course, major changes on the surface belong to the remote

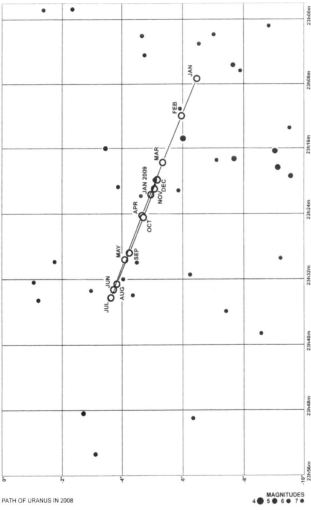

Figure 18. The path of Uranus against the stars of Aquarius during 2007. The brightest stars in the diagram are composed of the little group of stars Psi 1, Psi 2 and Psi 3 Aquarii (lower centre on the chart) and also Phi and Chi Aquarii (located above this little group). The positions of the brighter stars are as follows: Phi Aquarii (magnitude +4.2, RA 23h 14.8m, Dec. –6.0°); Chi Aquarii (magnitude +5.1, RA 23h 17.2m, Dec. –7.9°); Psi 1 Aquarii (magnitude +4.2, RA 23h 16.4m, Dec. –8.7°); Psi 2 Aquarii (magnitude +4.4, RA 23h 18.4m, Dec. –9.1°); and Psi 3 Aquarii (magnitude +5.0, RA 23h 19.4m, Dec. –9.6°).

past; even the youngest large impact craters, such as Copernicus, must be of the order of a thousand million years old, and violent vulcanism goes back even further in time. But since close telescopic observation began there have been persistent reports of small-scale glows, local obscurations and occasional flashes. They are known generally as Transient Lunar Phenomena, or TLP – a term for which I believe I was originally responsible, at some time during the 1950s.

One area where TLP had been reported was the floor of the huge crater Alphonsus, in the Ptolemaeus chain; there is a central mountain, and the floor contains a mass of detail, including a system of rills. (Rills are crack-like features, alternatively known as rilles or clefts.) I had suggested to various observers that Alphonsus would be worth monitoring, and one of these observers was N.A. Kozyrev, of the Crimean Astrophysical Observatory in what was then the USSR. His method was to take regular spectrograms with the Observatory's 50-inch (1.27-metre) telescope. While doing this at 0100 hours GMT on 3 November 1958, he noticed that the central peak of Alphonsus had become blurred, and was apparently enveloped in a reddish cloud. The central peak of Alphonsus then became abnormally bright, and things did not revert to normal until 0345 hours. Spectrograms showed that there had indeed been emissions of hot gas. Kozyrev stated that on the spectrogram taken at 0100 hours, 'the central peak of the crater appears redder than normal. Probably at this time the peak was being observed and illuminated by the dust and ashes being thrown out by the eruption,' and he estimated the temperature to have risen by around 2,000°C.

This explanation was immediately challenged, and I admit that I cannot accept it. There is no reasonable doubt that activity did take place, but certainly not a violent volcanic outburst; a comparatively gentle release of gases from below the surface seems much more likely. But the next step was to see whether the event had left any detectable traces.

During the next few months, red patches were reported by skilled observers, notably Brian Warner, now one of South Africa's leading astronomers but then working at the London Observatory. Using the 18-inch telescope there, he described the patch as 'bright red'. I was less successful, and I was never able to see the patch at all. It is certainly not there now.

The mystery remains – what did Kozyrev really see? Since then there have been other reports of obscurations and red TLP in the area, but none with photographic or spectrographic confirmation, so they cannot be accepted as conclusive. The reality of TLP was finally proved in 1992 by the French astronomer Audouin Dollfus, who recorded glows on the floor of the crater Langrenus: 'they are apparently due to dust grains levitated above the lunar surface, under the effect of gas escaping the soil. The Moon appears to be a celestial body which is not totally dead.'

N.A. Kozyrev. Nikolai Alexandrovitch Kozyrev, the distinguished Russian astronomer, certainly had a colourful career. At one stage he was even sentenced to be shot by a firing squad!

He was born a century ago, on 2 September 1908, in St Petersburg, and by 1928 he had graduated from the Leningrad State University; in 1931 he joined the staff of the Pulkovo Observatory, near Leningrad, and was widely regarded as one of the country's most promising astrophysicists. Alas, politics intervened, and almost at the start of Stalin's reign of terror most of the astronomers at Pulkovo were shot. Kozyrev was arrested in November 1936 for 'counter-revolutionary activity' (whatever that may mean) and in 1942 was sentenced to death. Somehow or other he managed to survive, and in December 1946 he was released from prison. However, he had lost what should have been his most productive years, and it is fair to say that this kept him from fulfilling his exceptional promise. He published some valuable papers, notably about the Ashen Light of Venus, but some of his theories were of doubtful validity, and he never really made up for his lost years. He died on 27 February 1983.

In late 1960, I spent a pleasant three weeks at the Crimean Astrophysical Observatory, and Kozyrev was there. We managed to talk, though he spoke no English and I was equally unversed in Russian – at least he did speak Norwegian, and I had just enough to 'get by' (I'm afraid I have forgotten it all now). Mars was at opposition. Every night we met at the dome of the newly completed 104-inch (2.65-metre) reflector, looked at the clouds, and said things in our respective languages. Not one clear night did we have throughout the whole of my stay!

October

New Moon: 28 October   *Full Moon:* 14 October

Summer Time in the United Kingdom ends on 26 October.

MERCURY is at inferior conjunction on 6 October and then moves out from the Sun to its greatest western elongation (18°) on 22 October. Thus it is a morning object, and for observers in northern temperate latitudes this will be the most favourable morning apparition of the year. Figure 19 shows, for observers in latitude 52°N, the changes in azimuth (true bearing from the north through east, south and west) and altitude of Mercury on successive mornings when the Sun is 6° below the horizon. This condition is known as the beginning of morning civil twilight, and in this latitude and at this time of year occurs about 35 minutes before sunrise. The changes in the brightness of the

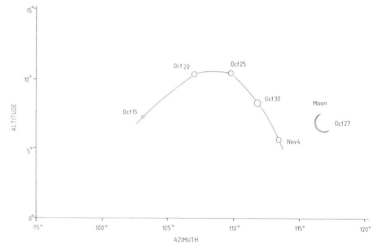

Figure 19. Morning apparition of Mercury, from latitude 52°N. The position of the crescent Moon is shown for 27 October as an aid to locating the planet. (Angular diameters of Mercury and the crescent Moon not to scale.)

planet are indicated by the relative sizes of the circles marking Mercury's position at five-day intervals. It will be noticed that Mercury is at its brightest after it reaches greatest western elongation. The planet is visible during the second half of the month to observers in the Northern Hemisphere and in the tropics, but not to observers further south. The diagram gives positions for a time at the beginning of morning civil twilight on the Greenwich meridian, on the stated date. Observers in different longitudes should note that the actual positions of Mercury in azimuth and altitude will differ slightly from those shown in the diagram. This change will be much greater still for the Moon, if it is shown, as its motion is about 0.5° per hour.

VENUS, magnitude −4.0, continues to be visible as a brilliant object in the western sky after sunset. The contrast in viewing the planet from different latitudes is quite marked at the end of the month, for whereas observers in the latitudes of the British Isles can only hope to see it for an hour after sunset, those in southern latitudes can expect three hours. Venus passes 3° north of Antares on 26 October.

MARS is not suitably placed for observation by those in the latitudes of the British Isles. Observers in the tropics and further south may be able to see it during the first half of the month, low above the western horizon as soon as the sky is dark enough after sunset, in the early evenings. Its magnitude is +1.6.

JUPITER is still visible in the western sky in the evenings, magnitude −2.2.

SATURN, magnitude +1.0, is slowly emerging from the morning twilight, becoming visible low above the eastern horizon for a short while before the morning twilight inhibits observation. Saturn is still in Leo.

Magnetic Mercury. Most planets have detectable magnetic fields – Venus being the glaring exception – though the field of Mars is very weak (when making your way around Syrtis Major, do not rely on your magnetic compass!). Rather surprisingly, it is found that Mercury, the smallest of the planets, does have an appreciable field. Its strength is only 1 per cent of the Earth's field, but its presence is undeniable.

Apart from the Earth, Mercury is the densest of all the planets, and the best models give it an iron-rich core larger than the whole globe of the Moon (Mercury is 4,878 kilometres in diameter). This poses new problems. The origin of a magnetic field is explained by a dynamo process, driven by the conductive flow of electrically conducting fluid in the planet's core. On this theory, the field of Mercury should be at least 30 per cent as strong as that of the Earth.

A new explanation for the weakness of the Mercurian field has been put forward by Ulrich Christensen, of the Max-Planck-Institut für Aeronomie in Germany. In his model, the outer part of Mercury's iron core does not convect, and a dynamo operates only in its deeper part, where a strong but fluctuating magnetic field is generated. This means that only a small fraction of the dynamo-generated field can escape through the inert part of the iron core.

We have to admit that our knowledge of Mercury is still very incomplete, but so far only one spacecraft (Mariner 10, during the 1970s) has flown past it. We must await results from MESSENGER, now on its way, and the ESA mission BepiColombo (see the article by David Rothery elsewhere in this *Yearbook*), but these spacecraft will not arrive there for several years yet.

Dr Olbers and the Minor Planets. Heinrich Wilhelm Mattäus Olbers was born a century and a half ago, on 11 October 1758, at Arbergren, near Bremen. His father was a Lutheran minister, but Heinrich became a medical practitioner; he studied at Göttingen and Vienna, and in 1781 set up a successful medical practice in Bremen, where he remained for the rest of his life.

He first became interested in astronomy when he was 13, and became one of Germany's best-known and best-loved amateurs; he set up his observatory on the roof of his house, and was very active in all sections of planetary research. In particular, he was concerned in the discoveries of three of the first four known asteroids, Ceres, Pallas and Vesta.

The well-known Bode's Law, linking the distances of the planets from the Sun, predicted the existence of a new planet in the wide gap between the orbits of Mars and Jupiter. In 1800 a team of astronomers, headed by Schröter and the Baron Franz Xavier von Zach, following a meeting at Schröter's observatory at Lilienthal, near Bremen, decided to make a systematic search. On 1 January 1801 Piazzi, at Palermo, discovered the first asteroid, Ceres (actually he was not then a member of von Zach's team, the 'Celestial Police', though he joined later). The postal service in nineteenth-century Europe was just as bad as it is today, and news of Piazzi's discovery did not reach other observatories until the object had been lost to the evening twilight. Fortunately the great mathematician Gauss was able to work out an orbit, using Piazzi's observations, and was able to predict the position of Ceres when it reappeared after conjunction with the Sun. Armed with this information, Olbers was able to locate Ceres a year after its original discovery, and on 28 March 1802 he independently discovered Asteroid no. 2, Pallas. His third and last asteroid discovery, of Vesta, was made on 29 March 1807.

It was some time before any more asteroids were found; the 'Celestial Police' gave up after 1815, when Schröter's observatory was destroyed by the invading French army (even his brass-tubed telescopes were looted, because the soldiers believed them to be made of gold!) and the fifth asteroid, Astraea, was not found until 1845.

Olbers' observational work was not confined to asteroids. Another of his main interests was in comets. In 1779 he devised a new method of calculating cometary orbits, and in 1811 he established that comets' tails are repelled by streams of tiny particles from the Sun, thereby anticipating the discovery of the solar wind by well over a century. In 1815 he discovered a comet now known as 13P/Olbers, which has a period of 69.5 years.

Heinrich Olbers died on 2 March 1840. He was known to be an exceptionally pleasant person, popular with everybody; he was always ready to help others, and was modest about his own very considerable achievements.

November

MERCURY, for observers in the tropics and the Northern Hemisphere, is still visible for the first few days of the month, low above the east-south-east horizon before dawn, magnitude −0.9. Further south the planet is unsuitably placed for observation at all this month. Mercury passes slowly through superior conjunction on 25 November.

VENUS, magnitude −4.1, is still visible for several hours after sunset in the western sky for observers in the Southern Hemisphere, while those in northern temperate latitudes may only see it for a much shorter period, low above the south-western horizon.

MARS is moving closer to the Sun as it approaches conjunction next month and is not suitably placed for observation.

JUPITER, magnitude −2.1, continues to be visible low in the western sky in the early evenings, though by the end of the month it is lost to view within three hours (or two for Northern Hemisphere observers) after sunset. At the end of November, Venus, which has been moving rapidly out from the Sun, will be seen passing 2° south of Jupiter. The Galilean satellites are readily observable with a small telescope or even a good pair of binoculars, provided that they are held rigidly.

SATURN continues to be visible as a morning object in the eastern sky, magnitude +1.0. The rings continue to close, and as a result the planet is not quite as bright as it was in the previous two oppositions. The south pole is presented towards the Earth, but the far side of the rings no longer appears clear of the body of the planet. Next year the Earth passes through the ring plane so that the rings will become invisible for a short time.

The Sun – from Epsilon Indi. The absolute magnitude of a star is the apparent magnitude that it would have if seen from a distance of 10 parsecs, or 32.6 light years. Absolute magnitude is therefore a measure of a star's true luminosity. Thus Sirius has an apparent magnitude of −1.45, and is much the brightest star in the sky; Rigel is not so brilliant, at +0.17, yet from the standard distance Sirius would fade to +1.4, about as bright as Regulus appears to us, while Rigel would blaze at magnitude −7, far superior to Venus as seen in our sky. Sirius is a mere twenty-six times more luminous than the Sun, while Rigel could match 40,000 Suns.

Most of the twenty closest stars would be easy naked-eye objects from the standard distance; but one would not – Epsilon Indi in the constellation of the Indian, too far south to rise over Britain (its declination is −57°). The apparent magnitude is 4.7, no test of visual acuity though it is not particularly easy to identify; it lies in the region of the 'Southern Birds' (Grus, the Crane; Pavo, the Peacock; Phoenix, the Phoenix; and Tucana, the Toucan). The absolute magnitude is +7, which is definitely below the limit for people of normal eyesight. The spectral type is K5, its mass is 0.8 that of the Sun, and the luminosity a mere 0.15 that of the Sun. Its diameter is just over a million kilometres (about three-quarters that of the Sun) and the surface temperature slightly below 4,000°C.

In January 2003 it was found that Epsilon Indi has a companion, moving round it at a distance of about 1,500 astronomical units. In the following August astronomers realized that this companion is actually a binary brown dwarf; both components are of spectral class T and their separation is only 375 million kilometres, much less than the distance between the Sun and Jupiter. One component is forty-seven times the mass of Jupiter, and the other twenty-eight Jupiter masses. Any inhabitants of a planet in the Epsilon Indi system would have an interesting sky. But what of our Sun?

Its absolute magnitude is +4.8, but from Epsilon Indi its apparent magnitude would be +2. The constellation patterns would be rather different from ours, and the Sun would shine as a second-magnitude star among the stars of Ursa Major, the Great Bear.

Is there really a planet orbiting Epsilon Indi? We cannot be sure, but it is by no means unlikely. Before long, we may find out.

Hypergiant in Cassiopeia. One of the most important of the Northern Hemisphere constellations is Cassiopeia, the Queen, whose five main stars make up a 'W' or 'M' shape. Cassiopeia never sets over Britain, and during November evenings it is almost overhead, so that the Great Bear is at its lowest in the north. Cassiopeia and the Bear are on opposite sides of Polaris, the Pole Star, and about the same distance from it. Two of the main stars in Cassiopeia are variable. Gamma, at the middle of the 'W', is usually about magnitude 2.2, but has been known to flare up to 1.6 and to fall to 3.2. Its neighbour, the orange Shedir or Alpha Cassiopeiae, is officially listed also as 2.2, but I have been watching it for many years, and I believe that it does show fluctuations of a few tenths of a magnitude. Beta, constant at magnitude 2.27, makes a good comparison star.

In 1572 there was a startling phenomenon – a supernova, close to Kappa Cassiopeiae (magnitude 4.2). The supernova became brighter than Venus, and was visible in broad daylight. The great Danish

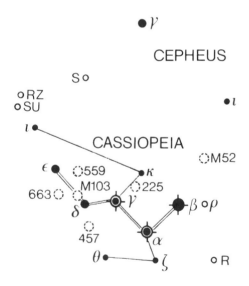

Figure 20. The familiar 'W' of Cassiopeia showing the positions of the interesting variable stars Rho and Gamma Cassiopeiae. Rho is a hypergiant and is located fairly close to Beta. Rho is the centre star in a line of three, with Tau above and Sigma below. Alpha Cassiopeiae is also suspected of variability.

astronomer Tycho Brahe left a full account of it, so it is always known as Tycho's Star. Its remnant has become very faint.

Supernovae are rare in the Galaxy; only one (Kepler's Star of 1604) has been seen since Tycho's time, but there must have been another, also in Cassiopeia, in the latter part of the seventeenth century. It was not observed, because it was hidden behind interstellar dust, but its remnant, known as Cassiopeia A, is the brightest X-ray source in the sky apart from the Sun, so we know its exact position.

Two supernovae in the Queen – could there be a third? The answer is 'yes', and it could be even more exciting – a hypernova of unbelievable power.

Close to Beta are three stars of just above the fifth magnitude: Tau, Rho and Sigma Cassiopeiae (Figure 20). Two of these are very ordinary, but the star Rho is a yellow hypergiant, over 80,000 times as luminous as the Sun. Its distance is around 8,000 light years (estimates vary somewhat); at present it varies only slightly, but it is very unstable, and it has a limited life expectancy. When it explodes, it will be spectacular in spite of its distance from us. Just when that will be, we know not; it may be tomorrow, or next week, or not for a million years, but sooner or later it might happen. At the moment it is rather obscure, but in the future it will, briefly, change the look of the whole of the sky.

December

New Moon: 27 December   *Full Moon:* 12 December

Solstice: 21 December

MERCURY becomes visible to observers in tropical and southern latitudes during the second half of December, low above the west-south-western horizon about half an hour after sunset, magnitude −0.7. Observers in northern temperate latitudes will have to wait until early in the New Year before having any chance to see the planet.

VENUS is a magnificent object in the early evenings, completely dominating the western sky for several hours after sunset. Its magnitude is −4.2. Venus is now moving northwards in declination, and by the end of the month observers in northern temperate latitudes will have similar opportunities to those in the Southern Hemisphere for seeing the planet, albeit at a lower altitude.

MARS passes slowly through superior conjunction on 5 December and therefore continues to be unsuitably placed for observation.

JUPITER is approaching the end of its 2008 apparition but is still a bright object in the western sky in the evenings during December. Its magnitude is −2.0. Although Jupiter is still in the constellation of Sagittarius in December it will move eastwards into Capricornus early in the New Year. Venus is moving steadily away from Jupiter, ending the month about 20° distant. Mercury is moving rapidly towards Jupiter and will actually pass 1° south of it on New Year's Day.

SATURN, magnitude +0.9, continues to move direct in the constellation of Leo and its path among the stars will be seen in Figure 14, given with the notes for July. On the last day of December, Saturn reaches its first stationary point and commences its retrograde motion. By the end of the year Saturn will be seen low above the eastern horizon shortly before midnight. Observers will note that the rings are slowly closing, before the Earth passes through the ring plane next year. This will be the first occasion since 1997 when the planet's magnitude has faded to this level. The rings will be difficult to observe as the angular width is now reduced to 1 arcsecond.

The Return of Halley's Comet. There is an interesting anniversary this month. Two hundred and fifty years ago, on Christmas night, Halley's Comet was recovered, making its first predicted return.

Before that time, comets had not been recognized as members of the Solar System; even Newton had thought that they travelled in straight lines, passing by the Sun only once. Halley's Comet was the first to make a predicted return to perihelion.

Records of it go back a long way. The orbital period is about seventy-six years, and all the returns since that of 240 BC have been observed. It may have been recorded by the Chinese as early as 1059 BC, and it is generally a fairly bright object (though, sadly, it was not at its best during its last return, that of 1986). It was at its very best in AD 837, when the tail stretched for over 90° and the coma became as bright as Venus. It was on view in 1066, and is shown in the Bayeux Tapestry (Figure 21); the Saxons apparently regarded it as an unfavourable omen! The return of 1301 was also very favourable, and the Florentine painter Giotto di Bondone used it as a model for the Star of Bethlehem in his painting *The Adoration of the Magi*. (*En passant*, Halley's Comet was not the Star of Bethlehem, either in 1301 or at any other time.) At the return of 1456 the comet was again bright; at that time the Turkish forces were on the rampage in Europe, and on 8 June it was said that 'a fearsome apparition appeared in the sky, with a long tail like a dragon'. The then Pope, Calixtus III, went so far as to preach against it as an agent of the devil. It is unlikely that he excommunicated it, as has sometimes been claimed – but even if he had taken this drastic step, it is unlikely that the comet would have paid much attention.

On 15 August 1682 the comet was recovered by G. Dörffel. Edmond Halley saw it a few nights later, and made a long series of observations. He realized that the orbit was strikingly similar to those of the comets of 1531 and 1607, and predicted the next return in 1758. He knew he could not hope to see it, but on Christmas night it was picked up by the German observer Palitzsch, and it came to perihelion in 1759. Since then it has been back in 1835, 1910 and 1986, and is due once more in

Figure 21. Halley's comet as it is depicted on the Bayeux Tapestry. The comet appeared in early April 1066, and was seen by some as a bad omen for King Harold, who had been crowned King of England only three months earlier. Here, Harold is shown sitting on his throne, with the comet above left in the Tapestry's upper border.

2061. This will not be a good return, but in 2137 the comet will be truly magnificent.

Johann Palitzsch. Palitzsch is remembered today only for his recovery of Halley's Comet, but he was an active observer and also had many other interests. Johann Georg Palitzsch was born on 11 June 1723 in Prohlis, near Dresden in Germany. He showed an early interest in science, and went to study at the Mathematischer Salon in Dresden. He seems to have used a reflector of focal length 8 feet, but whether or not he personally built it is unclear. It is said that he was an independent discoverer of the variability of Algol, but it was Halley's Comet that made him well known, and in 1760 he was called to the court of the Elector of Saxony to give astronomical instruction to Prince Friedrich

August. He was then made a member of the Ökonomische Sicietät (Economical Society). He paid attention to microscopy, and introduced the lightning rod to Saxony. When he died, on 21 February 1788, he left behind a library of 3,518 books, some of which were in his own handwriting. A formation on the Moon is named after him, and so is asteroid 11970 Palitzsch.

The Christmas Quiz. It's quiz time. Try some of these questions:

In what constellation is the star Rho Aquilae? In Delphinus. In 1993 its proper motion carried it over the boundary, into the neighbouring constellation.

What is peculiar about the star 34 Tauri? It is the planet Uranus. Flamsteed saw it when compiling his catalogue, and mistook it for a star.

What is the diameter of Saturn's satellite Themis, the discovery of which was announced by W.H. Pickering in 1904? 0 kilometres, because it doesn't exist. It was never confirmed, and what Pickering saw was certainly a star.

What do the stars Delta Pegasi, Gamma Aurigae and Gamma Scorpii all have in common? They have all been transferred to different constellations. Respectively, they are now Alpha Andromedae, Beta Tauri and Sigma Librae.

Where will you find the star Alpha Velorum? You won't. When the vast constellation of Argo Navis was split up, Alpha Argûs (Canopus) was given to Carina, the Keel of the ship.

Eclipses in 2008

During 2008 there will be four eclipses, two of the Sun and two of the Moon.

1. *An annular eclipse of the Sun* on 7 February is visible as a partial eclipse from New Zealand, the western part of the South Pacific Ocean and south-eastern Australia. The partial phase begins at 01h 38m and ends at 06h 12m. The path of annularity starts in the South Pacific Ocean and ends in Antarctica. Annularity begins at 03h 20m and ends at 04h 31m. The maximum duration of annularity is 2m 12s.

2. *A total eclipse of the Moon* on 21 February is visible from central and western Asia, the western Indian Ocean, Europe, Africa, the Atlantic Ocean, Iceland, Greenland, the Americas and the extreme north-east of Asia. The partial phase begins at 01h 43m and ends at 05h 09m. The total phase begins at 03h 00m and ends at 03h 51m.

3. *A total eclipse of the Sun* on 1 August is visible as a partial eclipse from north-east Canada, Greenland, northern Europe and Asia. The partial phase begins at 08h 04m and ends at 12h 38m. The path of totality starts in islands north of the mainland of Canada, and then crosses northern Greenland, Novaya Zemlya, central Russia and extreme western Mongolia, before ending in China. Totality begins at 09h 21m and ends at 11h 21m. The maximum duration of totality is 2m 27s.

4. *A partial eclipse of the Moon* on 16 August is visible from Australasia, Asia (except the extreme north-east), the Indian Ocean, Antarctica, Europe, Africa, Iceland, the Atlantic Ocean, the southern tip of Greenland, the north-east of North America, southern Central America and South America. The eclipse begins at 19h 35m and ends at 22h 44m. At maximum eclipse 81 per cent of the Moon's surface is obscured.

Occultations in 2008

In the course of its journey round the sky each month, the Moon passes in front of all the stars in its path, and the timing of these occultations is useful in fixing the position and motion of the Moon. The Moon's orbit is tilted at more than 5° to the ecliptic, but it is not fixed in space. It twists steadily westwards at a rate of about 20° a year, a complete revolution taking 18.6 years, during which time all the stars that lie within about 6.5° of the ecliptic will be occulted. The occultations of any one star continue month after month until the Moon's path has twisted away from the star, but only a few of these occultations will be visible from any one place during the hours of darkness.

There are twelve occultations of bright planets in 2008: five of Mercury, two of Venus, four of Mars, and one of Jupiter.

Only four first-magnitude stars are near enough to the ecliptic to be occulted by the Moon: these are Aldebaran, Regulus, Spica and Antares. Only Regulus and Antares are occulted during 2008.

Predictions of these occultations are made on a worldwide basis for all stars down to magnitude 7.5, and sometimes even fainter. The British Astronomical Association has produced a complete lunar occultation prediction package for personal-computer users.

Occultations of stars by planets (including minor planets) and satellites have aroused considerable attention.

The exact timing of such events gives valuable information about positions, sizes, orbits, atmospheres and sometimes the presence of satellites. The discovery of the rings of Uranus in 1977 was the unexpected result of the observations made of a predicted occultation of a faint star by Uranus. The duration of an occultation by a satellite or minor planet is quite small (usually of the order of a minute or less). If observations are made from a number of stations it is possible to deduce the size of the planet.

The observations need to be made either photoelectrically or visually. The high accuracy of the method can readily be appreciated when one realizes that even a stopwatch timing accurate to a tenth of a second is, on average, equivalent to an accuracy of about 1 kilometre in the chord measured across the minor planet.

Comets in 2008

The appearance of a bright comet is a rare event that can never be predicted in advance, because this class of object travels round the Sun in enormous orbits with periods that may well be many thousands of years. There are therefore no records of the previous appearances of these bodies, and we are unable to follow their wanderings through space.

Comets of short period, on the other hand, return at regular intervals, and attract a good deal of attention from astronomers. Unfortunately they are all faint objects, and are recovered and followed by photographic methods using large telescopes. Most of these short-period comets travel in orbits of small inclination that reach out to the orbit of Jupiter, and it is this planet that is mainly responsible for the severe perturbations that many of these comets undergo. Unlike the planets, comets may be seen in any part of the sky, but since their distances from the Earth are similar to those of the planets their apparent movements in the sky are also somewhat similar, and some of them may he followed for long periods of time.

The following periodic comets are expected to return to perihelion in 2008, and to be brighter than magnitude +15.

Comet	Year of Discovery	Period (years)	Predicted Date of Perihelion 2008
8P/Tuttle	1790	13.61	Jan 26
6P/d'Arrest	1678	6.54	Aug 15
19P/Borrelly	1904	6.88	July 22
46P/Wirtanen	1948	5.44	Feb 2
85P/Boethin	1975	11.54	Dec 16

Some ephemerides of comets that should be visible to observers with small telescopes in 2008 are given below:

Comet 8P/Tuttle

Date 2008 0h	2000.0 RA h m		Dec. ° '		Distance from Earth AU	Distance from Sun AU	Elongation from Sun °	Mag.
Jan 0	1	33.7	+29	51	0.253	1.106	112.8	+5.0
Jan 5	1	51.3	+9	29	0.258	1.080	105.3	+4.9
Jan 10	2	05.9	−7	57	0.292	1.059	97.0	+5.0
Jan 15	2	18.4	−20	43	0.346	1.043	90.1	+5.3
Jan 20	2	29.3	−29	39	0.411	1.033	85.0	+5.6
Jan 25	2	38.9	−35	59	0.480	1.028	81.3	+5.9
Jan 30	2	47.6	−40	38	0.551	1.028	78.5	+6.2
Feb 4	2	55.6	−44	11	0.621	1.035	76.5	+6.5
Feb 9	3	03.2	−46	57	0.689	1.047	75.0	+6.8
Feb 14	3	10.6	−49	12	0.754	1.064	74.0	+7.1
Feb 19	3	18.1	−51	05	0.816	1.086	73.3	+7.4
Feb 24	3	25.9	−52	41	0.873	1.113	73.1	+7.7
Feb 29	3	34.1	−54	04	0.926	1.144	73.2	+8.0
Mar 5	3	42.9	−55	18	0.974	1.178	73.6	+8.3
Mar 10	3	52.7	−56	25	1.018	1.216	74.4	+8.6
Mar 15	4	03.4	−57	27	1.058	1.256	75.4	+8.9
Mar 20	4	15.3	−58	25	1.094	1.298	76.7	+9.2

Comet 85P/Boethin

Date 2008 0h	2000.0 RA h m		Dec. ° '		Distance from Earth AU	Distance from Sun AU	Elongation from Sun °	Mag.
Oct 26	20	11.1	−19	32	0.953	1.351	87.8	+9.0
Nov 5	20	32.4	−17	32	0.942	1.285	83.2	+8.5
Nov 15	20	58.0	−15	02	0.927	1.229	79.7	+8.1
Nov 25	21	27.3	−12	00	0.909	1.186	77.4	+7.8
Dec 5	22	00.1	−8	20	0.891	1.159	76.1	+7.5
Dec 15	22	36.4	−4	06	0.877	1.148	75.9	+7.4
Dec 25	23	15.6	+0	37	0.873	1.154	76.6	+7.4

Minor Planets in 2008

Although many thousands of minor planets (asteroids) are known to exist, only a few thousand of them have well-determined orbits and are listed in the catalogues. Most of these orbits lie entirely between the orbits of Mars and Jupiter. All these bodies are quite small, and even the largest, Ceres, is only 913 kilometres (567 miles) in diameter. Thus, they are necessarily faint objects, and although a number of them are within the reach of a small telescope few of them ever attain any considerable brightness. The first four that were discovered are named Ceres, Pallas, Juno and Vesta. Actually the largest four minor planets are Ceres, Pallas, Vesta and Hygeia. Vesta can occasionally be seen with the naked eye, and this is most likely to happen when an opposition occurs near June, since Vesta would then be at perihelion. Below are ephemerides for Ceres, Pallas and Vesta in 2008.

1 Ceres

Date		RA (2000.0)		Dec. (2000.0)		Geo-centric Distance	Helio-centric Distance	Elong-ation	Visual Magni-tude
		h	m	°	′			°	
Jan	1	2	35.56	+9	35.7	2.152	2.773	120	+8.2
Jan	11	2	36.64	+10	27.4	2.269	2.764	110	+8.3
Jan	21	2	40.15	+11	27.1	2.394	2.756	101	+8.5
Jan	31	2	45.84	+12	32.8	2.522	2.748	93	+8.6
Feb	10	2	53.48	+13	42.8	2.652	2.739	85	+8.7
Feb	20	3	02.85	+14	55.5	2.779	2.731	77	+8.8
Mar	1	3	13.72	+16	09.2	2.903	2.723	70	+8.9
Mar	11	3	25.91	+17	22.5	3.020	2.715	63	+8.9
Mar	21	3	39.28	+18	34.1	3.130	2.706	56	+8.9
Mar	31	3	53.66	+19	42.8	3.231	2.698	50	+9.0
Apr	10	4	08.97	+20	47.5	3.323	2.690	44	+9.0
Apr	20	4	25.07	+21	47.3	3.403	2.682	38	+8.9
Apr	30	4	41.88	+22	41.2	3.473	2.674	32	+8.9
May	10	4	59.31	+23	28.5	3.532	2.667	27	+8.9

1 Ceres – *cont.*

Date		RA		Dec.		Geo-centric Distance	Helio-centric Distance	Elong-ation	Visual Magni-tude
		h	m	°	′			°	
Aug	18	8	08.36	+24	06.2	3.465	2.598	26	+8.8
Aug	28	8	26.91	+23	29.8	3.396	2.593	32	+8.8
Sep	7	8	45.09	+22	48.7	3.316	2.587	37	+8.8
Sep	17	9	02.83	+22	04.2	3.227	2.582	43	+8.8
Sep	27	9	20.07	+21	17.5	3.129	2.577	49	+8.8
Oct	7	9	36.73	+20	30.2	3.023	2.573	54	+8.8
Oct	17	9	52.72	+19	43.9	2.909	2.569	60	+8.7
Oct	27	10	07.96	+19	00.4	2.789	2.565	67	+8.7
Nov	6	10	22.31	+18	21.7	2.664	2.561	73	+8.6
Nov	16	10	35.63	+17	50.0	2.534	2.558	80	+8.5
Nov	26	10	47.75	+17	27.5	2.403	2.555	87	+8.4
Dec	6	10	58.45	+17	16.6	2.272	2.552	95	+8.3
Dec	16	11	07.48	+17	19.7	2.143	2.550	103	+8.1
Dec	26	11	14.54	+17	38.7	2.019	2.548	111	+8.0

2 Pallas

Date		RA		Dec.		Geo-centric Distance	Helio-centric Distance	Elong-ation	Visual Magni-tude
		h	m	°	′			°	
Sep	7	4	56.20	−9	37.7	2.208	2.471	93	+8.9
Sep	17	5	07.26	−12	07.7	2.091	2.448	98	+8.8
Sep	27	5	16.61	−14	53.6	1.983	2.424	104	+8.7
Oct	7	5	23.88	−17	52.0	1.884	2.402	109	+8.5
Oct	17	5	28.73	−20	57.1	1.797	2.380	114	+8.4
Oct	27	5	30.83	−24	01.4	1.723	2.358	118	+8.2
Nov	6	5	29.96	−26	54.8	1.662	2.337	121	+8.1
Nov	16	5	26.13	−29	25.5	1.616	2.317	124	+8.0
Nov	26	5	19.71	−31	21.6	1.585	2.297	125	+8.0
Dec	6	5	11.46	−32	32.6	1.568	2.278	125	+7.9
Dec	16	5	02.59	−32	52.2	1.565	2.260	123	+7.9
Dec	26	4	54.39	−32	19.2	1.575	2.243	121	+7.9

4 Vesta

Date		RA (2000.0)		Dec.		Geo-centric Distance	Helio-centric Distance	Elong-ation	Visual Magni-tude
		h	m	°	′			°	
Apr	10	23	50.86	− 5	58.0	3.213	2.346	25	+8.1
Apr	20	0	08.44	− 4	16.8	3.169	2.356	30	+8.1
Apr	30	0	25.65	− 2	38.8	3.115	2.366	35	+8.1
May	10	0	42.47	− 1	04.9	3.051	2.376	41	+8.1
May	20	0	58.87	+ 0	23.8	2.979	2.386	46	+8.1
May	30	1	14.80	+ 1	46.4	2.898	2.396	51	+8.1
Jun	9	1	30.22	+ 3	02.1	2.810	2.406	57	+8.1
Jun	19	1	45.02	+ 4	09.9	2.714	2.415	62	+8.1
Jun	29	1	59.10	+ 5	09.3	2.612	2.424	68	+8.0
Jul	9	2	12.33	+ 5	59.2	2.504	2.434	74	+8.0
Jul	19	2	24.51	+ 6	39.1	2.393	2.443	81	+7.9
Jul	29	2	35.45	+ 7	08.3	2.278	2.451	87	+7.8
Aug	8	2	44.87	+ 7	26.3	2.162	2.460	95	+7.7
Aug	18	2	52.49	+ 7	32.6	2.047	2.468	102	+7.5
Aug	28	2	57.98	+ 7	27.1	1.936	2.476	110	+7.4
Sep	7	3	01.01	+ 7	09.8	1.831	2.484	119	+7.2
Sep	17	3	01.29	+ 6	41.5	1.736	2.492	129	+7.1
Sep	27	2	58.68	+ 6	03.7	1.655	2.499	139	+6.9
Oct	7	2	53.23	+ 5	19.3	1.592	2.506	150	+6.7
Oct	17	2	45.38	+ 4	32.8	1.552	2.513	160	+6.5
Oct	27	2	35.90	+ 3	49.5	1.537	2.519	168	+6.4
Nov	6	2	25.91	+ 3	15.6	1.551	2.525	166	+6.5
Nov	16	2	16.61	+ 2	55.9	1.592	2.531	157	+6.6
Nov	26	2	09.02	+ 2	53.4	1.658	2.536	146	+6.9
Dec	6	2	03.84	+ 3	08.8	1.746	2.541	135	+7.1
Dec	16	2	01.39	+ 3	40.8	1.852	2.546	125	+7.3
Dec	26	2	01.67	+ 4	27.1	1.971	2.550	115	+7.5

Meteors in 2008

Meteors ('shooting stars') may be seen on any clear moonless night, but on certain nights of the year their number increases noticeably. This occurs when the Earth chances to intersect a concentration of meteoric dust moving in an orbit around the Sun. If the dust is well spread out in space, the resulting shower of meteors may last for several days. The word 'shower' must not be misinterpreted – only on very rare occasions have the meteors been so numerous as to resemble snowflakes falling.

If the meteor tracks are marked on a star map and traced backwards, a number of them will be found to intersect in a point (or a small area of the sky) that marks the radiant of the shower. This gives the direction from which the meteors have come.

The following table gives some of the more easily observed showers with their radiants; interference by moonlight is shown by the letter M.

Limiting Dates	Shower	Maximum	RA		Dec.	
			h	m	°	
Jan 1–6	Quadrantids	Jan 4	15	28	+50	
April 19–25	Lyrids	Apr 22	18	08	+32	M
May 1–8	Aquarids	May 4	22	20	–01	
June 17–26	Ophiuchids	June 19	17	20	–20	M
July 29–Aug 6	Delta Aquarids	July 29	22	36	–17	
July 15–Aug 20	Piscis Australids	July 31	22	40	–30	
July 15–Aug 20	Capricornids	Aug 2	20	36	–10	
July 23–Aug 20	Perseids	Aug 12	3	04	+58	M
Oct 16–27	Orionids	Oct 20	6	24	+15	M
Oct 20–Nov 30	Taurids	Nov 3	3	44	+14	
Nov 15–20	Leonids	Nov 17	10	08	+22	M
Nov 27–Jan	Puppids-Velids	Dec 9–26	9	00	–48	M
Dec 7–16	Geminids	Dec 13	7	32	+33	M
Dec 17–25	Ursids	Dec 22	14	28	+78	

Some Events in 2009

ECLIPSES

There will be six eclipses, two of the Sun and four of the Moon.

26 January:	Annular eclipse of the Sun – Africa, Asia, Australasia
9 February:	Penumbral eclipse of the Moon – Asia, Africa, Australasia, Europe, North America
7 July:	Penumbral eclipse of the Moon – Australasia, North and South America
22 July:	Total eclipse of the Sun – Asia, Indonesia, Pacific Ocean
6 August:	Penumbral eclipse of the Moon – Asia, Europe, Africa, North and South America
31 December:	Partial eclipse of the Moon – Australasia, Asia, Africa, Europe, northern Canada

THE PLANETS

Mercury may be seen more easily from northern latitudes in the evenings about the time of greatest eastern elongation (26 April) and in the mornings about the time of greatest western elongation (6 October). In the Southern Hemisphere the corresponding most favourable dates are 24 August (evenings) and 13 February (mornings).

Venus is visible from January to March in the evenings. From April onwards it is visible in the mornings.

Mars does not come to opposition in 2009.

Jupiter is at opposition on 14 August in Capricornus.

Saturn is at opposition on 8 March in Leo.

Uranus is at opposition on 17 September in Pisces.

Neptune is at opposition on 17 August in Capricornus.

Pluto is at opposition on 23 June in Sagittarius.

Part II

Article Section

C/2006 P1 (McNaught): a Truly Spectacular Comet

MARTIN MOBBERLEY

On 7 August 2006 an apparently routine comet discovery was made by the British astronomer and devoted comet hunter Robert McNaught, using the Uppsala Schmidt telescope in New South Wales, Australia. This famous instrument and its equally well-known discoverer are based at Siding Spring Observatory, near Coonabarabran. The discovery itself might have been routine, but Comet C/2006 P1 (McNaught) would turn out to be anything but. It will be remembered as one of the most awesome cometary spectacles of the last hundred years.

THE DISCOVERY SYSTEM

Prior to the discovery of C/2006 P1 the Uppsala Schmidt had already been used to capture twenty-eight comets since the early months of 2004. The telescope is the southern component of three sky-scouring systems operated by the University of Arizona and, not surprisingly, the other two instruments reside in that US state. The patrol work carried out by the trio of instruments is known as the CSS/SSS or Catalina Sky Survey/Siding Spring Survey. The principal purpose of these telescopes is to discover Near Earth Objects (NEOs) and, specifically, Potentially Hazardous Asteroids (PHAs) that could pose a threat to the Earth. Not surprisingly, a significant number of comets is also detected in the course of these surveys. Comets discovered by the CSS/SSS can end up having a variety of names, as, unlike the robotic LINEAR and NEAT discovery machines, which automatically search for fast-moving objects, there is still a human element to the checking process. Thus comets named McNaught, Garradd, Christensen, Gibbs, Kowalski and Hill are more common than comets simply named 'Siding Spring' or 'Catalina'. Rob McNaught and Gordon Garradd are the Siding Spring investigators and, in 2006, both already had an impressive tally of comets named after them. However, C/2006 P1, Rob McNaught's thirty-first comet discovery, would be, by far, his greatest find and take him within one discovery of being the greatest human comet discoverer of the modern era. The undisputed record of thirty-two was held by Eugene and Carolyn Shoemaker up to McNaught's subsequent thirty-second comet, C/2006 Q1, although the nineteenth-century French astronomer Jean Pons probably discovered at least thirty-seven comets (twenty-six actually bear his name). As an aside, the designation 'P1' simply means that comet C/2006 P1 McNaught was the first comet discovered in the half-month 'P' period, i.e. the 1–15 August window. Twenty-four letters split the year up, with the letters I and Z being unused.

The Uppsala Schmidt telescope, used by Rob McNaught to discover Comet 2006 P1, was originally based at Mt Stromlo Observatory from 1957 to 1982. Tragically, that observatory was destroyed by fire in 2003, but fortunately the Schmidt telescope had been moved to Siding Spring twenty-one years earlier. The Schmidt telescope has a relatively modest aperture of 52 centimetres (corrector-plate diameter) and a focal length of 175 centimetres, making it an f/3.4 system. In 2000 and 2001 this photographic telescope was modernized and the Schmidt focus was diverted outside the tube so that optically (if not mechanically) it is not dissimilar to a 52-centimetre f/3.4 field-flattened reflector, i.e. not all that different from some larger amateur Newtonians, at least in aperture and focal length. This focus modification enabled a top-quality 4096×4096 pixel CCD detector, cooled to $-90°C$, to be employed, rather than the old photographic plates. The CCD chip is a massive 60 millimetres across and features 15 micron pixels. This gives a field of view of just over 2° and a resolution just under 2 arcseconds per pixel. With short exposures down to nineteenth or twentieth magnitude, and the telescope working throughout the night, considerable swathes of sky can be searched with little competition from other competing surveys, which are mainly based in the Northern Hemisphere.

A PROMISING DISCOVERY

On 7 August 2006, discovery day, the new Comet McNaught was in Ophiuchus (RA 16h 40m, Dec. −18°) and gave no indication that it would prove to be one of the most spectacular comets of the last hundred years. It was a small, seventeenth-magnitude fuzz, moving slowly westwards at 40 arcseconds per hour against the background stars. At that time it was 370 million kilometres from the Earth and 460 million from the Sun, and at 116° elongation it was well away from the solar glare. By 10 August a total of twenty-three measurements enabled a preliminary parabolic orbit to be calculated and things started to look quite promising. Of particular interest was the predicted solar distance at perihelion, on 17 January, of only 0.18 Astronomical Units (1 AU = 149.6 million kilometres) from the Sun, i.e. 27 million kilometres. Later refinements to the orbit modified these values slightly to 0.17 AU (25 million kilometres) and a slightly earlier perihelion date of 12 January (Figure 1). Few decent-sized comets pass this close to the solar surface at perihelion but, occasionally, when they do, a truly spectacular comet can result; the intense heating results in huge quantities of gas, and dust being released. For such a comet the dust factor is especially important as this dust is essentially reflecting sunlight, which is vital if such a comet is to appear bright against the twilight sky. Comets that travel close to the Sun will inevitably only be seen in morning or evening twilight when the Sun is below the horizon, but the comet is a few degrees above it.

It should perhaps be explained that the standard way in which any comet brightens as it moves into the inner solar system is described by a logarithmic magnitude law, namely: Magnitude = H_0 + 5 log Δ + 10 log r, where H_0 is the absolute magnitude of the comet (its basic size/activity level), Δ is the Earth-comet distance in AU, and r is the Sun–comet distance in AU. As the magnitude scale is itself logarithmic (5 magnitudes = 100×) this innocent-looking formula tells us that we can expect a comet to brighten by an inverse square law relative to its distance from Earth, and an inverse fourth-power law relative to its distance from the Sun! So, in words, halve the Earth–comet distance and the comet will appear four times brighter, but halve the Sun–comet distance and the comet will appear sixteen times brighter. Now it is obvious why a comet passing very close to the Sun can be so dramatic.

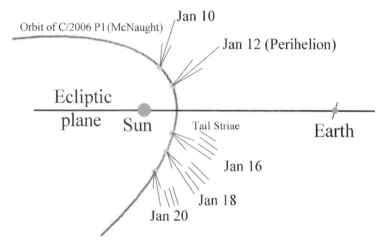

Figure 1. The plane of Comet McNaught's orbit was tilted at 78° to the ecliptic (the plane of the Earth's orbit around the Sun), in other words, tilted at almost a right angle. The comet passed downwards through the ecliptic on 14 January 2007, between the Earth and Sun, just two days after perihelion. A few days later it became visible in a darkening evening twilight sky for lucky Southern Hemisphere observers, including the discoverer himself. The discs depicting the Sun and Earth are not to scale. (Diagram by the author.)

All other things being equal, a typical comet passing only 0.17 AU from the Sun, like McNaught, will be 1200 times (7.7 magnitudes) brighter than one passing a mere 1 AU from the Sun. However, some caution is always needed in these situations as various comets have disappointed us in the past. Comet Kohoutek in 1973 and Comet Austin in 1990 both failed to live up to the media hype, even though they were still very nice comets from a keen amateur astronomy perspective. Kohoutek, in particular was a very bright but much-maligned comet, simply because the media hype was so extraordinary. The problem is that the 10 log r 'solar heating' part of the cometary magnitude law is only a generalization for the 'typical' comet – and there is no such thing as a 'typical' comet! As the comet discoverer David Levy once remarked, 'Comets are like cats: they have tails and they do what they want!' Comets that are on their first visit to the inner Solar System can show great promise as they first encounter the Sun's heat and initially brighten rapidly, but they often just fizzle out at perihelion. Small sun-grazing comets often break up under the enormous stresses of solar heating, upon which there may be a momentary rise in activity before they too fizzle out. However, the perihelion distance of 0.17 AU certainly raised observers' hopes in August 2006, even if a few dour veteran comet observers were urging much caution.

AMATEUR ASTRONOMERS WATCH AND WAIT

Less than three weeks after Comet McNaught was discovered the first visual observations were being made by amateur astronomers. Veteran Australian comet observer David Seargent at Cowra, New South Wales, estimated its magnitude as 13.9 in a 25-centimetre Newtonian on 25 August. On the face of it this might seem to indicate that the comet had leaped three magnitudes in as many weeks; however, CCD discovery magnitudes are often much fainter than the comet's total visual magnitude, as they do not record the full contribution from the cometary coma. Seargent's observation and, at the same time, Terry Lovejoy's digital estimate of fourteenth magnitude indicated that the comet could have an absolute magnitude, H_o, of 7, indicating a healthy 'sized' comet that would probably not break up at perihelion. (It would ultimately turn out that Comet McNaught obeyed a very healthy magnitude law of Mag. = $6.0 + 5 \log \Delta + 10.0 \log r$ right up to perihelion and beyond.) There were certainly grounds for optimism, even if a few cynical veteran observers still seemed only too keen to quash any enthusiasm for a comet that might have a highly negative magnitude in the coming January. How wrong those killjoys would prove to be! The comet brightened steadily during September as it tracked along the Ophiuchus/Scorpius border. By early October it was a twelfth-magnitude object. By mid November, now on the Ophiuchus/Serpens border (Figure 2), it edged above tenth magnitude with a 3-arcminute-diameter highly condensed coma visible on CCD images secured by Michael Jager and Gerald Rhemann in Austria, with the comet close to the horizon in deepening twilight.

It had been obvious since August that the comet would probably enter a long period of invisibility from mid November and throughout December 2006, as its angular elongation from the Sun would prevent it being seen in a dark sky, but its distance from perihelion would be too far for it to be a naked-eye object. This was a challenge to CCD and digital-SLR-equipped observers who could image the comet against

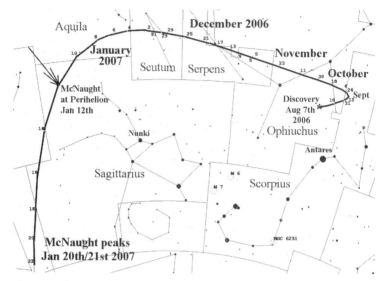

Figure 2. The path of Comet McNaught against the background constellations, from discovery in August 2006 to its peak in mid to late January 2007.

the twilight glare, using short exposures. In addition the comet was moving steadily north, while the Sun was moving south towards its winter solstice low point. For this reason, at perihelion Northern Hemisphere observers would, briefly, have the best view, before the comet plunged south once more. However, CCD imagers continued to persevere with following the comet in strong twilight. They were keen to know if it was going to be a monster at perihelion, and there was much competition between observers too. Jager and Rhemann imaged 2006 P1 on 26 November in strong twilight when it was only 18° from the Sun, declaring that it had now reached magnitude 8.0 with a highly condensed 4-arcminute coma and a 15-arcminute tail to the ENE. By December only a few diehard imagers were managing to cope with the twilight problem, the aforementioned Jager/Rhemann team in Austria and Mike Holloway in Van Buren, Arizona, being the keenest. Reliable magnitude estimates proved almost impossible during this time, but it is clear that the comet brightened from eighth to fourth magnitude before it became available to visual observers again around 1 January 2007. On 26 December the comet had passed, unobserved, from the constellation of Serpens and into Scutum. Despite all the doom and gloom predictions of a comet that would simply fizzle out at perihelion, C/2006 P1 (McNaught) was on track to become a spectacular object at perihelion. Was this the long-awaited successor to Comet West that blazed across the dawn sky for a few precious mornings in March 1976?

McNAUGHT EXPLODES FROM THE TWILIGHT GLARE

With the comet peaking at its highest declination of −7 degrees on 3–4 January, some 15° further north than the Sun, the first twelve days of January would see the comet as the sole property of Northern Hemisphere observers, as it would rise just before, and set just after, the Sun. However, December had been one of the cloudiest in memory for many UK and European amateur astronomers; would anyone actually see the comet in the critical twilight period? As it turned out, UK observers (including this author) were, for the most part, very lucky. A cloudy high pressure moved away from our skies in the second week of January, to be replaced by wet and very windy conditions, but with large periods of crystal-clear skies in between, especially on the mornings of 8 and 9 January and the critical last evenings of 10 and 11 January, prior to the comet heading south. The comet was now on the Aquila/Sagittarius border but, in twilight, these constellation boundaries were somewhat academic. On these four consecutive days I was able to view the comet when the head was barely 1° above the horizon and the Sun as little as 5° below it! For me, despite a quarter-century as a dedicated comet photographer and imager, this was a unique experience, as was a tripod-mounted photographic system with exposures of only two seconds maximum (Figure 3). In the evening sky Venus (and Mercury) provided a useful magnitude reference when estimating the brightness of the comet's head. The comet was clearly almost as bright as Venus on 10 and 11 January, with a magnitude of at least −3.

On 12 January Comet McNaught entered the field of view of the LASCO C3 detector on the SOHO spacecraft, used for detecting solar flares and, therefore, pointed permanently towards the Sun. This detector has a radius of just over 8°, so any comet with a solar elongation of 8° or less will be visible with the instrument. Apart from

C/2006 P1 (McNaught). 2007 January 10th. 17:07 UT. Canon 300D + 300mm f/5.6 lens. 2 secs. 3.4° x 2.3°.
M.P. Mobberley

Figure 3. This UK image of Comet McNaught was taken by the author on 10 January 2007 at 17.07 UT, just two days before perihelion. The Sun was only 9° below the WSW horizon at the time of the exposure and the magnitude −3 head of the comet was 1° above the horizon. Canon 300D + 300 mm f/5.6 lens, 2-second exposure at ISO 400. The field is just over 3° wide. (Image courtesy of the author.)

Venus, no other object that bright had ever entered the instrument's field of view (Figure 4), and after McNaught peaked in brightness at an estimated magnitude of −5 or −6, Venus would have to be content with second place. McNaught passed, in a line-of-sight sense, close to Mercury on 14 January but the magnitude −1 planet looked totally unimpressive next to a comet almost 100 times brighter! On the same day, in the UK, the President of the British Astronomical Association, Richard Miles, carried out precise photometry on the comet in *broad daylight* with it only a few degrees from the Sun! His measurement, with a 60-millimetre refractor and neutral-density filters, recorded the comet at close to a magnitude of −5 with a 90-arcsecond photometric aperture (Figure 5). C/2006 P1 would remain in the LASCO C3 field until 16 January but, for lucky Southern Hemisphere observers, the show had only just begun!

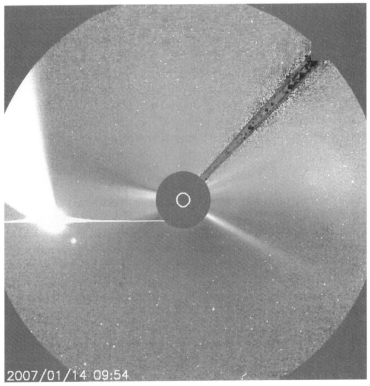

2007/01/14 09:54

Figure 4. Comet McNaught at magnitude −5 totally saturates the SOHO LASCO C3 coronograph on 14 January 2007 at 09.54 UT, two days after perihelion. The Sun is hidden behind the dark occulting disc at the centre. The central white circle represents the solar diameter. The dot near the comet's head is Mercury, on the other side of the Sun, shining at magnitude −1, but insignificant next to the comet's head. The white horizontal streak is caused by excess charge on the detector's pixels, overloaded by the brightness of the comet. (Image courtesy of SOHO/LASCO consortium. SOHO is a project of international cooperation between ESA and NASA.)

Comet C/2006 P1 (McNaught)
2007 Jan 14.624

Comet C/2006 P1 (McNaught)
2007 Jan 14.658

Figure 5. These extraordinary images of Comet McNaught were taken in broad daylight (!) by British Astronomical Association President Richard Miles, on the afternoon of 14 January 2007, using a 60 mm refractor and a neutral density/V band filter. Two hundred 4-second exposures were stacked and averaged for each. The comet was only 5.7° from the Sun at the time! The field spans 10 × 7 arcminutes. (Image courtesy of Richard Miles.)

AN AWESOME POST-PERIHELION SPECTACLE

Typically comets peak in activity a week or two after perihelion, when the ball of ice and rock has had time to really soak in the solar energy: McNaught was no exception. As this extraordinary comet plunged south, and its elongation from the Sun increased, moving it out of twilight and into a darkening evening sky, cometary activity increased. Even more fortunate was the fact that the closest approach to the Earth (120 million kilometres) occurred on 15 January, three days after perihelion, and New Moon occurred on 19 January, thus ensuring no significant moonlight interference for several days. During this time the comet's elongation from the Sun increased rapidly, reaching 20° by the 20th. The comet was, at last, visible in a dark sky, with its head fractionally above the horizon, from the country where it was discovered some five months earlier, i.e. from Australia. The spectacle seen in Southern Hemisphere evening skies around this time was truly awesome (Figure 6). Not since Comet West in March 1976 had such a sight been seen from any place on Earth. C/2006 P1 was producing vast amounts of dust and a classic curved dust tail, easily visible even to casual onlookers in the evening sky. From 17 to 25 January the sight was remarkable, peaking around 20 January with the comet some eight days past perihelion and in the southern constellation of Microscopium. As well as a main tail with a height of 10° above the comet's coma, fainter multiple tails, the remnants of previous days' emissions, stretched horizontally (and vertically) across the horizon for at least 50°, equivalent to a 150-million-kilometre swath in space. As the comet's orbital plane was at 78° to the ecliptic and well away from the

Figure 6. A 130-second exposure at ISO 200 of the magnificent Comet McNaught, taken with a Canon 350D + 100 mm f/2.8 lens at f/3.5 on 20 January 2007 by Australian Terry Lovejoy, who was at Lake Leslie near Warwick, Queensland. (Image courtesy of Terry Lovejoy.)

Earth there would, sadly, be no chance of a spectacular meteor storm as Earth ploughed through the débris.

Even to non-astronomers looking at the Southern Hemisphere early-evening sky it was as if dozens of comets were trailing behind the main one. Including the faintest visible extent of the tails, the cometary spectacle was covering a swath of sky 50° wide by 25° in height (Figure 7). The popular technical term for the intricate details in the tail(s) of comet McNaught is 'striae'. A comet's dust tail, driven by the solar wind, will initially point directly away from the Sun and be driven outside the comet's orbit. Unlike gas particles, the dust particles have significant mass, and so tend to lag behind the position of the comet's head, producing the traditional curved dust tail. The remarkable striations in McNaught's tail have to be related to gravity, solar wind and radiation forces acting on the dust. The time of particle release from the rotating nucleus as well as the dust-grain sizes will define the patterns seen. The multiple tail effect caused by dust grains released at the same time, and then released again over many days, are called synchrones, whereas the more horizontal patterns caused by dust grains of similar mass are called syndynes. McNaught easily displayed both patterns, even to the casual naked-eye observer!

Figure 7. Another image by Terry Lovejoy, acquired on 20 January. This time a 23 mm lens was used to capture a 50°-wide field in a 172-second exposure at f/3.2. The full extent of the incredible tail striations has been recorded and the comet is reflected in the water. (Image courtesy of Terry Lovejoy.)

These visible striae stretched so far across the sky that their ends could even be photographed by observers in the far Northern Hemisphere, despite the fact that the comet's head was (sadly) now 30° below the horizon by 20 January! As January 2007 came to a close the awesome spectacle faded. Not only was McNaught moving rapidly away from the Sun and the Earth, the Moon was waxing too. But for those who had seen C/2006 P1, from either hemisphere, it was a comet they would never forget.

C/2006 P1'S PLACE IN HISTORY

Comets are generally referred to as being 'Great' if they reach zero magnitude or brighter. The cometary term Great (i.e. massive and awesome) is one that has roots in antiquity, from the days when the original discoverer was usually unknown and every brilliant naked-eye comet instilled a sense of awe and wonder, and they were all simply known as 'The Great Comet of . . . (e.g.) 1744'. In the modern era, with so many comets called LINEAR it is good to see that all the truly 'Great' recent comets still seem to bear human discoverers' names!

Looking back over the last sixty years, and including all comets brighter than magnitude 2.0, we find a mere sixteen candidates (listed in Table 1). Many of these names will be well known to amateur astronomers, especially the more recent blockbusters like Hale–Bopp and Hyakutake. Older observers will recall West, Bennett, Kohoutek and Ikeya–Seki and even the 1950s comets Arend–Roland and Mrkos. UK observers will recall, with pride, IRAS–Araki–Alcock as George Alcock's fifth discovery, made when he was 70 years old and sweeping the skies with binoculars through his double-glazed upstairs landing window!

Comets generally become 'Great' for three reasons. They are sometimes simply 'massive' gas and dust producers (like Hale–Bopp), or they pass very close to the Earth (like Hyakutake and IRAS–Araki–Alcock), or they pass very close to the Sun and survive, like Ikeya–Seki and McNaught. Very rarely, Great Comets may satisfy all three criteria. One such example was Comet Donati in 1858. That comet was very active and passed reasonably close to the Earth and the Sun. Massive comets, like Hale–Bopp, have a big advantage in that they

Table 1. The sixteen brightest comets of the last sixty years

Comets in perihelion date order	Perihelion Date	Perihelion Dist.(AU)	Peak Mag.	Outstanding Characteristic
C/2006 P1 (McNaught)	12 Jan 2007	0.17	−5.5	Small q
C/2002 V1 (NEAT)	18 Feb 2003	0.10	0	Small q
C/1998 J1 (SOHO)	8 May 1998	0.15	1	Small q
C/1995 O1 (Hale–Bopp)	1 Apr 1997	0.91	−1	Massive H_0
C/1996 B2 (Hyakutake)	1 May 1996	0.23	0	Small Δ
C/1983 H1 (IRAS–Araki–Alcock)	21 May 1983	0.99	1.5	Small Δ
C/1975 V1-A (West)	25 Feb 1976	0.20	−3	Small q
C/1973 E1 (Kohoutek)	28 Dec 1973	0.14	0	Small q
C/1970 K1 (White–Ortiz–Bolelli)	14 May 1970	0.0089	1	Sungrazer
C/1969 Y1 (Bennett)	20 Mar 1970	0.54	0	Good q & H_0
C/1965 S1-A (Ikeya–Seki)	21 Oct 1965	0.0078	−10	Sungrazer
C/1962 C1 (Seki–Lines)	1 Apr 1962	0.031	0	V. small q
C/1957 P1 (Mrkos)	1 Aug 1957	0.35	1	Good q & H_0
C/1956 R1 (Arend–Roland)	8 Apr 1957	0.32	−0.5	Good q & H_0
C/1948 V1 (Eclipse Comet)	27 Oct 1948	0.14	0	Small q
C/1947 X1-A (Southern Comet)	2 Dec 1947	0.11	−3	Small q

The final column shows that comets become exceptional because:

1. They get close to the Sun, i.e. they have a small q (perihelion distance), or even 'graze' the Sun's inner atmosphere (Sungrazers have a q < 0.01 AU).
2. They have a massive 'size'/activity level, i.e. their absolute magnitude H_0 is large.
3. They come close to the Earth (small Δ).
4. A combination of all of the above.

can usually be seen for many months in a truly dark sky; thus they are seen by huge numbers of people. Comets that simply pass close to the Earth or the Sun are 'Great' for a shorter period of time. Comet 2006 P1/McNaught was outstanding in its sheer brightness. Only one comet was brighter in the last sixty years, namely Ikeya-Seki, briefly, at perihelion, but the dust tail was far less spectacular. McNaught was also exceptional with regard to its phenomenally intricate tail detail seen in the ten days after perihelion from the Southern Hemisphere (Figure 8). It seems to have exceeded even the performance of Comet West in this regard, and the clear visibility of multiple 'tails' hours after sunset is most reminiscent of a comet of the eighteenth century, namely de Chéseaux's comet (C/1743 X1) also called Comet Klinkenberg–Chéseaux of 1744, which was said to have had six or seven tails visible long after sunset on 8–9 March of that year, and also had a magnitude estimated as around −7. Perhaps we really do have to go back in time by those 263 years to find a comet with such an incredibly large and striated dust tail, visible long after the head has set.

For a Northern Hemisphere observer like me, who missed Comet West, the comets Hyakutake and Hale–Bopp are more awesome in the memory than Comet McNaught will ever be. However, McNaught for me (and many others) completes a trio with those other comets. I have now seen Great Comets in all three categories of 'Monster', 'Earth fly-by' and 'Small perihelion/Sungrazer'. I was beginning to wonder if I would ever see a comet in that latter category. However, for Southern Hemisphere observers, Comet McNaught, post-perihelion in January 2007, may well be the greatest cometary spectacle they will ever see. But

Figure 8. This final image by Terry Lovejoy was taken on 21 January 2007 with a 19 mm lens at f/3.2 and a 117-second exposure. The picture was taken from Cunningham's Gap in Queensland and the glow around the thin crescent Moon can also be seen. Terry measured the distance from the comet's head to the rightmost extent of the tail as an incredible 49°. (Image courtesy of Terry Lovejoy.)

of course, there could be another one just around the corner. That is the real beauty of comet observing: you just never know what is coming next!

One Hundred Supernovae and Counting

TOM BOLES

Little did I suspect when I started to patrol for supernovae that I would discover enough of them even to reach double figures. The thought of achieving over a hundred would have been a mere pipedream. In those early days the discovery of each supernova was typically months apart. In fact, the gap between my first and second discoveries was just ten days short of a year in length.

THE EARLY YEARS

In the latter part of the 1990s, when patrolling for supernovae was just beginning in the UK, the methods available for discovering them were much more primitive than today. Before then many observers had attempted to discover supernovae (SNe) using photographic techniques. (See Ron Arbour's article in the *2000 Yearbook of Astronomy*.[1]) When we look today at statistics showing the discovery rate compared with the number of images taken then, it is little surprise that so many hours were spent exposing and developing photographic emulsions without success. Today it is not uncommon for 4000+ frames to be taken between each discovery. If that is translated into time these early patrollers were indeed heroes of the first degree. If we add the cost of 4000 frames of film and developer then the whole exercise looks overwhelmingly daunting. Despite that, discoveries were made and our respect and admiration must go to those early patrollers.

The Revd Robert Evans (Figure 1) in Australia used an alternative and very successful method. Bob searched for SNe visually. This was indeed a lot faster and less expensive. He could patrol over 400 galaxies

---

[1] Moore, P. (ed.), *2000 Yearbook of Astronomy*, Macmillan, London, pp. 223–40.

Figure 1. (Left to right) The author, Sir Patrick Moore and the Revd Robert Evans, Selsey 2006. (Image courtesy of the author.)

each clear night. This did, of course, mean that Bob had to memorize the appearance of each of the galaxies that he observed if he were to keep up his patrol and resulting discovery rates.

A major breakthrough came in the 1990s when affordable Go To telescopes became available. These telescopes utilized new low-cost micro circuitry to enable the observer to point them to an astronomical target quickly and with relative ease. In many cases only the name of the object needed to be input and the telescope would 'go to' that object at the press of a button. This breakthrough was soon followed by affordable charge-coupled device (CCD) cameras that had become accessible, for the first time, to other than professional astronomers. These two pieces of equipment were to revolutionize how supernovae were discovered. The revolution, however, came slowly.

One of the first improvements was the use of a planetarium program to help input the names of targets into a desktop computer. This had the ability to send the correct coordinates to the telescope and slew it to 'almost' the correct spot in the sky. Minor imperfections in the telescope's mechanical construction and its encoders, aided by imperfect polar alignment, meant that the telescope had to be resynchronized regularly with nearby stars to keep the target galaxies in view. This was still a de luxe method of patrolling. Exposures as short as sixty seconds could be made and stars as low as magnitude 18.5 could be reached on the best of nights. This meant that, with a list of galaxies that were planned in advance, it was possible to image between twenty and twenty-five galaxies an hour. If the observer were clever enough to choose his galaxies with care, it was possible to get multiple galaxies in the same (tiny) CCD frame and so increase his productivity.

At this stage it was possible to record images with relative ease. What was more difficult was finding a satisfactory method of checking those images. Shortly after I took delivery of my camera my employer relocated me to Germany for two years. This made some excellent skies available to me and helped me to improve my imaging skills with the newly delivered camera. Also around this time an article appeared in *Sky & Telescope* which showed a novel way of inspecting images. It was relatively simple and looked very effective to me. It consisted of mounting a transparent foil from an overhead projector in front of the CCD monitor. Any field stars that were visible on the image were marked on the foil with a marker. The template produced would then become the comparison chart of that galaxy the next time it was observed. One of the problems I had was that the galaxy never lined up on the monitor in the same way twice. This meant that the mount had to be discarded, and the foil held by hand so that it could be manually aligned with the known field stars. I persevered with this for some months, but became determined to find a better method.

After I returned to the UK the first task was to build a permanent observatory and pillar for the telescope. By this time Mark Armstrong had discovered SN1996bo. This was the first SN discovered from the UK. Mark was a member of the UK Nova/Supernova patrol, which was organized by Guy Hurst in Basingstoke. I contacted Guy and joined the patrol.

The camera I was using at that time was a Starlight Xpress, a UK-manufactured camera that had a double-sized frame store. This is the memory that is used to store the images once they are downloaded from the camera. I discovered that the upper part could be used to load master images into, and a switch on the front panel could be manually thrown to simulate a plate comparator by effectively blinking two images. One would be the new image just taken, and the other would be a library image taken at an earlier date and loaded into this higher area of the memory. This system worked quite well for me. I used it for nearly two years and my first two discoveries were made by this method.

Throughout this period of patrolling, it was necessary to sit by the monitor in the observatory. Each image and telescope slew command had to be loaded via the keyboard. This is fine in the warmer months but in winter it can become very uncomfortable and even dangerous. You are sitting stationary for long periods and can become extremely cold without realizing it. In February, for example, it is possible for your core body temperature to drop. Even a slight drop can be danger-ous. One option is, of course, to wrap up very well, which I did. I added several layers of clothing and substantial gloves, but this made the keyboard very difficult to use. I had to use a rubber-tipped pencil in each hand to push the keys, and any call of nature resulted in a major undressing and dressing exercise. The obvious and superior method of doing this was to devise a system that enabled me to work indoors while keeping the telescope and camera where they operated more efficiently – in the cold. It would be some time before that would be possible.

WHY PATROL FOR SUPERNOVAE?

Let's face it, the UK is not the ideal place to search for nineteenth-magnitude objects in faint distant galaxies. Light pollution there has become a very serious problem. Observers in the UK who hope to succeed have to choose their area of interest with care depending on where they live and what they find motivates them. Where I lived in Northamptonshire, and the site of my first fixed observatory, con-ditions were not ideal. My local council was proud that it had rates that were among the lowest in the country, achieved through encouraging distribution firms to surround the town where I lived with depots which were protected by powerful security lights. This resulted in a circular halo of orange glow that rose from the horizon and nearly reached the zenith. I can remember going to the town centre with some visiting astronomers to discover that I could see more from the town's cark park than from my home at the edge of town. These conditions severely limited just how faint I could see. It did mean that exposures had to be lengthened to see faint enough. It also meant that not as many nights as I would have wished were available for patrolling. When conditions are as poor as this it restricts what can be done and still achieve worthwhile results. Supernova patrolling, I felt, was one thing that could be successfully done, albeit with difficulty, from a light-polluted area. If the equipment that you are using is capable of recording faint enough stars, then in theory you are making a simple binary decision. Either a new star is there or it isn't. In practice it isn't quite as simple as that because noise caused by polluted skies can generate false 'stars' and artefacts in your images. These are not necessarily showstoppers, but they do result in wasted time re-imaging galaxies a second, third and sometimes even fourth time, which affects your productivity. As we shall see, the secret to successful supernova patrolling is doing everything possible to increase the productivity of your imaging. I can say with confidence that if we enjoyed skies of the quality of, for example, Arizona in the USA, the UK supernova discovery tally would be many times higher.

WHAT PATROLLING IS ALL ABOUT

The theory of patrolling for supernova is really quite simple. The idea is to take an image of a galaxy and then compare that image with another image, taken some time previously, and then look for differences. To be successful, however, you have to take a very large number of images. There are several ways of achieving this. The first is to patrol on a very large number of nights. This can be difficult in the UK because the number of cloudless nights is not that large. If you are willing to sit up on nights that are partially clear or clear for only part of the time this can be improved, but it is much harder work. Given that the number of patrolling hours available is outside your control, then the next best thing is to patrol faster. There are several ways of achieving this. You can take shorter exposures, which gets you through your galaxy list quicker. The larger the aperture of your telescope the fainter you can get with any given exposure. This is obvious, so I will not dwell on it here. The choice of camera is critical if you wish to optimize the imaging speed. The type of mount that you use will also play a crucial role in how fast you can patrol. I shall discuss each of these in turn.

CHOICE OF CAMERA

The camera's contribution is to keep your exposures as short as possible, and to do this means that you need to have the most sensitive camera available to you. I chose a camera with a back-illuminated, thinned CCD chip. These cameras invariably have larger-sized pixels. Pixels are equivalent to the grain that was present in standard camera film. It was usually that the larger the grain size, the faster was the film. So it is with CCD cameras. My camera has large pixels measuring 24 microns, which are square in shape. The larger pixels give me more sensitivity and the square pixels make it easier for software to measure the positions of the stars in the images. However, one problem with larger pixels is that they create more electrical noise. The amount of noise generated must be checked in the camera's specifications before a purchase is made. There is one way of reducing noise in these cameras; the chip can be cooled. The lower the temperature at which the chip operates, the less noise is generated. It is normal to cool these faster chips to around 50° below ambient. Some of the really expensive ones use liquid nitrogen to chill them by a hundred or more degrees. One disadvantage of a camera operated at these temperatures is that it takes longer at the start and end of the night to get the camera back to ambient temperature without damaging the chip. To ensure this doesn't happen, the chip has to be cooled and warmed slowly. The lower the temperature, the longer it takes to stabilize. This type of chip is expensive, and I need to emphasize at this point that you can succeed without its enhanced features. Indeed, my first discoveries were made with a much more modest camera. The pixels were smaller, and slower, but this was partially offset by the lower noise levels that the smaller pixels produced.

CHOICE OF MOUNT

Some mounts move faster than others, and some mounts only *appear* to move faster than others. There is little point in a mount moving your telescope fifteen degrees in a few seconds if it takes another thirty seconds to stop shaking after it comes to rest. The mount has to be both powerful and robust. It must be capable of both moving quickly and coming to rest quickly. There will be thousands of telescope movements between each discovery, so the gears need to be strong and accurate: the mount must be capable of pointing to your chosen galaxies accurately and consistently. The quality of the mount is crucial if this is to happen. Inaccurate pointing will result in your having to stop and repoint the telescope throughout the night and will lose you much valuable patrolling time.

The aperture of your chosen telescope and the sensitivity of your camera affect the faintness of the stars that you can record. What most people might not recognize is that the mount also plays an important rôle in how faint you can get. A mount that causes the stars to drift across the field of view, for whatever reason, will detract from the good work done by the telescope and camera. A badly polar-aligned mount can cause drifting, but with the short exposures used in patrolling it would do more damage to pointing accuracy than sensitivity. A mount with badly manufactured gears and without some kind of error correction is much more deadly. The lateral east to west drift caused by periodic error in a poorly machined worm gear can lose you a large percentage of the sensitivity of your system. A high-quality mount will have both top-quality gears and periodic error correction built in.

GOING FASTER

What hasn't been mentioned so far but which has been inferred is how the telescopes are controlled. To attain the maximum possible speed the system must be automated. Without the use of computers controlling the telescopes and cameras, the opportunity to maximize the use of the available clear skies will be lost. Automation of the imaging process increases the speed at which the images are recorded in several ways. Of course, a computer can do some things faster than the observer could, so let us discuss gains in speed for other reasons. Firstly, the computer will make fewer errors than a manual observer will. This in turn eliminates the need to back up and reset the system each time an error is made. Secondly, an automated system does not tire. It will not slow down in the small hours of the morning when we humans are starting to sag and collapse; it preserves whatever energy and concentration the observer has for accurately checking images, thus reducing the chances of missed candidates, especially faint or poorly recorded ones that have been recorded under poorer-quality skies. Thirdly, mundane things like building a time delay into the process to allow each telescope to settle so that no shake is apparent in the final image can be programmed. This can be done so that sufficient time, but no more than absolutely necessary, is used. Similarly, the programming can accommodate additional tasks such as carrying out error correction on the pointing coordinates sent to the telescope so that the target is always centred in the field of view. This means that the telescope can maintain its pointing accuracy across the entire sky, thus eliminating the need to resynchronize the telescope on a regular basis due to its drifting off over time as the pointing errors accumulate.

A computer can also do more than one task simultaneously. For example, with older CCD cameras, such as the type I use, it takes several seconds to download each image from the camera, which is normally wasted time. However, a cleverly written control program can be slewing the telescope while this is going on. Often the telescope will be at rest before the image is fully downloaded. This saves valuable settling time and the whole process runs faster.

If a telescope and computer are properly protected from the harshest of the elements then their performance will be far superior to that of a human observer in cold weather. Once an automated system has been set up, it is possible to control the computer from another one that is safely and comfortably sitting indoors. The computers are linked together by a simple local area network (LAN). From the warmth, it is possible to carry out most functions easily. These can include changing the list of galaxies to be imaged, the camera temperature and even focusing of the telescope. This is of course much more comfortable than sitting in the cold, but it also means that the observer can concentrate better, go on for longer and, in general, make fewer mistakes than when outside.

Once this is set up the real skill comes from choosing the galaxies that you wish to patrol. By selecting the correct galaxies by their characteristics and perhaps position, it is possible to increase the observer's discovery rate considerably.

GOING EVEN FASTER

One very common method of increasing your productivity is to operate more than one telescope. At present I run three 14-inch Schmidt Cassegrain reflectors simultaneously. Each of these will be patrolling a different area of sky, the thinking being that with three telescopes working I can cover three times as much sky as I would with one. If you live in a country with a hundred clear nights a year, then using three telescopes is equivalent to having 300 clear nights. Having additional telescopes therefore helps combat the effect of our poor climate and increases the discovery rate. There are, however, a few disadvantages to this. The first is that you have more than one telescope to manage throughout the night. This can sometimes be onerous, especially if the weather is being changeable and unpredictable. Covering up three telescopes, in a rush at the threat of rain, can be quite good exercise but very stressful. I can recall one evening when I was imaging galaxies in an area of very clear sky close to the horizon while several inches of snow were falling immediately above the observatory. The secret here is to get brushing and shovelling before the snow has a chance to melt. Another great disadvantage (but of course the main advantage) is that you acquire three times as many images with three cameras. It is not easy to stay ahead of the game and be able to check the images as fast as the telescopes can store them. The result is that several hundred often remain to be studied and searched for supernovae after the Sun rises. This is the time when the observer should be sleeping and recovering. In November, the patrol period could be as long as fourteen hours if a night is clear throughout. If you are 'lucky' enough to have two or three clear nights in succession then things can become critical.

Even in summertime with its shorter nights things aren't necessarily any easier. The beauty of August, for example, is that there are many clear nights and nights with good seeing because of thin, high mists. A backlog of images can build up easily. Added to this is that clear days often follow clear nights and while everyone else can be enjoying the summer sunshine the patroller must check his images, for the next evening might be clear again. I know this can sound very negative, but I assure you that it isn't in practice. The whole point of doing astronomy is because you enjoy doing it. If you cease to enjoy it, change your area of interest or even give it up. The golden rule is that astronomy must be fun, go out and enjoy it. When I cease to enjoy patrolling or it becomes a chore I will give up and do something else.

BASIC TIPS IN PLANNING AN EFFICIENT PATROL

The whole secret of high productivity in any area is to work as little as possible. Or, if you need to put in a high number of hours, as in SN patrolling, to get as much done per hour by taking the time to plan your work carefully. I shall describe some obvious and some not so obvious tips to help increase productivity.

Choose galaxies carefully. The first objective is, of course, to discover supernovae. The type of galaxy that you choose can make a big difference to your productivity. Supernova types that are believed to result from a binary system containing a white dwarf and a giant companion (type Ia) are more frequently seen in older star populations. Those that are believed to come from the demise of massive stars are more commonly found in younger star populations. From this you would expect to see type Ia SNe in elliptical galaxies and nearer the cores of spiral galaxies, and the core collapse of the larger stars (mainly type II) in the spiral arms of galaxies. This is not, however, an absolute rule, as older stars have moved around and been mixed with the rest of the stellar population. With a little experience it is even possible to guess the type of a newly discovered SN just from the galaxy type, its position within it and the SN's apparent brightness. The latter is based on the fact that type Ia SNe are intrinsically more luminous than type II SNe. I estimate that I can work out the types of newly dis-covered SNe in about 70 per cent of the cases before the official spectra become available. So choose the galaxies carefully. Spiral galaxies can be host to both types of SNe, so start with these. Choose face-on spirals. This will let you observe deeper into the galaxy and you will spot more of its SNe. Edge-on galaxies present dust lanes towards the observer, which obscures many of the SNe that occur and causes the reddening and dimming of many others. Choose galaxies nearby whose SNe will appear brighter. If, like me, your galaxy list extends to many thousands then this criterion is less critical.

Minimize telescope movement. To make your telescope image as many galaxies as possible, plan a run so that it has to move around the sky as little as absolutely necessary. To achieve this I patrol the sky in segments. I choose 15° segments each represented by an hour of right ascension (RA). The sky therefore breaks up into twenty-four segments, which are from RA00 to RA23. I then patrol each segment in a single direction from north to south. Using this approach the telescope never has to backtrack on itself in declination and so saves time. It also has the additional advantage that the declination gears are always driven in the same direction, thus reducing any slack that they might have.

Fighting back against bad skies and bright moonlight. These cannot be completely eliminated, but the effects can be reduced. Not only do I set my patrols up in RA segments but I also produce up to three plans for each segment. These are: the brighter galaxies, i.e. brighter than magnitude 14; those between magnitudes 14 and 15; and finally between magnitudes 15 and 16. It is then possible to choose to patrol your brighter galaxies when the Moon is visible or the sky is less transparent. The faintest galaxies are held in reserve for those exceptional nights.

Use a logbook and planning sheet. All observers should keep a logbook. This tells you which galaxies you have looked at and when you did so, though it can be a little unfriendly if you try to use it to help you to choose an area to patrol on any given night. To help with this I have designed a planning sheet. This is a single A4 sheet that summarizes the seventy-two scripts that I have by RA and brightness. It also shows the number of galaxies in each list. The sheet is dated and each box contains the number of days since that area was last patrolled. The boxes can also contain multiple entries for each area. This will occur if a patrol was broken off early because of the weather or because it was getting too close to the horizon. The whole objective here is to ensure that you don't 'neglect' any area for too long, and that you don't patrol an area more frequently than every four days (unless you are up to date with all the others). This is a very simple visual tool and very easy to use.

Beat the wind. I have two of my telescopes in a run-off shed and the third in a traditional dome observatory. The dome gives that telescope some additional protection from the wind, but the two in the shed are exposed. The walls are necessarily low to allow fuller access to the sky nearer the horizon. To assist against wind, I have three large wooden boards that can be hoisted to sit on the observatory walls and temporarily increase their height. Two boards are needed for the long walls and a third is used for the short ones. They are only installed on the windward side. I then choose a patrol facing the opposite direction and the effects of wind are minimized. If this is insufficient, the dew shields are removed. If there is still a problem then there is no option but to close for the night. Never make a decision regarding wind strength immediately after sunset. I have noticed that on most nights the wind will increase temporarily at this time. It usually calms within an hour.

Eliminate false alarms – use a checklist. During the small hours of the morning it is so easy to make mistakes. Your body is tired but you might not necessarily feel it. A lot of the work that a patroller does is repetitive. Most of the manual tasks are simple and can be carried out often without much thought. The more challenging tasks are the mental ones. These occur most commonly when a suspect is found or when a report is being written. The greatest fear of any regular supernova patroller is the dread of discovering that a false claim has been made. With experience there are many ways to ensure that errors can be avoided. The development of the Internet and the resources that are available now make it much easier than before to check for likely problems. To do this efficiently, it is necessary to construct a checklist. This is simply a list of standard checks that the observer carries out on any SN suspect to try to eliminate it. There is no way to prove that what you have found is an SN (unless you have access to a telescope larger than one metre in diameter and a spectrograph), but there are ways to prove that a candidate is *not* an SN. It is so easy to forget to do one of the checks due to tiredness, and the checklist ensures that this does not happen. The checks range from eliminating asteroids to even checking if your suspect is indeed a genuine SN but has been reported before. Each check is done to eliminate a common possible cause. In some cases the checks can eliminate several causes, and some redundancy is built in, which makes them more secure. If the reader is interested, then a table showing all the common checks and what they are testing for, including the logic for and where to find the resources for each test, is available in the *Journal of the British Astronomical Association*.[2]

THE FIRST DISCOVERY

I was still in full-time employment when I started patrolling. This meant that, with the exception of weekends, it was rare that I was able to patrol throughout the night. On occasions I managed to patrol until the dizzy time of 2 a.m., but this was not usual, and it was even more unusual to be able to patrol to this time on consecutive nights. The night of 29 October 1997 was one of the few times when I was able to patrol into the early hours. This was exceptional, as the patrol had begun on the evening of 28 October, which was a Tuesday and a workday. I can remember that I was finding it very hard to keep myself motivated on that night, and to do so I made a deal with myself that if I continued to patrol to the end of the current list of galaxies then I would call it a night and retire to the welcoming warmth of my bed. This was not to happen.

There were some six galaxies still to patrol when I imaged Galaxy NGC 3451. You would imagine that, having searched for many months, I would have been overjoyed at finding a previously unrecorded star sitting on the limb of this galaxy (Figure 2). It was 04.15 in the morning and sunrise was not that far off. I continued to take images for almost another hour before I reported my 'suspect' to the Nova/Supernova patrol. We need to remember that in 1997, the discovery of a supernova was a less common event. All the necessary checks still had to be completed. These took a lot longer as some of the facilities available today were not then available. NGC 3451, although being in the New General Catalogue of galaxies, was not a popular subject for photographers, so few images existed that could be used for comparison. Nothing was visible on the first version of the Digital Sky Survey (DSS1), but that is often misleading and can be unhelpful.

The next day was the 1997 Annual General Meeting of the British Astronomical Association in London. While all the financial reporting and updates on the past year's activities were taking place, a small group huddled at the back of the room exchanging floppy disks of

2 Boles, T., 2006, *J. Brit. Astron. Assoc.*, **116**(5), 229–38.

Figure 2. The author's first supernova discovery, on 29 October 1997: SN1997dn in NGC 3451. (Image courtesy of the author.)

images and discussing whether or not this could really be a supernova. Guy Hurst had previously visited the library of the Royal Astronomical Society and searched for any atlases that might contain other images of this galaxy. Nick James kindly carried out astrometry on what was a very poor image. Later that evening details about the suspect were sent to Brian Marsden at the Central Bureau for Astronomical Telegrams (CBAT). From then, the whole passage of time seemed to slow down. Hours seemed like days and when I look back on the events it felt as though a week had passed before I heard anything. In reality the opposite was true. Things really happened very quickly. A spectrum taken by the Fred Whipple 1.5-metre telescope (Figure 3) on the night of 30 October confirmed that the suspect was indeed a type II supernova. It was later that day that I was told that it had been given the designation 1997dn and that the results were published in IAUC 6763. It was only after the circular appeared that I was able to relax and enjoy the marvellous feeling of satisfaction at having discovered an extra-galactic supernova.

From somewhere, *The Times* in London found out about the discovery. On 3 November it produced a nice, almost half-page story about a supernova being discovered from a back garden. The accompanying picture let it down and indicated that a whole galaxy had been discovered. Then the lesser media got hold of the story. I was inundated with calls from small newspapers and smaller radio stations asking for details. Not all of them were interested in serious reporting. I can recall one interview on commercial radio where loud pop music was blasting away while rather banal questions were asked. I will leave the reader to guess what popular record was playing in the background.

The important thing about the discovery of SN1997dn[3] was that it demonstrated to me that my equipment and methods worked. It fuelled my motivation enough to make me want to go on and try to repeat the experience. Of all the supernovae that I was to discover from then on, SN1997dn is the one that will be remembered as giving the greatest 'buzz'.

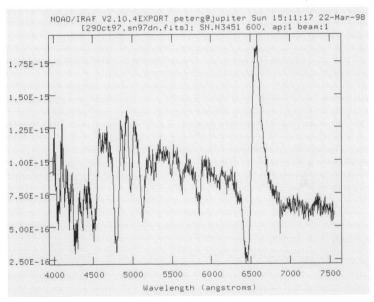

Figure 3. Spectrum of SN1997dn, acquired by the Fred Whipple 1.5-metre telescope, confirming that the object was a type II supernova. This spectrum was taken as part of the Center for Astrophysics (CfA) Supernova Program, which is funded in part by the National Science Foundation through grant AST 06–06772.

3 IAU Circular 6763.

THE ONE-HUNDREDTH DISCOVERY

There are many differences between the first and one-hundredth discoveries. The first discovery was unpredictable; indeed, I hadn't even any confidence that it would be made. As time passed, the frequency of discoveries increased and the experience that this brought also brought with it the almost certain knowledge that, if I persevered, the hundredth supernova must come.

As it turned out, the supernova SN2006bk[4] (Figure 4) that took me into triple figures was quite a bright example at magnitude 16.9. The galaxy, MCG +06−33−020, was one of the lesser-known ones in the Morphological Catalogue of Galaxies (MCG). It is a small but

Figure 4. The author's one-hundredth supernova discovery, SN2006bk in MCG+06−33−020. (Image courtesy of the author.)

4 IAU Circular 8698.

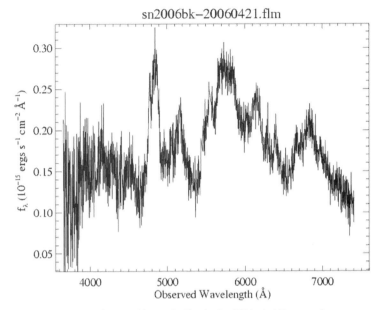

Figure 5. Spectrum of SN2006bk, acquired by the Fred Whipple 1.5-metre telescope, confirming that the object was a type Ia supernova. This spectrum was taken as part of the Center for Astrophysics (CfA) Supernova Program, which is funded in part by the National Science Foundation through grant AST 06–06772.

bright, elliptical galaxy. There was some confusion early on with the classification of SN2006bk. Gunma Astronomical Observatory considered it to be over-bright for its distance and classified it as a type Ic from its spectrum, which was taken in poor conditions. This excited me somewhat (see the section on SN2003L). I was hoping for an association with a gamma-ray burst (GRB), but the excitement was short-lived. The Whipple 1.5-metre followed up with a spectrogram, under better conditions, that showed it to be a type Ia (Figure 5). The confusion apparently arose due to a 'W' feature in the spectrum around 500 nm caused by unresolved Fe lines. These are common to both types Ia and Ic SNe after they have reached maximum brightness.

The more images that you record, the more supernovae you will discover; the pattern of discovery is, however, completely random. Just to emphasize that fact, discovery 101 came less than two hours after the hundredth. This was in another MCG galaxy, MCG +02−40−009, which is a small spiral galaxy in the constellation of Serpens. It is not that far away from the earlier discovery, which was in Boötes. SN2006bl was slightly fainter at magnitude 17.3, which was partly owing to it being a type II SN albeit at maximum light.

The discovery of SN2006bk was still every bit as exciting as 1997dn had been, even though the excitement was of a different kind. After a hundred discoveries, the excitement comes more from the thrill that arises from the appreciation of what you have discovered and its astronomical significance, though some stress is still present from the worry that you have not carried out all your tests on the subject properly so as to prevent making a false claim. This is good, as it prevents you from becoming careless and taking short cuts, which could easily happen as the years pass and the tally of successful discoveries increases.

HOW SUPERNOVA DISCOVERIES ARE ATTRIBUTED AND COUNTED

All discoveries are vetted and announced by the Central Bureau for Astronomical Telegrams (CBAT). For a long time it was a simple matter of relying on CBAT to announce the discovery, to give the SN a designation consisting of the year the discovery was made followed by a lettering code to signify the sequence of discovery, and name the discoverer(s).

That is no longer as simple as it was, as discoveries are now being claimed by groups of individuals. These are often involved in some kind of collaborative venture, and the claim can often read like a published research paper where a list of 'co-authors' follows the lead authors. Although this is very acceptable in research situations, it does not fit so comfortably when discoveries are made: it is often very likely that many of the names on the list haven't even observed the object.

I have counted my discoveries based on the following criteria:

- I have discovered the object and not been told about it by someone else;
- I have observed the object;
- I have reported the object to CBAT before a circular appears announcing the discovery;

- The suspect has been imaged on a second night, either independently or by myself;
- The discovery has been reported immediately to allow independent follow-up by anyone interested.

Using these criteria, SN2006bk was my one-hundredth discovery, though I could, of course, take an even more strict definition than this. Whereas it is fairly certain that a suspect that reaches publication in the circulars is indeed a bona fide supernova, that alone is no guarantee. Until a supernova is classified, doubt still exists as to its identity. Using this additional criterion, since six of my discoveries have not had spectra taken, my true hundredth supernova should perhaps be number 106. Going one stage further, I also have a discovery that has been classified but the classification has not appeared in a formally published circular. So perhaps I should count 107 as the hundredth supernova?

SN2003L – A SPECIAL SUPERNOVA

There is no doubt that the first supernova discovery is the one you cherish the most. This is for nostalgic and emotional reasons, but if I were to name a discovery that stood out for scientific reasons it would be, without doubt, SN2003L. This was discovered in January 2003 in a small pretty galaxy, NGC 3506. The whole background to SN2003L would take far too long to describe here. In the supernova rankings, it was the second most energetic radio supernova ever recorded. Only SN1998bw, which was the optical counterpart of a GRB, was more energetic. (Discovered in September 2006, the pair instability supernova SN2006gy subsequently outshone both of these.) The interesting discovery about the supernova was that, given its immense energy output, the speed of the ejecta that resulted from the explosion was relatively slow. Current theories explaining the central engines of core-collapse supernovae fail when such low-energy ejecta is observed. This led Alicia Soderberg to suggest that it might be a new sub-type of supernova.[5] These very high-energy supernovae (hypernovae) are very rare and so proof or otherwise of this suggestion will take some time; hence the short-lived excitement when

[5] Soderberg, A.M. et al., 2005, *Ap.J.*, **621**, no. 2, pp. 908–20.

SN2006bk was thought to be a type Ic and over-bright for its distance.

In addition to being very interesting scientifically, SN2003L was very satisfying because of the amount of resource that was put into following it up. Telescopes that observed it included the Katzmann Automatic Imaging Telescope (KAIT), which independently discovered it several hours after I did. The Asiago 1.8-metre reflector obtained a spectrum. The spectral type encouraged the Very Large Array (VLA) in New Mexico to follow up and discover that it was extremely loud at radio wavelengths. Following this, the Chandra X-ray Observatory observed it and recorded its high-energy output in X-rays. A new spectrum was recorded by the Fred Whipple 6.5-metre reflector, which confirmed the Asiago findings that the ejecta had a very low velocity.

Because of the high energy being emitted and the fact that it was a type Ic (type Ic supernovae can often be associated with GRBs), observations from the 3D Interplanetary Network (IPN) were used to attempt to match it with a previously recorded GRB. The IPN is made up of any suitable space probes that happen to be in transit and that could detect a reasonably strong GRB. It is used to triangulate the position of any GRB by measuring the time when the signal arrives at each of the probes. Three probes must return a measurement to pinpoint the position of a GRB in the sky. In this case it was also known that the GRB must have been of long duration if it were to be connected with a type Ic supernova.

Six probes were in place, and in the right orientation, to possibly detect the signal. These were: Hete-2; Integral; Konus-Wind; Rhessi; Ulysses; and Mars Odyssey. It turned out that both Hete-2 and Konus-Wind detected a long duration GRB within the expected time frame. The detection by Hete-2 had a low probability of coincidence with the location of SN2003L, but the one from Konus-Wind was more promising with a probability of 83 per cent that it was associated with the supernova. To be 100 per cent certain there would need to have been three almost simultaneous detections. This one at the end of December 2002 was likely but not proven conclusively to have preceded SN2003L.

AND EVEN ONE THAT I DIDN'T DISCOVER

SN2006jc[6] was discovered by K. Itagaki (Teppo-cho, Yamagata, Japan) on 9 October 2006. An independent discovery was made by T. Puckett and R. Gorelli in Georgia, USA. What was very interesting about this discovery was that in almost the same astrometric position Itagaki had also recorded a faint (confirmed) transient in 2004. Stephen Smartt, of the Queen's University of Belfast, found that the two phenomena were 'exactly' coincident. The peculiar spectra that were observed from the SN and this coincidence suggested that the earlier transient might have resulted from the brightening of its progenitor. If this were indeed the case, this would be a very valuable contribution as to the possible progenitors for core-collapse supernovae, such as 2006jc, resulting from the death of massive stars.

Since I started patrolling on a regular basis I have archived every image that I have taken (Figure 6), including the very poor ones. The

Figure 6. The author's 190 gigabytes of archived patrols. (Image courtesy of the author.)

[6] IAU Circular 8762.

galaxy that was host to these seemingly related phenomena was UGC 4904, a small, spiral galaxy in the constellation Lynx. I had many images of UGC 4904 in my archive. The observations went back almost to when I started patrolling and I had a very comprehensive set of images surrounding the transient that Itagaki observed in 2004.

None of my images showed the transient to a limiting magnitude well below that recorded in Japan. This is a good example of where negative observations can be crucial in helping to make a significant contribution. As a result Stephen Smartt et al. subsequently produced a paper for *Nature* in 2007[7] to which I was privileged to have made a contribution and be listed as a co-author. There is a lesson to be learned here. Always record your observations so you can find them again, and never throw any of them away. All those old observations and drawings that you have stored away are valuable and could be used to provide proof for something in the future.

WHAT NOW?

What of the future? Will I continue patrolling or not? I think there is one very important thing about doing astronomy of any kind, be it as an armchair astronomer or a 'serious' observer, whatever the definition of that is. It is essential that you enjoy what you do. If you are satisfied with what you get from astronomy, then continue to do it. Astronomy is all about enjoying oneself; it is essential that it is fun. If it isn't, you should stop it. That is the approach that I have taken since my first look at the Seven Sisters through a small telescope. It captivated me for ever.

One thing that will certainly change in the coming years is the increased amount of professional interest that exists in supernova patrolling. Over the past years large-scale professional patrols have been organized specifically for nearby supernova discovery. The continuing work done by the Sloan Digital Sky Survey (SDSS) has reported large numbers of SNe discoveries in the course of its survey. Most of these are relatively faint with magnitudes greater than 20, but there are many appearing that are within the normal detection range of amateurs. Many of these are unfortunately never analysed

[7] Smartt, S., et al., *Nature*, **447**, pp 829–832 (2007)

spectrographically because of their low brightness. The SDSS strives to image the sky using its newly introduced set of filters. Any SNe fortunate enough to be imaged with the full complement of colour filters should have a sufficiently detailed colour profile recorded to provide useful information even though a full classification might not be possible.

Other new patrols such as the space-based SNAP observatory and the ground-based Pan-Starrs, with its huge billion-pixel detector and adaptive optics, will produce very serious competition for amateur discoverers. I have been hearing about the demise of the amateur astronomer for a few decades. What will always be certain is that he/she will adapt to any new challenges that might come along. We are far from being an extinct species. Room exists for amateurs, no matter at what level or niche they become involved. Remember, the important issue is to enjoy what you do, be it observing, reading about the subject or bringing the pleasure of astronomy to others.

I for one will continue for as long as the pleasure and satisfaction remain. Based on past experience, that could be a very long time.

The First Modern Telescope: the Mount Wilson 60-inch Reflector

ANTHONY MISCH AND WILLIAM SHEEHAN

At the beginning of the twentieth century, the largest telescope in operation was a refractor 40 inches in diameter; by the century's end, the title belonged to a reflector ten times that size. Along the way, a series of landmark telescopes appeared. This year we celebrate the centenary of one of the greatest of them, the 60-inch reflector of the Mount Wilson Observatory. Though its predecessors – notably the nineteenth-century reflectors of Draper, Grubbs, and Commons – showed the way, the many optical and mechanical innovations that first appeared in the 60-inch and that have since become standard features of telescope design, distinguish it as the patriarch of today's big telescopes, and would ensure its prominence even had it not contributed so importantly to our knowledge of the stars.

Scores of gifted observers used the 60-inch during its long and productive career. Its logbooks are a roll call of twentieth-century astronomers, and its contributions touch on every aspect of the science. Allan Sandage, in his excellent history of Mount Wilson, calls the telescope 'a – perhaps *the* – key tool in cracking [the stellar evolution] conundrum'.[1] Harlow Shapley, one of the telescope's most celebrated users, wrote that 'More discoveries were made with the Mount Wilson 60-inch reflector than any telescope in the world except, perhaps, than Galileo's tiny optic tube.'[2] Sandage points out that the famously immodest Shapley, in saying that, no doubt had his own discoveries in mind but, excesses of pride notwithstanding, the 60-inch shines as an instrument of surpassing importance. In the present article, we focus

[1] Sandage, A., *The Mount Wilson Observatory*, p. 169.
[2] ibid., p. 307.

on the story of its creation, and the first, remarkable, decade of its operation.

A MIRROR IN SEARCH OF A TELESCOPE

The 60-inch came into the world in stages. Its beginnings are entwined with the early years of the University of Chicago's Yerkes Observatory, the founding of Mount Wilson Observatory, and the careers of two giants of American astronomy, George Ellery Hale and George Willis Ritchey.

The tale begins with a devoted father's extraordinary gift to his extraordinary son. George Ellery Hale was a child of the Gilded Age, a scion of Chicago's wealthy aristocracy. His father William had made a fortune supplying hydraulic elevators to a city rebuilding from the Great Fire; he had the means and the desire to nurture his son's early curiosity about the natural world, providing him with the tools he needed to further his interests. By the time George Ellery finished high school, he had assembled his own small machine shop and the beginnings of a spectroscopy laboratory in the family home, fore-shadowing the arrangement of the great observatories he would later bring into being. Each would be equipped with a first-class shop and lab, reflecting both the importance Hale placed on instrumentation and his forward-looking commitment to the 'new astronomy' – astrophysics, as it came to be called – where work in the lab was an indispensable companion to work at the telescope.

In 1886, the 18-year-old Hale enrolled at Massachusetts Institute of Technology. While there, he offered his services to Edward Pickering, the astrophysics-minded director of nearby Harvard College Obser-vatory, as a volunteer researcher. In his last year at MIT, Hale dis-tinguished himself by his brilliant invention of the spectroheliograph, an ingenious device that, attached to a telescope, made it possible to photograph the Sun for the first time in the light of a single element. Back in Chicago his father, more convinced than ever of George's bright future in his chosen field, redoubled his programme to provide the material requirements for his son's enterprise. Hale came home from his second year at MIT to a completely equipped spectroscopy lab in a building of its own, on his parents' estate in Chicago's elite Kenwood area (at 4545 Drexel Boulevard). The following year his father added a

Figure 1. George Ellery Hale, at age 20. His expression conveys the intensity and purposeful determination of a man who would move mountains. (Image courtesy of the Yerkes Observatory.)

12-inch Clark refractor and dome, completing a private observatory for his son that would have been the envy of many universities.

Not far from Kenwood, the University of Chicago was taking shape with the help of John D. Rockefeller, among the most golden of the robber barons of the Gilded Age. Hale, with his demonstrated ability, his wealthy father, and a private observatory, naturally came to the attention of the new university's president, William Rainey Harper. In 1892 Hale was appointed to the faculty, and was soon spearheading the effort to secure funding for a giant telescope. The university's Yerkes Observatory, on the shore of Lake Geneva in Williams Bay, Wisconsin, with its 40-inch refractor and imposing building, stands to this day as witness to his success.

Always a fundraiser extraordinaire, Hale approached the tight-fisted but vain Chicago streetcar magnate Charles Tyson Yerkes with the idea of building the world's biggest refractor, but even then he was convinced the future lay in the power of big reflectors. He asked his father to purchase for him a huge disc of high-quality glass for a mirror around which to build the next world's-largest telescope. Estimates for discs from 48 to 84 inches in diameter were sought from France's Saint-Gobain glassworks, the only firm then equipped to undertake castings on that scale. In 1896, with Yerkes' telescope and building still more than a year from completion, Hale placed the order for a 60-inch disc, and for the smaller discs from which the secondary and tertiary mirrors would be shaped. It was to be the last major gift from his doting father, and would prove to be the most far-reaching.

A piece of glass of any size is a far cry from a finished telescope, and Hale did not know where the money would come from to bridge the gap. But he was a gambler with a vision, banking on his certainty that a way would be found. Astronomy demanded it.

In the meantime, Hale had immediate plans for the big disc. Six years earlier he had met George Willis Ritchey at a meeting of the short-lived Chicago section of the Astronomical Society of the Pacific, which Hale had organized with the blessing of the Society's founder, Edward Holden, after Hale's visit (on his honeymoon!) to Lick Observatory, where Holden was director. When they met, Ritchey was a high-school woodworking teacher with a young wife, an infant daughter, and a second child on the way. What spare time remained between work and family, he spent in the small home shop he called his astronomical laboratory, quietly reinventing the reflecting telescope.

'ALL DIFFICULTIES HAVE BEEN SUCCESSFULLY SOLVED'

Ritchey was only a few years older than Hale. They had in common their great enthusiasm for astronomy and for telescopes, though the gulf in their backgrounds could never be bridged. In contrast to Hale's impeccably aristocratic upbringing, Ritchey had endured a hardscrabble existence after his father, a cabinetmaker, had lost everything in a fire that destroyed his Ohio furniture business. George Willis was seven when the family was forced to start over from scratch. Like his father, Ritchey became a fine craftsman, skilled with wood and machine tools and adept at all things mechanical. His interest in astronomy began with a visit to the Cincinnati Observatory during a year's stint as a student at Cincinnati University's School of Design.

Though Ritchey's student days were few, the interest in astronomy kindled in the 18-year-old grew into a strong desire to become a

Figure 2. Yerkes Observatory group, 1898. Sitting on the wall, second from the far right, is Ritchey. Hale is in the top row at far right. Next to Hale is Edwin Frost, who succeeded him as Director of Yerkes, and next to Frost is the legendary observer E. E. Barnard. Ferdinand Ellerman, who, with Ritchey and Walter Adams, followed Hale to Mount Wilson, is in front of Hale on the steps below. (Image courtesy of the Yerkes Observatory.)

professional astronomer. But jobs in astronomy were few and far between, and to support himself and his family he settled in as a woodworking teacher in a Chicago high school. But his passion for astronomy remained undiminished.

Ritchey must have sensed immediately the younger man's energy and self-assurance, his grand vision for the future of the new astronomy, and his wealth and standing. For his part, Hale believed that a fine instrument-maker was essential to successful research, and saw in Ritchey a rare combination of gifts perfectly suited to the demands of an astrophysical observatory. Their meeting marked the beginning of a productive association, if not quite a partnership, that lasted until a bitter falling-out a quarter of a century later.

For Ritchey, the meticulous craftsman, perfection was the only acceptable goal. His systematic mind unsparingly criticized his own work, always seeking ways to improve process and product. He made himself indispensable to Hale, and by 1896 had left his teaching job to become Hale's full-time assistant, entrusted with negotiating the purchase of the 60-inch blank. By the time the glass was delivered, in the summer of 1897, Ritchey was installed at Yerkes, building the massive grinding machine on which the huge disc was to be given its exquisitely precise parabolic curve.

Ritchey brought with him to Yerkes a superb 24-inch mirror that he had made in his home workshop. Over the next four years, while also engaged in a variety of other projects, including work on the 60-inch disc, he put the 24-inch at the heart of a new telescope that in many important respects became the prototype for the 60-inch. The 24-inch mirror was exceptionally fast for the time (i.e. it was designed with a short focal length compared with its diameter); though difficult to figure, it made the mirror well suited to celestial photography. Ritchey intended the 24-inch mirror to be carried in a sturdy fork mounting he had worked out before coming to Yerkes, but was forced to compromise his design to accommodate a mounting already partly completed and awaiting him in the observatory shop – one that he considered flawed.

Notwithstanding the compromise over the mount, the 24-inch was a resounding success. Ritchey managed to correct what he considered to be the worst of its shortcomings, and to incorporate many of the innovations of his original design. He used it to make a series of striking celestial photographs, some of which far surpassed, in their definition of detail, anything that had been done before. Their wonder-inspiring beauty provided Hale with his most eloquent argument for promoting the 60-inch. Yerkes Observatory published a selection of the best images, accompanied by an article in which Ritchey enunciated the importance he attached to the 24-inch reflector:

> It is almost superfluous to state that the great reflectors of the past, without exception, have been in many respects extremely crude instruments; in all cases without the great rigidity and stability of construction which are absolutely essential to the successful performance of a reflector; and in all cases without the refinement of workmanship, in both optical and mechanical parts, which are attained in the great modern refractors.[3]

After assuring the reader that he intends no criticism of the 'able and skillful men' who pioneered reflectors, he writes of his 24-inch: 'It is

[3] Ritchey, G.W., *Photography with the Forty-inch Refractor and the Two-foot Reflector.*

safe to assert that the peculiar difficulties of the reflecting telescope are now thoroughly understood, and that all difficulties which relate to its mechanical and optical construction have been successfully solved.'[4]

This is a remarkable statement from a self-taught telescope maker with but one significant instrument under his belt – but it is essentially correct.

Figure 3. The 24-inch reflector made by Ritchey for Hale at Yerkes – in many respects, this telescope was Ritchey's warm-up for the 60-inch. (Image courtesy of the Yerkes Observatory.)

[4] ibid.

Yerkes Observatory was officially dedicated on 21 October 1897. Hale organized a professional conference for the days leading up to the dedication. Many of the luminaries of late-nineteenth-century astronomy attended. Members of the Yerkes staff gave presentations to their distinguished guests to show off the new observatory. Ritchey demonstrated the operation of his large grinding machine, on which he had recently begun shaping the 60-inch glass. On the day of the dedication, 700 guests came by train from Chicago, filling the huge dome to hear long-winded speeches given beneath the enormous refractor. After the ceremony, on an inspection tour of the observatory, they, too, would have seen the big mirror.

These casual visitors could hardly have appreciated the importance of what was taking shape in the basement optical shop, though some of the astronomers attending the conference may have recognized its significance. In retrospect, the pathos of the day is inescapable: the great lens just finished and the great mirror just begun are symbols of an era at its end and of another at its beginning. The magnificent 40-inch was the king of the great refractors, but it was to be the last – already half an anachronism on the day of its christening; a decade later, the 60-inch glass, slowly taking form in the basement below, would establish a new dynasty.

THE ROAD TO MOUNT WILSON

Hale's personal research interest was the Sun, but his energies as a scientist and entrepreneur of astrophysics encompassed the broader question of stellar evolution. His early reading exposed him to the Uniformitarian model of a slowly evolving Earth, and to Darwin's ideas about the origin of species. The imaginative young Hale projected these principles on to a universe of evolving stars. The conviction that the secrets of stellar evolution were within the reach of the creative scientist with the independence to 'leave the familiar path' is a leitmotif that runs through Hale's career. He saw the observatory as a special kind of physical laboratory adapted to the solution of this problem, a concept that is already evident in the arrangement of Yerkes – an observatory designed from the outset as an astrophysical lab. But even before the 40-inch had seen first light, Hale's plans ranged far beyond the shores of Lake Geneva.

In his 1915 recap of Mount Wilson's first decade,[5] Hale quotes the well-known passage from Newton's *Opticks*: 'For the Air through which we look upon the Stars, is in perpetual Tremor. . . . The only remedy is a most serene and quiet Air, such as may perhaps be found on the tops of the highest Mountains above the grosser clouds.' A decade before the founding of Yerkes, the University of California's Lick Observatory in central California had borne out Newton's surmise, conclusively demonstrating the superiority of a mountain-top location, but Charles Yerkes had insisted that his telescope be sited within a hundred miles of Chicago. (James Lick himself had at first envisioned *his* telescope in the heart of downtown San Francisco, before being persuaded to locate it, more usefully, on Mount Hamilton.) Hale knew that Williams Bay could not compete with observing conditions on either Mount Hamilton or Wilson's Peak, near Pasadena, where Harvard College Observatory had briefly considered operating a major observatory in collaboration with the University of Southern California.

It is impossible to know exactly when Hale began planning for a California observatory – it is quite likely that he intended the 60-inch mirror for just such a destination from the very outset – for he kept his own counsel on the subject, not wishing to give the University of Chicago reason to suppose that the young director of its new observatory was already casting his eyes towards other horizons. So when, in 1903, with the future of the 60-inch still uncertain, Hale was awarded $10,000 (the equivalent today of about $200,000) by the newly created Carnegie Institution of Washington, it was for the ostensible purpose of mounting an expedition to establish a *temporary* outpost of the Yerkes Observatory on the same Wilson's Peak that Harvard had been eyeing, in order to carry out solar research. (In those days, a scientific enterprise on a California mountain could still be called an expedition.)

Hale's private ambitions went far beyond the stated aims of the Carnegie/Yerkes expedition. Again staking his future on a daring gamble, Hale proceeded full steam ahead, on his own authority, with preparations for a permanent solar observatory on the summit along with support facilities in Pasadena in the valley below. When the $10,000 ran out, Hale supplemented it with an additional $15,000

[5] Hale, G. E., *Ten Years' Work of a Mountaintop Observatory.*

(about $300,000 today) from his own pocket, betting on the Carnegie Institution's favourable reception of – and further support for – his independent, if highly irregular, initiative.

As a member of Carnegie's scientific advisory committee, Hale had earlier made the case (not without opposition) for a mountain-top astrophysical observatory devoted to the study of the Sun and to the problem of stellar evolution. To complement the solar work, it would include a large reflecting telescope (no doubt Hale had his 60-inch mirror in mind) for high-resolution spectroscopy of stars, an undertaking he called the 'wider plan'. Late in 1904, already deeply committed but with growing doubts about Carnegie's support as the days passed and expenses mounted, Hale finally received word that Carnegie had granted him $150,000 a year for two years to establish his observatory.

The Carnegie grant opened a floodgate. Hale's plans, held in abeyance as long as the future of his California ambitions remained uncertain, tumbled out in the succeeding months. The 'Mount Wilson Station of the Yerkes Observatory' became the 'Mount Wilson Solar Observatory'. Hale resigned as director of Yerkes and gave up his post on the University of Chicago faculty, taking with him much of the 'first team' at Yerkes: Ritchey, Ferdinand Ellerman (who became the first of a line of legendary observers at Mount Wilson), and Walter Adams (pioneering spectroscopist who twenty years later would succeed Hale as director of Mount Wilson). Hale took a 99-year lease on forty acres of the summit, and purchased a property on Santa Barbara Street in Pasadena on which to build a permanent home for the observatory's support facilities. On the mountain, living quarters were improved and construction of the Snow solar telescope – the first of the mountain's permanent solar instruments – was completed.

These were heady days for Hale and his associates, a time of boundless possibilities awaiting them on the summit of Mount Wilson. For Ritchey, it was an opportunity for which he was well prepared. At last he could realize *his* telescope, built entirely according to *his* designs and under *his* direction. Today, designing and building a large telescope (much less the world's largest) would involve the talents of a whole cadre of experts in a variety of specialized disciplines. Remarkably, the 60-inch was, in all essential parts, the product of one man's genius.

The basic design of the telescope had been worked out while Ritchey

Figure 4. The 60-inch disc in the basement optical shop at Yerkes Observatory, about 1900. Both surfaces have been given a preliminary polish, but the mirror is still years from its final figure. (Image courtesy of the Huntington Library, San Marino, California.)

was still at Yerkes, and published by the Smithsonian in 1904 in his classic monograph *On the Modern Reflecting Telescope, and the Making and Testing of Optical Mirrors*, illustrated with full-page plates of Ritchey's characteristically unpeopled photographs of apparatus – the only human scale provided by his signature empty chair.

Many of the mechanical and optical innovations Ritchey in-corporated in the 60-inch are now standard design, but in 1904 they were groundbreaking: a 'clean room' environment for optical work;

optical testing in the mirror's focal plane; a compensating mirror-support system; interchangeable Newtonian, Cassegrain, and Coudé foci; a permanent, highly stable Coudé spectrograph; push-button, electric slow-motion controls; backlash-free gear trains; and scrupulous attention to equalizing temperature, among others.

At the time of the Carnegie grant, the 60-inch mirror – stalled for several years after the first fine grinding – was still in the optical shop at Yerkes, but the glass belonged to Hale, who had offered it to the university on the condition that it provide a mounting and dome. Hale now took possession, settled with the university for the costs incurred for the grinding and polishing thus far, signed the mirror over to the Carnegie Institution, and instructed Ritchey to send it, post-haste, to Pasadena. Ritchey designed a special case, equipped with double sets of heavy steel springs, to give the precious disc a smooth ride over the continental divide as it wended its way from chilly Wisconsin to sunny southern California.

The contracts for the large steel and cast-iron parts of the mounting

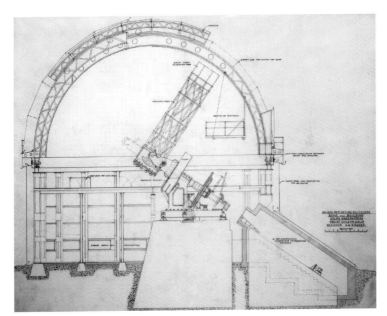

Figure 5. A 1906 elevation drawing of the 60-inch and dome, showing a remarkably modern design. (Image courtesy of the Huntington Library, San Marino, California.)

204 | 2008 YEARBOOK OF ASTRONOMY

were quickly awarded. The Warner & Swasey Company of Cleveland – the established builder of large telescopes in America – was the obvious choice, but Hale and Ritchey opted instead for the Union Iron Works of San Francisco – a builder of ships and large machinery – on the strength of its California location and expertise with the industrial-scale castings needed for the 60-inch. Union, which twenty years earlier had built the dome for the Lick 36-inch refractor, also won the contract for the 60-inch dome.

As the large pieces were turned out in Union's factory on the shore of San Francisco Bay, the mounting was assembled for testing, where it survived, miraculously undamaged, through the devastating 1906 earthquake and fire that destroyed much of the city. The telescope was disassembled, packed, and shipped south to the Santa Barbara Street shops, where the huge parts were machined to a perfect fit, the intricate driving clock assembled, the gearing cut, and the complex mirror support system fabricated, transforming more than twenty tons of castings and steel assemblies into an instrument of exquisite precision. The telescope was again assembled and tested in an erecting shed built for the purpose, but still minus its primary mirror, which had yet to reach the high pitch of perfection Ritchey demanded.

But another obstacle had to be overcome before the pieces of the telescope could be hauled to the summit. When Hale wrote in 1905 that 'the first problem that confronts one in undertaking the con-struction of buildings and the erection of instruments on Mount Wilson is that of transportation over the trail from the valley',[6] the best route to the summit was little more than a broad trail – though in places as narrow as two feet – climbing for nine miles through rugged canyons and across steep traverses, used by hikers who wished to spend a few days roughing it at one of two camps near the mountaintop.

The New Trail, as it was known, had already been widened in places to permit the transportation of the observatory's first solar telescope, virtually every piece of which was carried by sometimes recalcitrant burros loaded with as much as 225 pounds per animal. (A few years later, the legendary Milton Humason, who shared in Hubble's dis-covery of the expanding universe, would make his Mount Wilson debut as a mule driver.) At $1.35 per hundred pounds, the cost of transportation doubled the price of a bag of cement from valley to

[6] Hale, G.E., 'The Solar Observatory of the Carnegie Institution of Washington'.

Figure 6. The telescope fully assembled in the erecting shed at Pasadena in 1907, shortly before disassembly for transport to the summit. (Image courtesy of the Huntington Library, San Marino, California.)

Figure 7. Midsummer, 1908: the main section of the telescope tube makes its slow journey up the narrow mountain road to the summit. (Image courtesy of the Huntington Library, San Marino, California.)

summit. The one piece too heavy even for the sturdy pack animals – a 400-pound equatorial head – was dragged up on an improvised cart over the course of two days. The heaviest single piece of the 60-inch mounting weighed 14,000 pounds! 'It was evident', Hale wrote, 'that a different arrangement would be required . . .'

Accordingly, further improvements to the road were undertaken. A total of 120 men, working in three gangs, widened it to ten feet overall, making it ready for a specially designed truck, driven by an electric motor at each of its four wheels, to carry the heavy pieces of the 60-inch. The truck proved capable, though the mule teams that continued to carry everyday provisions and the lighter parts of the telescope to the summit were often called in to provide a 'power assist'.

'THE 60-INCH HAS SPOILED THE MOUNTAIN'

The Pasadena optical shop had been designed with every precaution against contaminating dust that could insinuate itself into the polishing and scratch the mirror's perfect surface. Windows were double-sealed, the air filtered, walls and ceilings were heavily shellacked. Canvas baffles hung above the grinding machine, and the floor was kept constantly damp. The obsessional Ritchey's meticulous measures were the optical equivalent of the first sterile operating rooms. Even so, on a morning in mid April 1907, with only finishing touches remaining, the mirror was found to be covered with scratches. The entire disc had to be repolished. The mystery has never been explained.[7]

Despite this frustrating setback, by August Ritchey had again brought the mirror to a near-perfect figure. But for Ritchey, near-perfect was never good enough. Though strikes at Union Iron Works were delaying delivery of the dome, and unprecedented rains and five feet of snow the following winter hampered roadwork, the mounting and dome were finished and waiting on the summit when, late in 1908, Ritchey finally conceded that the mirror was perfect enough to follow the other parts to the summit. The first visual observations came at last on the night of 13 December; the first plates were exposed a few nights later. Ritchey knew at once that he had achieved a masterpiece. Never a slave to false modesty, he described it as 'the most complete and refined and powerful photographic telescope yet constructed'. In his 1909 article in the *Astrophysical Journal*, he wrote:

Mere bigness is no criterion of efficiency; if a great telescope is to yield a gain in results even approximately proportional to its increase in size, the utmost care must be given to meeting all those conditions which experience in the use of large telescopes has shown to militate against their successful performance. It was a most serious question

[7] Many decades later, the grinding machine on which the 60-inch mirror had been made found its way to the Lick Observatory optical shop in Santa Cruz, where, in 1987 and 1988, it was used to repolish the crazed surfaces of the lens of the Great 36-inch refractor. For a time it was considered as a possible grinding machine for the 1.5-metre (60-inch) secondary mirror of the first 10-metre Keck Telescope. Though in the end it was not used, it would have been a satisfying symmetry if, eighty years after grinding the world's largest primary, it had been used to make the world's largest secondary.

Figure 8. The dome of the 60-inch in May, 1908. The heavy trusses that will carry the shutter are in the foreground, ready to be hoisted into place. (Image courtesy of the Huntington Library, San Marino, California.)

whether it would be possible to give as fine a figure to the 60-inch mirror as was attained in the case of the 24-inch Yerkes mirror; the difficulties were of course incomparably greater, but the final figure of the 60-inch is decidedly better that that of the smaller mirror . . . Similarly, it was a serious question whether the moving parts of the 60-inch telescope, weighing 23 tons, could be made to follow the stars as smoothly as those of the 24-inch . . . It is therefore a great satisfaction to see the star in the guiding eyepiece of the 60-inch remain perfectly bisected on the spider-lines for several minutes at a time, without perceptible tremor.[8]

Years earlier, with the troubled history of large reflectors in mind, Hale wrote that, 'According to a well-known saying, a reflecting telescope can be successfully used only by its maker.' By contrast, the optical and mechanical perfection of the 60-inch made it accessible to

[8] Ritchey, G.W., 'The 60-inch Reflector of the Mount Wilson Solar Observatory'.

Figure 9. The massive polar axle and worm gear (the latter encased in a protective covering), ready to be lowered into place beneath the observing floor. The large disc at the far end of the axle will float in a fitted tub of mercury, carrying much of the telescope's weight, relieving the thrust on the axle, and providing a virtually frictionless bearing. (Image courtesy of the Huntington Library, San Marino, California.)

any trained observer. Yet the man responsible for the telescope's excellence at first resisted its use by the scientists for whom it was intended. Ritchey hindered the transition from work in progress to completed telescope by his uncompromising perfectionism and imagined proprietary rights. Allan Sandage writes:

> Ritchey rightly attributed the perfection and resultant success of the 60-inch almost entirely to his own efforts. Its optics were superior, its design and realization flawless. Pride turned to possessiveness, however, as Ritchey grew unreasonably reluctant to open the completed instrument to the scientific staff, who were eager to begin the many long-range scientific programmes they had planned for the instrument.[9]

Though he regarded himself as a professional astronomer, Ritchey – the unsurpassed artisan of astronomy – remained a gifted amateur for whom the telescope was a tool with which to make beautiful celestial portraits that affirmed the perfection of his craft. He was not interested in the rigorous, quantitative, usually unglamorous kind of observing that is the lifeblood of research astronomy, and which began occupying the 60-inch soon after commissioning. Though he continued to use the telescope to make direct photographs, some of real importance, Ritchey's role began to recede as a new cast of characters took the stage. Increasingly at odds with Hale, and even more so with Adams, he was dismissed soon after completing work on the mirror for Hale's next great telescope, the 100-inch reflector, which became operational in 1917.

Until the appearance of the 60-inch, the mountain top belonged to the daytime astronomers who used the two large solar telescopes that comprised the observatory's first scientific apparatus. But the arrival of the big reflector initiated a new era not only in the scientific life of the observatory, but also in its social life which, as long as observing had focused on the Sun, had been regulated by its risings and settings. Walter Adams, recounting those early days on Mount Wilson from a vantage point of forty years, recalled the nightly gatherings for cards and conversation around the library fire in the Monastery – the astronomers' communal quarters – writing that

[9] Sandage, A., *The Mount Wilson Observatory*, p. 168.

Figure 10. This finished telescope conveys the muscular stability of Ritchey's design, in this 1910 photograph (probably taken by Ritchey himself). The Cassegrain spectrograph grows from the tube like a prominent dorsal fin, and the mercury flotation tank, carrying the whole, seems to rise like an iceberg out of the floor. The counterweights of the self-adjusting mirror-support system can be seen ringing the bottom of the telescope. (Image courtesy of the Huntington Library, San Marino, California.)

'Hale's amazing breadth of interests, his great personal charm, and his stories of important figures in science and national affairs make these evenings stand out in memory'. But with the arrival of the 60-inch, this convivial routine was largely undone by the introduction of night-work. Adams recalls the Smithsonian solar observer Charles Greeley Abbot's 'pathetic lament that the 60-inch telescope had spoiled the mountain'.[10]

[10] Adams, W. S., 'Early Days at Mount Wilson'.

THE DECADE OF PRE-EMINENCE

In the decade before the 100-inch reflector came online, the 60-inch was the most powerful research telescope on earth. In his annual *Report of the Director* for 1909, Hale wrote that the observing programme for the 60-inch is 'not yet definitely arranged', though its goal of unlocking the secrets of stellar evolution had never been in question. But Hale's view of the problem had broadened through his acquaintance with the work of the eminent Dutch astronomer Jacobus Kapteyn. Kapteyn was seeking the cooperation of major observatories worldwide in a programme he called 'The Plan of Selected Areas', aimed at nothing less than the large-scale dynamics and structure of the universe – a universe then still thought by most astronomers to be a sidereal system bounded by the Milky Way Galaxy.

Kapteyn's plan called for applying methods of statistical analysis to 206 'selected areas' – representative swatches evenly distributed around the celestial sphere. Kapteyn could only hope to realize this ambitious plan by enlisting the participation of a number of observatories. Hale was convinced. He argued that Kapteyn's work, especially his putative discovery that stars moved in one of two opposing streams, bore directly on the problem of stellar evolution. Accordingly, he committed substantial 60-inch time to Kapteyn's programme, redefining the observatory's mission, in a single bold stroke, to include the investigation of the structure of the universe.

Though neither Kapteyn's star streams nor his model of the universe survived the test of time, the programmes begun with the 60-inch in the selected areas proved far-reaching. Much of the telescope's working life was to be bound up in the great, interwoven quests for the answers to stellar evolution and galactic structure. Both gained momentum from Kapteyn's programme. 'So solid was Hale's intuition,' writes Sandage, 'that 50 years later [the survey programmes for the selected areas] unlocked the origin of the Galaxy. Eventually they furnished the keys to stellar evolution itself.'

From 1909 until 1914, Kapteyn spent most summers as a visiting researcher on Mount Wilson (the small residence built for his use is still known as the Kapteyn Cottage), advising Hale on the scientific course for the big telescope. Intensive programmes were initiated in high-resolution spectroscopy of bright stars at the Coudé focus for

Figure 11. A rare candid shot of Hale, at right, with a group of astronomers on the summit of Mount Wilson. The photograph was probably taken in 1910 during the fourth meeting of the International Union for Cooperation in Solar Research (later to become the IAU), hosted by the observatory. The 60-inch never had a formal dedication, but the 1910 meeting served as its coming-out. (Image courtesy of the Yerkes Observatory.)

direct comparison with solar spectra, medium-resolution spectroscopy at the Cassegrain focus to obtain radial velocities and determine spectral types, and direct photography at the Cassegrain and Newtonian foci for parallax measurements, photometry and the study of nebulae and clusters.

These soon bore important fruit. A decade earlier, Annie Jump Cannon at the Harvard Observatory had introduced the stellar equivalent of DNA sequencing: a system for classifying stars from their spectra that correctly reflected their physical properties. Cannon's approach was adopted for Harvard's monumental *Draper Catalog* of stellar spectra. By the time the 60-inch classification programme was in full swing, the Harvard system had become widely accepted.

In attempting to fit the many new 60-inch spectra on to the Harvard system, discrepancies emerged. While trying to account for them, Adams and Arnold Kohlschütter noticed a relationship between a star's proper motion – an indirect indicator of distance – and the intensities of certain spectral features. They realized that these 'interesting peculiarities' offered a new means of obtaining a star's absolute magnitude, and thereby its distance, simply by examining its spectrum. They presented their findings in a 1914 paper[11] that Sandage describes as 'a gem of spectroscopic literature'. Spectroscopic parallax, as their method became known, was of incalculable value, extending distance determination far beyond the reach of classical trigonometric parallaxes to any star whose spectrum could be recorded.

In a separate article, published just before the announcement of spectroscopic parallax, Adams and Kohlschütter foreshadowed another important discovery in their report on high radial-velocity stars, measured from the same plates used for the discovery of the spectroscopic parallax. In that paper they mention, without further conjecture, that for stars of large radial velocity there is a 'great preponderance of large negative over large positive values'.[12] This seemingly simple observation hinted at the later discovery of the rotation of the Milky Way Galaxy by stellar kinematics.

The enormously demanding photometric portion of Kapteyn's programme in the 139 selected areas observed from Mount Wilson was conducted at the 60-inch's Newtonian focus by Frederick Seares. He began with the difficult task of developing techniques to assure photometric accuracy in the presence of bedevilling aberrations inherent in the Newtonian's wide field. Next came the equally painstaking job of extending the magnitude scale from existing measurements to much fainter stars. His 60-inch work supplied an invaluable collection of data and a toolbox of new techniques for future investigations. Along the way, Seares virtually reinvented photographic photometry and produced his famous North Polar Sequence of faint magnitudes, all culminating in the 'scriptural' *Mount Wilson Catalog of Photographic Magnitudes.*

[11] Adams, W. S. and Kohlschütter, A., 'Some spectral criteria for the determination of absolute stellar magnitude'.
[12] Adams, W. S. and Kohlschütter, A., 'The radial velocities of one hundred stars with measured parallaxes'.

The most celebrated discovery to come out of the 60-inch's early years is what Sandage has called the 'galactocentric revolution'. Its principal protagonist was Harlow Shapley – a charming, imaginative, immodest, occasionally rash, 29-year-old Princeton PhD, newly arrived at Mount Wilson in 1914 to assist Seares in his photometric work. Shapley was also granted telescope time to pursue independent research. Taking advantage of the 60-inch's unequalled power, and with the help of techniques he had learned from Seares, he began photometric measurements of the stars in globular and galactic clusters, taking plates at the telescope's Newtonian focus.[13] He did not then know that this line of investigation would ultimately lead to unlocking the structure of the Galaxy and the Sun's position in it.

Shapley recalls his process of discovery in the sometimes unconvincingly folksy voice of his autobiography: 'I stayed with the Cepheids and clusters during those early years at Mount Wilson,' he writes, 'until I crashed through on the distances and outlined the structure of the universe.'[14] As usual the actual story is much more complicated. The path to his galactocentric revolution stretches across four years and more than a dozen papers, and is strewn with missteps and wrong turns, but is, in the end, brilliantly illuminated.

Shapley began by measuring the colours and magnitudes of stars in the globular cluster M13. He soon realized that for this – and, as he later established, other globular clusters – the colours and magnitudes were markedly different from those of field stars and the stars of galactic clusters or 'open' clusters. The fundamental importance of this difference remained hidden for decades, until Walter Baade recognized the existence of two stellar populations – a breakthrough discovery that showed the way to cracking the stellar evolution puzzle.

From these first observations Shapley drew several incorrect conclusions. He vastly overestimated the size and distance of the clusters, inferring that they were not part of the Galaxy, and similarly overestimated the size of the Galaxy itself, a conclusion that in turn contributed to his mistaken view that the spiral nebulae were local, not 'island universes' as some believed. He had correctly concluded that absorption of light by interstellar matter was negligible in directions

[13] Shapley began his cluster observations at the suggestion of Harvard astronomer Solon I. Bailey, to whose earlier observations of cluster variables Shapley's eventual success is indebted.
[14] Shapley, p. 52.

away from the galactic plane, but unfortunately his subsequent observations of stars in galactic clusters led him to erroneously extend that result to the galactic plane, a misconception that confounded attempts to measure cosmic distances until Robert Trumpler and others years later proved the importance of interstellar absorption.[15]

Then, in 1917 Shapley made his breakthrough. 'In [his sixth paper],' writes Sandage, 'Shapley invented three powerful and (it turned out) highly reliable methods to determine cluster distances. It was a singular achievement.'[16] Armed with these tools, his 60-inch observations, and earlier plates taken by Solon Bailey at Harvard, Shapley was able to map the distribution of the globular clusters, demonstrate its asymmetry with respect to the Sun, and reveal the Sun's place in the Galaxy. The galactocentric viewpoint that emerged has been compared in importance with Copernicus' introduction of the heliocentric system. In the end, it displaced the smaller, Sun-centred Kapteyn universe.

In November, the same month that Shapley's pivotal sixth paper appeared in the *Astrophysical Journal*, the decade of the 60-inch's pre-eminence came to an end with the first tests of the observatory's 100-inch Hooker Reflector. The vanguard of observational astronomy follows new instruments that promise to bring hitherto intractable problems within reach. In the first half of the twentieth century, aperture was key to opening up new realms in cosmology, and the central rôle of the 100-inch in the breathtaking extragalactic discoveries that followed its commissioning is well known. The spotlight naturally shifted 500 feet to the north, from the 60-inch to the telescope that would dominate astronomy for the next thirty years.

The 60-inch remained heavily subscribed into the 1970s, and its logs continued to be filled with the names of legendary observers, but with the arrival of the 100-inch its unique rôle becomes more difficult to distinguish than in the decade of its dominion. Many of the celebrated discoveries that flowed from the summit of Mount Wilson in the decades that followed were made using observations from both instruments.

From the 60-inch dome, a short path leads north through the pines, meeting a narrow wooden footbridge running south from the back

[15] Both Shapley's missteps and triumphs from this period are well remembered from the so-called Great Debate of 1921, in which he and Lick astronomer Heber D. Curtis each argued for his view of galactic structure and the nature of the spiral nebulae.
[16] Sandage, A., *The Mount Wilson Observatory*, p. 300.

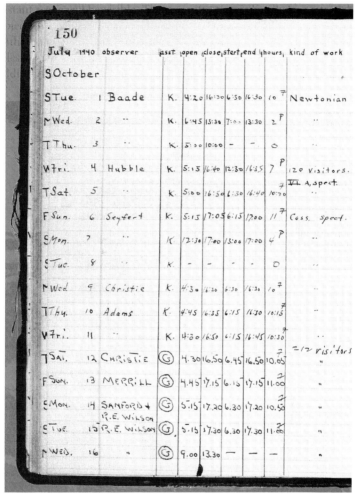

July 1940	observer	asst	open	close	start	end	hours	kind of work
150								
SOctober								
STue. 1	Baade	K.	4:20	16:30	6:30	16:30	10	Newtonian
MWed. 2	..	K.	6:45	13:30	7:00	13:30	2 P	..
TThu. 3	..	K.	5:30	10:00	-	-	O	..
WFri. 4	Hubble	K.	5:15	16:40	12:30	16:35	7 P	120 visitors.
TSat. 5	..	K.	5:00	16:50	6:30	16:40	10:20	ᵧ Ⅺ A.spect.
FSun. 6	Seyfert	K.	5:15	17:05	6:15	17:00	11 ⫶	Cass. spect.
SMon. 7	..	K.	12:30	17:00	13:00	17:00	4 P	..
STue. 8	..	K.	-	-	-	-	O	..
MWed. 9	Christie	K.	4:30	16:30	6:30	16:30	10 ⫶	..
TThu. 10	Adams	K.	4:45	16:35	6:15	16:30	10:15	..
WFri. 11	..	K.	4:30	16:50	6:15	16:45	10:30	..
TSat. 12	CHRISTIE	G	4:30	16:50	6:45	16:50	10:05	=12 visitors
FSun. 13	MERRILL	G	4:45	17:15	6:15	17:15	11:00	"
SMon. 14	SANFORD + R.E. WILSON	G	5:15	17:20	6:30	17:20	10:50	"
STue. 15	R. E. WILSON	G	5:15	17:30	6:30	17:30	11:00	"
MWed. 16	"	G	9:00	13:30	-	-	-	"

Figure 12. The 60-inch logbooks are filled with names that loom large in twentieth-century astronomy. This single page includes, in the first two weeks of April 1930, Walter Baade, the discoverer of stellar populations, Edwin Hubble, the father of modern cosmology, Carl Seyfert, whose name is linked to the active galaxies he identified, and Walter Adams, the great spectroscopist and by then the observatory's director. Note that Hubble, and a week later Adams, played host to the visitors who weekly flocked to Mount Wilson for a peek through the telescope and a lecture from the astronomer. (Image courtesy of Dave Jurasevich.)

door of the 100-inch. Near where they meet stands the Galley, a plain, one-room building where astronomers and night assistants from both telescopes ate their midnight lunches. On any given night, some of the greatest astronomers of the time might be gathered at the Galley's wooden table – an informal, communal arrangement that reflects the close connection between the two telescopes.

In the decades that followed the completion of the 100-inch, the 60-inch played an important rôle in our present understanding of the universe, but the story of the 60-inch after 1918 is closely intertwined with that of the 100-inch, and is beyond the scope of this article, even were it within the power of the authors to tell it.

In the early 1970s, the 60-inch logbooks begin, for the first time, to show significant numbers of unscheduled nights. The decline in 60-inch subscription coincided with the opening of Carnegie's Southern Hemisphere observatory at Las Campanas, Chile, whose dark skies and new instruments were, not surprisingly, preferred by many of the staff astronomers. It is likely that by the end of the decade the 60-inch would have fallen into disuse, had not a project appeared that was perfectly suited to the telescope, unaffected by the increasingly light-polluted skies above Mount Wilson and able to make use of every available night.

The H and K project bought the 60-inch an extra fifteen years of highly productive observing, carrying its working life a decade beyond Carnegie's 1985 withdrawal from operations on Mount Wilson and the mothballing of the 100-inch the following year.[17] The project – the brainchild of observatory astronomers Olin Wilson and Arthur Vaughan – sought to identify and monitor activity cycles, analogous to the Sun's 22-year sunspot cycle, in a large sample of solar-like stars. Tens of thousands of observations of the H and K lines of ionized calcium – sensitive markers of magnetic activity in a star's upper atmosphere – were amassed, yielding excellent results. With bookend symmetry, this last major undertaking on the 60-inch was a study of the same phenomenon in stars that Hale had set out to understand in the Sun more than a century earlier.

The H and K project came to a close in 1996. Intermittent scientific

[17] The 100-inch has been maintained in working condition and has seen sporadic use as an adaptive optics test bed and as a telescope for hire. Solar observing, stellar interferometry, and astronomy education continue under the umbrella of the Mount Wilson Institute, founded in 1985 to fill the post-Carnegie vacuum.

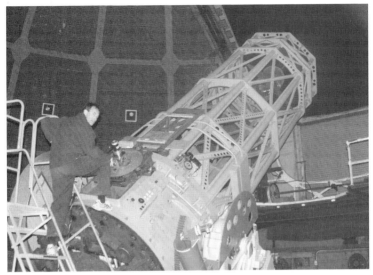

Figure 13. The 60-inch as it appears today. William Sheehan climbs to the eyepiece mounted at the telescope's folded Cassegrain focus. The photograph was taken during an evening of visual observations of the 2005 opposition of Mars. (Image courtesy of William Sheehan.)

use was made of the telescope until 2001. The 60-inch is now available for hire for visual observing, reviving a tradition of public access that began with the telescope's commissioning and continued until the Second World War. Throughout those years, the first hours of every Friday night were given over to visitors who made the long trip to the summit, sometimes in throngs (one Friday in 1940 saw 740 visitors!), to look through the telescope and to have their questions answered by the astronomer in charge. One of those early visitors, mining tycoon and Los Angeles philanthropist Griffith J. Griffith, was so moved by his view through the telescope in 1912 that he bequeathed to the city the famous Griffith Observatory and Planetarium. 'If everyone could look through that telescope,' he said of his night on the 60-inch, 'it would change the world.'

ACKNOWLEDGEMENTS

The authors owe a particular debt to two books: Donald Osterbrock's *Pauper and Prince: Ritchey, Hale, and Big American Telescopes* was an essential reference for the years leading up to the foundation of Mount Wilson Observatory, and Allan Sandage's *The Mount Wilson Observatory: Breaking the Code of Cosmic Evolution* was an indispensable guide to the scientific terrain. We also thank Victoria Scott and Nina Misch for their careful reading of the manuscript and excellent suggestions, Larry Webster, Chief Solar Observer at Mount Wilson, for generously sharing his time and knowledge, and Dan Lewis of the Huntington Library, Dave Jurasevich of Mount Wilson, and Rich Dreiser of Yerkes Observatory for their help with the illustrations.

FURTHER READING

Adams, Walter S., 'Early Days at Mount Wilson' (part 1), *PASP*, **59**, no. 350, p. 213 (1947).

Adams, Walter S., 'Early Days at Mount Wilson' (part 2), *PASP*, **59**, no. 351, p. 285 (1947).

Adams, W.S. and Kohlschutter, A., 'The radial velocities of one hundred stars with measured parallaxes', *Ap.J.*, **39**, p.341 (1914).

Adams, W.S. and Kohlschutter, A., 'Some spectral criteria for the determination of absolute stellar magnitudes', *Ap.J.*, **40**, p.385 (1914).

Arp, H., 'The Hertzsprung-Russell Diagram', *Astronomical Society of the Pacific Leaflets*, vol. 8, p.73 (1959).

Dyson, Freeman J., 'Two Revolutions in Astronomy', *Proceedings of the American Philosophical Society*, vol. 140, no. 1 (1996).

Hale, G.E., 'Minor Contributions and Notes: the Dedication of the Yerkes Observatory', *Bulletin of the Yerkes Observatory of the University of Chicago*, vol. 4, p. 54 (1897).

Hale, G. E., 'The Solar Observatory of the Carnegie Institution of Washington', *Ap.J.*, **21**, p.151 (1905).

Hale, G.E., *Ten Years' Work of a Mountain Observatory*, Carnegie Institution of Washington (1915).

Hale, G.E., *Report of the Director*, various (1905–18).

Keeler, James, E., 'The Importance of Astrophysical Research and the Relation of Astrophysics to Other Physical Sciences' (Address delivered at the dedication of the Yerkes Observatory), *Bulletin of the Yerkes Observatory of the University of Chicago*, vol. 4, p.3 (1897).

Osterbrock, Donald E., *Pauper and Prince: Ritchey, Hale, and Big American Telescopes*, University of Arizona Press (1993).

Ritchey, G.W., 'A support System for Large Specula,' *Ap.J.*, **5**, 143 (1897).

Ritchey, G.W., 'The Two-foot Reflecting Telescope of the Yerkes Observatory', *Ap.J.*, **14**, pp. 217–33 (1901).

Ritchey, G.W., 'Photography with the Forty-inch Refractor and the Two-foot Reflector', *Publications of the Yerkes Observatory of the University of Chicago*, vol. 2, p. 389 (1904).

Ritchey, G.W., 'On the Modern Reflecting Telescope and the Making and Testing of Optical Mirrors', *Smithsonian Contributions to Knowledge*, part of vol. 34 (1904).

Ritchey, G.W., 'On Methods of Testing Optical Mirrors During Construction', *Ap.J.*, **9**, p. 53 (1904).

Ritchey, G.W, 'The 60-inch Reflector of the Mount Wilson Solar Observatory', *Ap.J.*, **29**, p. 198 (1909).

Ritchey, G.W., 'The Making of a Great Telescope', *Harpers' Monthly*, no. 121, p. 740 (October 1910).

Ritchey, G.W., 'The Modern Astronomical Telescope and the New Astronomical Photography', Part III, *JRASC*, **22**, no. 8, p. 303 (1928).

Sandage, Allan, *The Mount Wilson Observatory: Breaking the Code of Cosmic Evolution*, Centennial History of the Carnegie Institution of Washington, vol. 1, Cambridge University Press (2004).

Sawyer Hogg, H., 'Harlow Shapley and Globular Clusters', *PASP*, **77**, no. 458, p. 336.

Shapley, H., *Through Rugged Ways to the Stars*, Charles Scribner's Sons (1969).

van de Kamp, P., 'The Galactocentric Revolution: A Reminiscent Narrative', *PASP*, **77**, no. 458, p. 325.

Mercury: the Anomalous Terrestrial Planet and ESA's BepiColombo Mission

DAVID A. ROTHERY

Mercury is an elusive object in the sky, because it never strays more than about 28° from the Sun and so, except in the tropics, it is barely above the horizon when the sky is truly dark. A favourable evening elongation (27.1°) occurs on 11 September 2008. I have only seen Mercury a few times myself, and yet I now find myself in the rôle of 'UK lead scientist' on one of the most important instruments flying on Europe's first mission to Mercury.

This mission is named BepiColombo, in honour of Professor Giuseppe (Bepi) Colombo (1920–84) of the University of Padua, whose suggestion led to the first Mercury mission (NASA's Mariner 10) using a gravity-assist swing-by of Venus to place itself in a solar orbit that allowed it to make three fly-bys of Mercury in 1974–5 rather than having only a single encounter. Each fly-by came from roughly the same direction, and so only about 45 per cent of the planet's surface was seen. However, details as small as 1 kilometre were imaged, which is a far better view than could be achieved by ground-based telescopes, revealing a heavily cratered rocky surface (Figure 1). However, the resemblance to the Moon is only superficial, as I shall explain later.

Since then, just one other mission has been sent to Mercury, NASA's MESSENGER, which was launched in August 2004 and is due to make fly-bys on 14 January 2008, 6 October 2008 and 29 September 2009 before achieving orbit around Mercury in March 2011. MESSENGER is a 'Discovery' class mission, like NEAR-Shoemaker (from which it inherited several subsystems), Lunar Prospector, Stardust, Genesis and Deep Impact. Discovery missions are relatively cheap (by NASA standards) and conservative in design, but even so, unless something

Figure 1. Mosaic of images recorded by Mariner 10 while it receded from Mercury after its first encounter in 1974. The Caloris Basin (see Figure 3) straddles the terminator. (Image courtesy of NASA.)

goes badly wrong, MESSENGER will considerably advance our understanding of Mercury by the time BepiColombo arrives.

BepiColombo is a European Space Agency (ESA) 'Cornerstone' mission due for launch in 2013 with insertion into orbit about Mercury in 2019. I wish MESSENGER well, but I am more excited about BepiColombo not just because I am involved with it but because it has a fuller complement of instruments, which will be placed in a much less eccentric orbit than can be achieved by MESSENGER. In fact, BepiColombo consists of two orbiters (Figure 2): the Mercury Polar Orbiter (MPO) to be operated by ESA, and the Mercury Magnetic Orbiter (MMO) to be operated by the Japan Aerospace Exploration Agency (JAXA). Sadly, initial plans for a third component – a lander – had to be abandoned early in the mission planning on cost grounds. BepiColombo will be launched from Baikonour (Kazakhstan) on a Russian Soyuz-Frégat rocket and flown to Mercury under ESA's direction. This six-year cruise will be powered by a solar electric propulsion module, and will include gravity-assist manoeuvres at

Figure 2. Artist's impression of the BepiColombo MPO (360 kg, foreground) and MMO (200 kg, background) at Mercury. However, the two craft will never actually be this close together once they are in their respective orbits. (Image courtesy of ESA.)

the Moon, Venus (twice) and the Earth, necessary to deliver a mission of this mass to Mercury with sufficient propellant in a chemical propulsion module for the orbit-insertion manoeuvres. When orbit has been achieved, MMO will separate and be handed over to JAXA control, and then the chemical propulsion module will continue to manoeuvre MPO into a lower orbit.

MMO will be placed into an elliptical polar orbit (400 kilometres at closest, on the sunward side, and 12,000 kilometres at its far point, above the night side) optimized to explore the planet's magnetosphere. However, MPO will be put into a lower and near-circular polar orbit only about 400 kilometres from the surface at its closest and 1,500 kilometres at its furthest point. This carries the instrument suite for studying the planet's surface, which is what, as a geologist, interests me most. MPO is designed to function for at least one Earth year in orbit around Mercury, with the option to continue for a further year if things go well. So, what do we know about Mercury, and what do I particularly want to find out? I can best summarize the latter as follows:

Big questions:
From what material did Mercury form, and how?
How and when did it become internally differentiated?
Is there both primary crust (crystallized from Mercury's primordial magma ocean) and secondary crust (produced by volcanic eruptions) on Mercury?

Secondary questions:
What is the history of crust formation?
How does crustal composition vary (i) across the surface, (ii) with depth?

Mercury is, of course, the closest planet to the Sun. It has a rocky surface, placing it in the class of 'terrestrial' (i.e. Earth-like) planets along with Venus, the Earth, Mars and (for geological purposes) the Moon and Io. Some basic physical properties of this group are listed in Table 1, in which Mercury may appear unremarkable. Other than being the closest to the Sun its properties do not appear extreme; it is in the middle of the size range and its density falls between that of the Earth and Venus. However, if you allow for Mercury's relatively small size, its density sticks out like the proverbial sore thumb. On a graph plotting radius against density, the other five bodies plot pretty much on a straight line, but Mercury falls well clear.

Table 1. Properties of the terrestrial (Earth-like) bodies of the Solar System

Name	Density (kg/m^3)	Radius (km)	Mass (relative to Earth)	Distance from Sun (AU)
Mercury	5.43	2,400	0.055	0.39
Venus	5.20	6,052	0.815	0.72
Earth	5.51	6,378	1.000	1.00
Moon	3.34	1,738	0.012	1.00
Mars	3.93	3,397	0.107	1.52
Io	3.53	1,821	0.015	5.20

The issue here is that if these were all made from the same recipe, we would expect the more massive ones to be denser, because the bigger the body, the stronger its gravity, and so the greater the pressure in its deep interior. Because Mercury is almost as dense as the Earth despite being so much smaller and less massive, it must be made of a greater proportion of *naturally dense* material, which has not had to be compressed to high density by the weight of the planet's outer layers.

So, although Mercury has a rocky crust it has a larger dense core than it should. This is almost certainly made largely of iron, and must extend about three-quarters of the way to the surface (Earth's core reaches barely halfway to the surface). Such a composition is consistent with Mercury's magnetic field discovered by Mariner 10, but those measurements could not distinguish whether the field is 'remanent' (frozen in) or is a consequence of an active dynamo in a fluid part of the core (like Earth's magnetic field). One of the prime goals of MMO is to find this out.

Mercury's cratered surface looks very much like that of the Moon. It even has a large, multi-ringed impact basin, named Caloris (Figure 3). However, although the terrain with the Caloris basin, and some of the adjacent terrain too, is relatively uncratered and may have been flooded by lava, there is no sign of the albedo contrast that makes the lunar maria stand out so well against the paler highland crust. Mariner 10 carried no spectroscopic devices, but such spectra as can with difficulty be collected by means of telescopes show a distinct lack of iron in

Figure 3. A mosaic of Mariner 10 images, covering about 1,200 km from side to side. The sunlit half of the Caloris Basin is on the left. (Image courtesy of NASA.)

Mercury's crust. It makes up about 1–3 per cent at most, barely a third of the iron abundance in typical basalt.

Thus, if there are lava flows on Mercury, they appear to be rather unlike the basalt that is so common on the other terrestrial planets, which are dark largely because of the presence of iron oxides. How then can Mercury have an enormous iron core, but so little iron in its mantle that it barely registers in the crust? Was it the process of core formation itself that somehow scavenged virtually all the iron out of Mercury's mantle? Maybe Mercury's crust is not actually poor in iron at all; perhaps 'space weathering' of the exposed surfaces has broken the iron-to-oxygen bonds in silicate minerals, leaving free atoms of iron that would not show up in visible and infrared spectra.

As for the disproportionately large size of the core, maybe the special conditions close to the Sun where Mercury formed (if indeed the planet formed where we now find it!) inhibited the accretion of rocky material and favoured that of metallic iron. Alternatively, Mercury could originally have had a 'conventional' composition, but later been stripped of most of its mantle by one or more giant impacts, or by exceptionally violent solar winds during the 'T Tauri' phase of the Sun's youth.

As for the nature of Mercury's crust, Mariner 10 images provide intriguing hints that should be resolved by BepiColombo's more detailed imaging. For example, some patches shown in Figure 4, notably 2–3 crater diameters above Holberg, are remarkably smooth. This could be relatively recent volcanic lavas, but there are other possible explanations such as patchy blanketing of the terrain by impact ejecta. When I say 'relatively recent' I am speaking geologically, and in the case of Mercury this means at least a billion years old, and maybe more than two billion. Even the youngest areas are unlikely to consist of bare rock but, as on the Moon, of a regolith of fragmented material produced by impacts. However, most of the regolith will be locally derived, and therefore reflect the composition of the underlying bedrock.

BepiColombo will carry visible and infrared imaging spectrometers (called SYMBIO-SYS and MERTIS), which will be able to detect 'colour' differences across the surface, and make lava stand out from impact ejecta. The size of the pixels on the best images will be only 5 metres across, and the entire globe will be mapped at <110-metre pixel size. Spectroscopic data from these instruments will be used to match the surface composition with mixtures of likely minerals, whose

Figure 4. A 600-km-wide Mariner 10 image centred near lat. 61° S, long. 61° W. The large degraded crater at top left is Rabelais, the prominent pair of 70-km craters towards the lower right are Holberg (above) and Spitteler (below). The escarpment running diagonally from lower left towards upper right is Adventure Rupes, and is evidence of an episode of global contraction relatively early in Mercury's history, but after some of its surviving craters were formed. (Image courtesy of NASA.)

spectral properties are known from laboratory studies. Mercury's topography will be mapped both by stereoscopic imaging and by a laser altimeter.

The instrument with which I am involved is the Mercury Imaging X-ray Spectrometer (MIXS), which will provide an independent but complementary set of data from those acquired by SYMBIO-SYS and MERTIS. MIXS works on the principle that Mercury's unprotected surface is bathed in X-rays from the Sun, which causes the atoms in the surface layer to fluoresce, giving off X-rays at characteristic energies that are specific to each element.

The planning, design and construction of MIXS is led by a UK team based at the University of Leicester, with major partners in Spain, Finland and Germany. The spatial resolution of MIXS will vary depending on the strength of the solar X-rays (a major solar flare would be a great advantage to us!), but under favourable conditions we should be able to measure the element abundances from some areas smaller than 10 kilometres across. Fine-scale spatial resolution such as this will enable us to compare crater peaks (which are uplifted portions of the lower crust) with more typical surface material. Because we need to allow for the strength of the solar radiation before we can fully interpret MIXS data, our Finnish colleagues are building BepiColombo's Solar Intensity X-ray Spectrometer, SIXS, which will look back towards the Sun while MIXS is imaging the surface.

MIXS will be able to detect X-rays from the following elements: O, Si, Ti, Al, F, Mn, Mg, Ca, K, P, S, Cr and Ni. In fact, there is no element occurring in the lunar crust or chondritic meteorites at >0.1 per cent abundance to which MIXS is not sensitive, so our picture of the major elements on Mercury's surface is likely to be fairly complete. All being well, between MIXS, SYMBIO-SYS and MERTIS we should end up with a good idea of the composition of Mercury's surface in terms of both the elements that are present and the minerals in which they occur. In particular, it should be clear whether relatively young, lightly cratered areas have been resurfaced by volcanism or by some other processes. If there *are* lava flows, then we shall be able to interpret variations in magma chemistry over time, and from region to region.

That is only the first step on a long journey of discovery before we can work out the *internal* composition of the planet. Some elements may have been implanted on the surface directly from the solar wind. Iron and nickel may be artificially high because of delivery by iron meteorites. Interpretation of X-ray fluorescence data is complicated by secondary effects such as surface roughness, and by the possibility that high-energy solar-wind particles can reach the surface during times of magnetic disturbance and cause additional X-ray fluorescence. We would dearly love a sample of Mercury's surface to analyse in the laboratory, to help calibrate the BepiColombo data and to measure 'trace elements' that are too low in abundance to be detected remotely, but which in some ways are more informative than the major elements. Planetary science is rarely straightforward, and I expect that in twelve years' time the list of unanswered questions about Mercury will have lengthened rather than shortened. But if so, it will be because BepiColombo has taught us to ask more, and more insightful, questions.

Stairway to Heaven: the Cosmic Distance Ladder

CHRIS KITCHIN

Led Zeppelin's 1971 folk-rock smash hit 'Stairway to Heaven' was partly inspired by the biblical account of Jacob's ladder – a mechanism whereby angels could travel between the Earth and Heaven. The possibility that such a stairway might become a reality (though probably with non-angelic travellers) has recently received some support. An extremely tough cable could be let down to the surface of the Earth from a satellite in geostationary orbit (with a massive counterweight much further out) that might then enable cargoes to be taken into space for a few pounds or dollars per kilogramme. Arthur C. Clarke has extensively explored the practicalities of such a space elevator or orbital tower in his novel *The Fountains of Paradise*.

However, should a Stairway to Heaven allowing real people and their goods and chattels to zoom up and down to space with little more fuss than taking a lift up to the next floor of a department store ever become a reality, the 'Heaven' that it reaches will still only be about a tenth of the distance to the Moon. Astrophysicists, though, have long been familiar with another set of steps that reach to beyond the outermost quasars – a hundred thousand million million times further away than the Moon. They have dubbed this stairway the 'Cosmic Distance Ladder'. It does not transport anything or anyone to anywhere except in the imagination, but it provides us with a yardstick to measure the Universe.

MEASURING THE SIZE OF THE EARTH

The numbers involved in determining the distances to astronomical objects are so large that in popular usage 'astronomical' has become a synonym for 'unimaginably gargantuan'. Distance, though, is absolutely fundamental to understanding the nature of the universe and its contents – the masses, sizes and many other properties of planets, stars, nebulae and galaxies can only be found if their distances are known. Attempts to measure astronomical distances therefore date back to the earliest recorded times – well over two millennia ago Aristarchus of Samos (c.310–230 BC) estimated the Sun to be at least twenty times further away than the Moon. The first measurement in absolute terms, however, had to await Eratosthenes' (c.276–c.195 BC) attempt to find the size of the Earth (Figure 1). He noted that at midday on the summer solstice, the Sun was directly overhead at Syene (modern-day Aswan) in Upper Egypt, since the bottoms of wells were illuminated by the Sun's rays. Further north, at the same time, at Alexandria, the Sun was one-fiftieth of a circle away from the zenith. Measuring the distance between Syene and Alexandria to be about 5,000 stades (one stade is thought to be equal to about 180 metres or 200 yards) enabled him to estimate the Earth's circumference as 250,000 stades (=5,000 stades × 50) or 45,700 kilometres in modern measurements. It followed therefore that its radius must be some

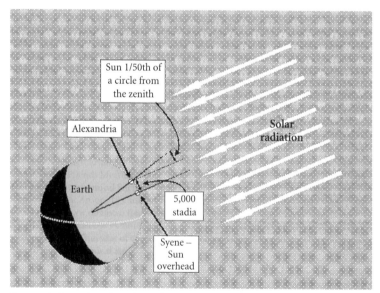

Figure 1. Eratosthenes' method of measuring the Earth's circumference – the first determination of the absolute size of any astronomical object.

40,000 stades (7,300 kilometres). Today's values for these quantities are 40,074 kilometres and 6,378 kilometres respectively – Eratosthenes' estimates were remarkably good for a first attempt.

The size of the Earth is the 'ground' upon which our Cosmic Distance Ladder rests – and the distance to the Moon is the first rung upwards on that ladder. Finding the Moon's distance may nowadays be accomplished in innumerable ways, but the earliest approaches relied upon its parallax. Parallax is the angular shift between the relative positions of nearby and more distant objects when observed from different locations. We rely upon the parallax between the views seen by our two eyes to estimate the distances of objects in everyday life (Figure 2). When the Moon is full and is observed as it rises and sets, we see it from locations separated by the full diameter of the Earth. The stars are millions of times further away than the Moon and so their positions can be taken as fixed (but see the discussion of stellar parallax later on). The position of the Moon in the sky can be measured against those background stars and observers seeing it rising and setting (Figure 3) will find it in different places. The angular distance between those two positions in the sky is the Moon's parallax across the diameter of the Earth. A single observer can make the same measurement by waiting while the Earth's rotation moves him or her from seeing the rising Moon to seeing the setting Moon, although an allowance will need to be made for the Moon's movement across the sky during that interval. An allowance will also need to be made for the latitude(s) of the observer(s) if they are not on the equator. However, ignoring such complications and using simple trigonometry, the distance of the Moon is related to the parallax shift for a pair of equatorial observers by:

$$\tan P = \frac{R}{D}$$

where P is half the angular change between the rising and setting Moon positions (usually called the parallax angle), D is the Earth–Moon distance and R is the radius of the Earth (in the same units as D).

Thus, finding the distance of the Moon is easy once the size of the Earth is known. Hipparchus, whether by this method or another (perhaps based upon eclipses), probably found the Moon's distance to lie between about 71 and 83 times the Earth's radius. This works out to be between 2.8 million and 3.3 million stades – 510,000 to 600,000

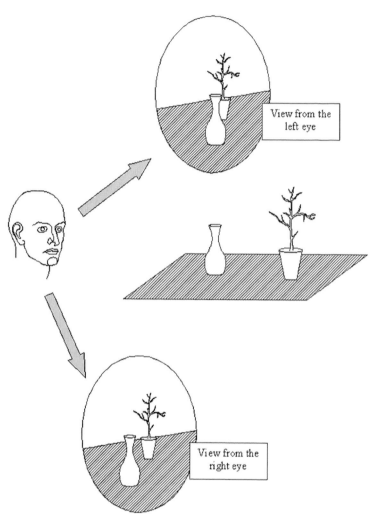

Figure 2. Parallax. The left eye sees the vase and flower almost superimposed, while the right eye sees them well separated. The brain combines these two differing images to enable us to judge the distances of the objects.

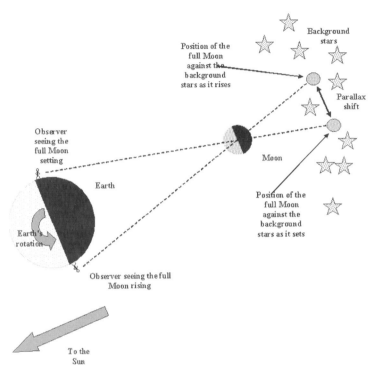

Figure 3. Lunar parallax (not to scale). An observer watching the full Moon rising sees it in a different position against the background stars when compared with an observer seeing it setting at the same time. The angular change in the position of the full Moon in the sky is its parallax shift across the diameter of the Earth.

kilometres. Again this is a remarkably good result compared with the modern value of 384,401 kilometres for the average Earth–Moon separation.

THE EARTH–SUN DISTANCE

The second rung on the Cosmic Distance Ladder is the distance between the Earth and the Sun – and this is an absolutely crucial measurement. Not only are all distances within the Solar System based upon the value of the Earth–Sun distance, but ultimately almost all other distances – out to the furthermost quasars and beyond – rely on it as well.

Even before an actual value was known for the Earth–Moon distance, Aristarchus had estimated the Sun's distance to be at least twenty times greater than that of the Moon. This translates, using Eratosthenes' values, to a distance of at least 10 million to 12 million kilometres. Even as a first attempt, though, this is a poor result – the average value of the Earth–Sun distance (usually called the astronomical unit, AU) is actually fifteen times larger than this early estimate.

Despite the importance of knowing a good value for the AU, nearly two millennia were to pass before a method that improved upon Aristarchus' work could be developed. In 1672 Giovanni Cassini (1625–1712) and Jean Richer (1630–96) managed to measure a value for the parallax of Mars as seen from observing sites at Paris and Cayenne (French Guiana). From this they deduced a value for the AU of 139 million kilometres – within 7 per cent of the true value. Then in 1716 Edmond Halley (1656–1742) suggested that the AU could be measured using the parallax of Venus and also that this could be determined accurately when Venus passed between the Earth and the Sun and was seen silhouetted against the solar disc while in transit (Figure 4). Such transits only occur in pairs at intervals of over a century, so the first available opportunity to use Halley's method did not occur until 1761. Halley therefore never saw his suggestion put into practice. Numerous observing teams, however, were ready for 1761 (and for 1769, the next of the eighteenth-century's pair of transits) and even in the face of unexpected problems with the observations, a good value for the AU was found – 153 million kilometres – within 2 per cent of the correct value. Continuing and improving observations of the parallax of Venus and more recently of asteroids passing close to the Earth, plus direct measurements of the distances to planets and asteroids using radar, have finally fixed the AU's value at a figure of 149,597,870.66 kilometres.

Once a realistic value for the AU was known, then, thanks to Johannes Kepler (1571–1630), all distances within the solar system were equally well known. Kepler's third law of planetary motion relates the size of a planet's (or asteroid's, comet's, etc.) orbit to its orbital period. Almost all orbits are elliptical in shape, so their sizes are measured using half the maximum diameter of that ellipse – usually

Figure 4. The transit of Venus on 8 June 2004. Similar events from 1761 onwards enabled astronomers to begin to tie down the value of the astronomical unit. (Image courtesy of the author.)

called the orbit's semi-major axis and labelled a. If the orbital period is T years, then the semi-major axis of the orbit, in AU, is simply given by:

$$a = T^{2/3}$$

The orbital periods are easy to observe. Thus given Jupiter's orbital period of 11.862 years, for example, we quickly find its orbital semi-major axis (and so its average distance from the Sun) to be 5.2 AU (778 million kilometres).

DISTANCES TO THE STARS

Even before the true scale of the solar system had been found, attempts were under way to try to step up to the third rung of the Cosmic Distance Ladder by finding the distances to the stars. Success in this task, however, had to await improvements in the accuracy and stability of telescopes and was not achieved until 1838. In that year Friedrich Bessel (1784–1846) announced that he had determined the distance to a fifth-magnitude star to be found about 10° south-east of Deneb (Alpha Cygni). This star (actually a binary star called 61 Cygni) was 96,000,000 million kilometres away from the Sun. Bessel just pipped another astronomer – Thomas Henderson (1798–1844) – to the post. A few weeks after Bessel's announcement, Henderson revealed the distance to Alpha Centauri as 30,000,000 million kilometres – one-third of the distance to 61 Cygni. Modern measurements put these two stars at 102,000,000 million and 40,000,000 million kilometres respectively away from us.

Bessel and Henderson and the thousands of other astronomers who have followed in their tracks used parallax to measure the distances of their stars. The parallax of even the nearest star (Proxima Centauri – 39,000,000 million kilometres) across the diameter of the Earth, however, is just 0.000 06 seconds of arc,[1] and this is much too small an angle to be detected even using the largest and most sophisticated of today's telescopes. Bessel and Henderson's measurements therefore used a base line that was much larger than the Earth – the diameter of the Earth's orbit. This is, of course, twice the value of the AU, so the distances to the stars could not be found until *after* the distance from the Earth to the Sun had been determined. However, once the AU was known (or at least a good approximation to it), then observing a nearby star over a six-month interval would show its parallax shift against the very, very distant stars whose parallaxes remain negligible even now (Figure 5).

Distances within the Solar System can conveniently use AUs as their units – even Pluto is only 40 AU outwards from the Sun. Proxima Centauri, though, is 260,000 AU away – and the most distant quasar is

---

[1] A second of arc is 1/3600 of a degree – about the size of a 2-kilometre crater on the Moon as seen from the Earth.

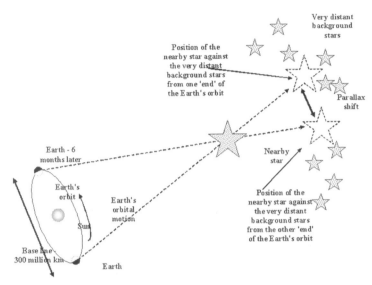

Figure 5. Stellar parallax (not to scale). The position of a nearby star against the very distant background stars changes over six months as the Earth moves from one 'end' of its orbit to the other – a baseline of 300 million kilometres.

800,000,000,000,000 AU distant. Outside the Solar System, therefore, the AU is too small a unit for ease of use. The method used to find the distances of stars, however, suggests a new unit – the distance at which one AU subtends an angle of one second of arc. This unit is called the parsec (abbreviation pc) from PARallax and SECond of arc, and a star one pc away from us would have a parallax shift (Figure 5) of 2 arc-seconds since its movement arises from the Earth's motion across the *diameter* of the Earth's orbit – i.e. 2 AU. Another unit is also in wide-spread use, the light year (ly), which is the distance travelled by light in one terrestrial year. The pc is just over three times larger than the ly, so

1 pc = 3.2616 ly
    = 206,265 AU
    = 30,857,000 million kilometres.

In these units we thus have the distances of 61 Cygni, Alpha Centauri and Proxima Centauri as 3.3 pc (10.8 ly), 1.3 pc (4.3 ly) and 1.26 pc (4.1 ly) respectively.

Since Bessel's time the parallaxes, and hence the distances, of many thousands of stars have been measured. Measuring very small angles is not easy, however, and from the surface of the Earth even the best measurements are still uncertain by some ±0.01 seconds of arc. The Hipparcos spacecraft (named after Hipparchus of Nicaea (*c.*190–*c.*120 BC), the first person to catalogue the stars) improved upon this by a factor of about five and measured over 100,000 stars. The best-known parallax values thus have uncertainties of about ±0.002 seconds of arc. For a star that is 10 pc away (parallax 0.1 seconds of arc) this translates into an uncertainty in its measured distance of between 9.8 pc and 10.2 pc – quite a reasonable degree of accuracy. However, for a star 250 pc away (parallax 0.004 seconds of arc) the same uncertainty in the value of the parallax angle means that the star's distance could be anywhere between 170 pc and 500 pc. Thus parallax, even with the best available modern equipment, only really gives us good distances for stars out to 100 pc (330 ly) or less. Typically, parallax distances are uncertain by ±10 per cent – a figure that would cause any self-respecting physics and most other scientific experiments to be thrown into the dustbin as quite useless!

BEYOND THE NEAREST STARS

Obtaining distances for stars and other objects beyond 100 pc requires a further step up on the Cosmic Distance Ladder – to rung 4. However, the next method and those that follow it almost all depend upon being calibrated using the results from the distance measurements based upon parallax. Their uncertainties *at best* are thus equal to the ±10 per cent of the parallax measurements, and can be very much worse than that.

In fact the calibration of the next distance measure was completely bungled to start with, and its initial results were wildly off beam. The approach for rung 4 of the ladder is the first example of a general method that is widely used, known as the 'Standard Candle Scheme'. It relies upon obtaining the actual brightness (luminosity) of an object via some method that does *not* require the distance of that object to be known. By comparing the actual brightness of the object (the standard candle) with its observed brightness in the sky we can immediately calculate its distance. In 1907, Henrietta Leavitt (1868–1921) discovered that the average observed magnitudes of a group of Cepheid variable stars within the Small Magellanic Cloud (SMC) were related to the periods of their brightness variations. Since the stars were all at effectively the same distance from us, this meant that their actual luminosities were also related to their periods. Potentially, therefore, observing the period of any Cepheid variable would tell us its actual brightness. Using it as a standard candle we could then at once obtain its distance – and Cepheids can be up to several tens of thousands of times brighter than the Sun, so they can be picked up even in nearby galaxies – so potentially this could also tell us the distances to those galaxies.

Unfortunately the SMC is too far away for its distance to be found by parallax, so Leavitt, though she had found the Cepheid period–luminosity law, was unable to calibrate it in absolute terms. Ejnar Hertzsprung (1873–1967) took on this task and looked for some nearby Cepheid variables to use. Unfortunately, even the nearest Cepheid (Delta Cephei, the prototype of the class) was too far away for its parallax to be measured at that time (even now its distance of 270 pc makes parallax a difficult measurement). Hertzsprung thus had to employ a series of complex and roundabout approaches to arrive at his calibration of the Cepheids as standard candles. Unfortunately he got it wrong – firstly by seriously underestimating the effect of interstellar absorption, and secondly by not realizing that the Cepheids close to the Sun were of a different type from those in the SMC. Thus for thirty years astronomers thought the Universe was only about a third to a half of its true size. Finally, in 1943, Hertzsprung's errors were corrected by Walter Baade (1893–1960) and our estimates of the distances to all galaxies had to be doubled overnight. Nowadays, Cepheids can be detected out to distances of ten to twenty million pc (Mpc) with uncertainties in their distances of ±15 per cent at best, thus taking us out into the region of the nearby galaxies.

The next few rungs of the Cosmic Distance Ladder are all based upon standard candle approaches of one sort or another. The candles range from the average luminosities of groups of stars estimated from their spectra (sometimes called spectroscopic parallax) through the luminosities of spiral galaxies estimated from their 21-centimetre hydrogen line emission (the Tully–Fisher relation) to type Ia supernovae whose peak absolute visual magnitudes are all close to −19. This takes us out to distances of several hundred Mpc. Beyond that, the brightest galaxy within a cluster of galaxies can be used as the candle – assuming that such galaxies are all very similar – to take us to a thousand or more Mpc, but the uncertainties in the distances are by now at least ±50 per cent to ±100 per cent.

Finally, the topmost rung of the Cosmic Distance Ladder uses the red shifts of the galaxies to estimate their distances. The relationship between the shift of lines to longer wavelengths (the red shift) within a galaxy's spectrum and its distance determined by one or other of the methods already discussed has been known since Edwin Hubble's (1889–1953) work in 1929. By assuming this relationship to be valid out to the edges of the visible Universe, the distances to the furthermost quasars and galaxies can be estimated. The most distant objects then turn out to be bright infrared galaxies some 4,100 Mpc (13,300 million ly) away from us and 97 per cent of the way back towards the Big Bang – a far cry from Eratosthenes' observations of the bottoms of water wells.

September 1608: Astronomy's Awakening

FRED WATSON

It was arguably the single most important event in the entire history of astronomy. For the first time, one of the human senses had been extended to reveal objects that had previously been invisible. It instantly transformed the study of the heavens from simple join-the-dots measurement into a dawning understanding of what those dots actually stood for. At a stroke, it gave new weight to Copernicus's Sun-centred theory of the Solar System, beginning an era in which robust models of our cosmic environment could be built on ever-increasing scales. Who could have guessed that those ideas would one day lead to the supremely powerful hot Big Bang model of the Universe that we all revere today?

All this came, of course, from the invention of the telescope. And what it achieved in its infancy in the hands of the 'Florentine Patrician', Galileo Galilei, can never be in doubt. You have only to read his little book *The Starry Messenger* of 1610 to sense the trembling excitement with which he plucked discovery after discovery from the sky with his new creation. Craters and mountains on the Moon, stars rather than milk coagulating in the Milky Way and – most dramatically – Jupiter's brilliant speck resolved into a disc and four orbiting moons. Truly, this was the dawn of modern astronomy.

WHO INVENTED THE TELESCOPE?

Contrary to popular belief, Galileo wasn't the inventor of the telescope. He tells us in *The Starry Messenger* that he first heard a rumour about a Dutch *perspicillum*, or spyglass, sometime around May 1609, and that it was confirmed by a letter from a former student, Jacques Badovere, in Paris. The story of how Galileo set about understanding this device (without actually having seen one), and then went on to build a succession of steadily improving telescopes, is the stuff of legend. Without question, the startling discoveries he made were a direct result of those efforts (Figure 1). But – invent the telescope he did not. So who did? It's a good question, and the short answer is that no one knows exactly. What we do know is that truly extraordinary events surrounded the invention of the telescope. And they make for a remarkable story.

In fact, the first name associated with the telescope's debut on the world stage is that of Hans Lipperhey, a humble spectacle-maker who petitioned the government of the fledgling Dutch Republic for a patent on the invention late in September 1608. His timing was perfect, coinciding with tense diplomatic negotiations between the Dutch and the Spanish, who had been at war since 1568. But in a farcical turn of events, two other individuals turned up within three weeks asking for similar patents, so it is questionable whether Lipperhey was the true originator of the telescope.

Many of the contemporary documents that refer to these extraordinary proceedings were uncovered early in the twentieth century by another Dutchman, Cornelis de Waard, and presented, together with related evidence, in his *De Uitvinding der Verrekijkers* (*The Invention of the Telescope*), published in The Hague in 1906. It was in assembling and translating those original sources for a wider readership that the modern historian Albert Van Helden performed perhaps the greater service to today's scholars. He wrote a detailed analysis of their contents in a comprehensive work also entitled 'The Invention of the Telescope', published as a complete issue of the *Transactions of the American Philosophical Society* (see 'Further Reading').

This study has become the yardstick against which all subsequent commentaries on the origin of the telescope have been judged. It should not be assumed, though, that Van Helden solved all the problems. Indeed, he made no claim to have done. The evidence is a maze of contradictory statements and reports, often with well-known historical names intermingled with shadowy figures in confusing circumstances. It is a *very* difficult area.

Then, into this minefield stepped another brave author, the late M. Barlow Pepin, who wrote a little book with the intriguing title of *The Emergence of the Telescope: Janssen, Lipperhey and the Unknown Man* (see 'Further Reading'). His stated purpose was to take a 'fresh look' at the circumstances under which the telescope emerged.

Figure 1. Galileo chatting up the muses of the sciences in the frontispiece of an early edition of his collected works. Although Galileo did not invent the telescope, he improved it beyond recognition, and the refined version shown here enabled him to make the extraordinary discoveries symbolically portrayed in the sky. (Image courtesy of the author and the Royal Observatory, Edinburgh.)

Although no significant new evidence had come to light since Van Helden's epic work in 1977, Pepin did manage to draw some previously unrecognized threads together in arriving at a conclusion not too different from de Waard's of a century earlier, but with rather greater emphasis (and a lot more entertainingly). The telescope was perfected not by Lipperhey, said Pepin, but by one Saccharias Janssen, a spectacle-maker, peddler and small-time crook who secretly presented an example to the authorities shortly before Lipperhey got around to it.

Although it does not by any means put the final verdict beyond dispute, *The Emergence of the Telescope* is a worthy adjunct to Van Helden's work, and a useful contribution to the scholarly literature. I wish I'd had a copy of it a few years ago, when I embarked on my own foray into this morass for *Stargazer: the Life and Times of the Telescope*. But, as we celebrate the four-hundredth birthday of the telescope, perhaps now is as good a time as any for one more 'fresh look' at the evidence – if for no other reason than to bring it to a wider readership.

A PRE-HISTORY?

'The disappearing telescope.' 'Viking conquest of the heavens?' 'Did an Englishman invent the telescope?' Headlines such as these have appeared at intervals over the last couple of decades, each one herald-ing some novel piece of evidence that the telescope was known to humankind before the remarkable events of September 1608. Such ideas range from an assertion that the ancient Assyrians had telescopes in the eighth century BC, enabling them to observe the rings of Saturn, to the far less fanciful notion that an Elizabethan gentleman called Leonard Digges made a telescope using a curved mirror in the 1550s. That, at least, retains some credible links with reality.

On closer examination, most of these claims turn out to be based on evidence that is highly circumstantial, if not wildly speculative. Readers interested in pursuing them are invited to consult the sources mentioned in 'Further Reading', particularly Van Helden's detailed account, and the analysis in Chapter 3 of *Stargazer*. Two of these claims, however, are sufficiently credible as to be worthy of note here.

The first appears in a book called *Natural Magick*, first published in 1589 and written by an Italian optician called Giovanbaptista della Porta (1538–1615). It is a throwaway line about the use of convex and concave lenses to correct poor eyesight that quickens the pulse of anyone wishing to place the invention of the telescope before the seventeenth century:

With a Concave you shall see small things afar off, very clearly; with a Convex, things neerer to be greater, but more obscurely: if you know how to fit them both together, you shall see both things afar off, and things neer hand, both greater and clearly.

Many readers of this *Yearbook* will be aware that when the telescope did finally make its undisputed first appearance, it was in a form that took a convex and a concave lens and 'fit them both together' at opposite ends of a tube. It is what is called a Galilean telescope in homage to its great champion, and, incidentally, is still found today in the guise of ordinary opera glasses. So, did della Porta know the secret of the Galilean telescope in the 1580s?

Maybe he did, although it is clear from the context of the quote that della Porta is really referring to the improvement of defective vision, rather than an instrument specifically for magnifying distant objects. I speculated in *Stargazer* as to whether della Porta's description may, in fact, have been pre-empting Benjamin Franklin's eighteenth-century invention of bifocal lenses, and still find that an intriguing possibility. Van Helden has a more interesting interpretation, however, suggesting that della Porta had, indeed, succeeded in making a weak Galilean telescope – but that he did not perceive its wider possibilities.

Credibility is lent to this idea by the fact that on 28 August 1609 (by which time Lipperhey's Dutch spyglass of 1608 had become well known), della Porta wrote to a noble friend that he had seen one of these supposedly new instruments. 'It is a hoax,' he went on, 'and is taken from the ninth book of my *On Refraction*' (see Figure 2). By 'a hoax' we can perhaps infer that della Porta meant there was nothing new in the Dutch invention, for hadn't he written about it himself twenty years previously? As it turns out, della Porta was getting his own books confused, since *On Refraction* (1593) doesn't mention the combination of lenses whereas, as we have seen, *Natural Magick* does. Notwithstanding that slip, this does seem to support a case for the Galilean telescope having originated in Italy, a theme that we shall return to.

The other credible description of a sixteenth-century telescope comes from a rather likeable friend of the Elizabethan gentleman mentioned above, Leonard Digges, and his son Thomas. This man was William Bourne (*fl.* 1565–88), a mathematician who corresponded with Sir William Cecil, the principal adviser to Elizabeth I. It is, in fact,

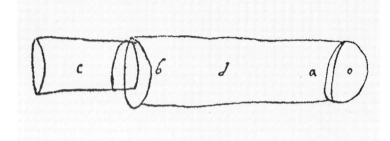

Figure 2. The first known depiction of a telescope, complete with sliding drawtube, from a letter written by Giovanbaptista della Porta on 28 August 1609. Della Porta was dismissive about it, claiming to have invented it himself twenty years earlier. (Image courtesy of the author and the Royal Observatory, Edinburgh.)

through a manuscript written for Cecil by Bourne in around 1585 that we know something of the Diggeses' endeavours with combinations of lenses and mirrors. That manuscript was analysed in some detail by the late Colin Ronan (see 'Further Reading').

But in an earlier document of Bourne's, published in London in 1578, we read what you might see on looking through a very large, long-focus convex lens (perhaps 40 centimetres in diameter) when it is stood up in a frame. If you stand immediately behind the lens and look at a distant object ('thing') through it, 'then your eye being neare unto it, it sheweth it[s] selfe according unto the thing, but as you doo goe backwardes, the thing sheweth bigger and bigger, untill that the thing shall seeme of a monstrous bignesse'.

This is an accurate, if flowery, account of the effect of the lens – and, remarkably, is also an exact description of something that was marketed 350 years later by a reputable London optical company as a 'window telescope' (Figure 3). Hanging in the window of the fashionable 1930s drawing room, this 38-centimetre-diameter lens would allow 'a person standing a few feet within the room [to] see through the lens the details of the distant landscape . . . From one's hall one may recognise the visitor far down the drive. Or one may watch birds and other creatures.'

Such a single-lens 'telescope' relies for its effect on a slight long-sightedness of the eye. When standing well back from it (but closer to it than its focal point), an acceptable, magnified, upright image of the distant scene will be visible. The magnification is hardly 'monstrous' – objects will appear no more than two or three times the size they are with the unaided eye – but it is significant. The lens has become a telescope of sorts. What would turn it into a genuine telescope is the addition of a concave eyepiece lens (which effectively renders a normal

Figure 3. Illustration from an optical catalogue issued by W. Watson & Sons Ltd in the 1920s. It depicts a 'window telescope' consisting of a large, long-focus lens that has a magnifying effect on the landscape. An added feature was that it could burn the house down in strong sunlight. This 'telescope' required a slight long-sightedness of the eye, the principle having been recognized some 350 years earlier. (Image courtesy of the author.)

eye artificially long-sighted), producing a conventional Galilean telescope. Nevertheless, Bourne's thinking was clearly going in the right direction.

The one thing that casts doubt on just how effective these putative sixteenth-century telescopes might have been is that they were not picked up as useful military or scientific devices, as they certainly were in 1608. (Very quickly, in fact; the news spread like wildfire throughout the following year.) In particular, the greatest scientist in Europe in the late sixteenth century – a man who not only corresponded with Thomas Digges, but with many other leading minds of the period – seems to have been completely unaware of them. This man was Tycho Brahe (1546–1601), the most prolific and accomplished instrument-builder of his day, and the greatest astronomer of the naked-eye era. Had he heard of a telescope in any form, he, more than anyone, would have checked it out – and would have either made one, or written about it. But he did neither.

SEPTEMBER 1608

Six years and eleven months after Tycho's untimely death, the telescope was a reality. That much is historical fact. We know from a number of original documents that have survived the ravages of time (and a few that remain only as copies, thanks to the attentions of the Luftwaffe in 1940) that sometime between Friday 25 and Tuesday 30 September 1608, a spectacle-maker turned up at The Hague carrying a telescope.

As it happens, that was quite a weekend in Dutch history. With both sides weary of conflict after forty years, the Dutch and the Spanish had taken tentative steps towards a truce, and peace negotiations had been taking place in The Hague throughout September. But things had not gone well, and on the last day of the month, the commander-in-chief of the Spanish forces in the southern Netherlands – a nobleman by the name of Ambrogio Spinola (1569–1630) – left The Hague with the talks in deadlock. Spinola's opposite number on the Dutch side was the commander-in-chief of the armed forces of the United Provinces of the Netherlands, Prince Maurice of Nassau (1567–1625). Not to be confused with its better-known namesake in the Bahamas, Nassau in present-day Germany was then a principality of the Holy Roman Empire.

Maurice was a formidably gifted man, and not only was he commander-in-chief, but he was also the Stadtholder, or leader, of the United Provinces government, an assembly known as the States General. This federal parliament was made up of representatives of the seven United Provinces of the Dutch Republic. And it was the delegate from the province of Zeeland who, on or around 27 September, received a strange letter from his fellow councillors at home, two days' journey away.

'*Den brenger van dese,*' it began:

The bearer of this, who claims to have a certain device, by means of which all things at a very great distance can be seen as if they were nearby, by looking through glasses which he claims to be a new invention, would like to communicate the same to His Excellency [Prince Maurice]. Your Honour will please recommend him to His Excellency, and, as the occasion arises, be helpful to him according to what you think of the device. . . .

Honoured, etc., the XXVth September, 1608.

Herewith,

Councillors.

That the parliamentary recipient of the letter did, indeed, introduce the bearer of the letter to Prince Maurice is borne out by other contemporary documents. The Hague was full of diplomatic emissaries from other nations, all with a vested interest in the peace process, and at least one of them wrote home to tell of a humble spectacle-maker who had been ushered into the Prince's presence carrying a remarkable tube with a lens at each end: 'the instrument for seeing far', it was called, for the word 'telescope' was not coined until three and a half years later, when an exclusive group of Italian and Greek intellectuals held a banquet to honour Galileo and his astronomical discoveries.

In order to test the instrument, Prince Maurice climbed the tower of his residence in the grounds of the Binnenhof, the imposing thirteenth-century building that was then the seat of the States General and remains its ceremonial home today. From there, we are told, he could clearly see through the instrument the clock of Delft and the windows of the church of Leiden, respectively one-and-a-half and three-and-a-half hours' journey away. The enormous military potential of the device was not lost on the Stadtholder.

That moment when Prince Maurice first held the telescope in his hands was an event of high drama, a turning point in history against a backdrop of international crisis. But it quickly turned into farce. Whether it was by dint of diplomatic etiquette, a misguided ploy, or simply to gloat, we have no way of knowing, but somehow the unthinkable happened. Within a day or two of Prince Maurice inspecting the telescope – or perhaps even at the same time – he had shown it to the Marquis Spinola. By the time the commander-in-chief of the enemy forces left The Hague on 30 September, he had not only held this new strategic deterrent in his hands, but had taken a look through it.

His reaction was one of amazement. 'From now on, I'll no longer be safe, for you'll see me from afar,' he had said to Prince Frederick Henry, Maurice's half-brother. 'Don't worry,' the Prince reassured him, 'we'll forbid our men to shoot at you.' No doubt everyone laughed. Of course, the members of the States General were eager to see for themselves the marvellous new device that Prince Maurice had received. He sent it to them, commenting that with its help, 'they would see the tricks of the enemy'. He seems to have neglected to add that the same enemy already knew of its existence.

Then, on Thursday 2 October, the spectacle-maker himself was interviewed by the States General at the Binnenhof. He put his cards on the table, asking them to grant him a patent for thirty years during which time no one else would be permitted to make telescopes. Failing that, he would be happy with a yearly pension in return for which he would make telescopes solely for the state. He was probably not the first person to try to make a fast buck out of the government in a time of national crisis – and he was certainly not the last.

The neat, measured handwriting of the duty clerk records for posterity the States General's predictable reaction. Even in those days, it was the time-honoured way of deciding what to do next. They formed a committee. They also made the curious request that the spectacle-maker should try to improve his invention so that it could be used with both eyes.

It is the minutes of that interview (Figure 4) that give us the identity of this man, for the Councillors' letter of 25 September didn't actually mention his name. But he was Hans Lipperhey, a German-born spectacle-maker who had settled in the town of Middelburg in Zeeland – and he was the first person to be identified with a verifiable, working

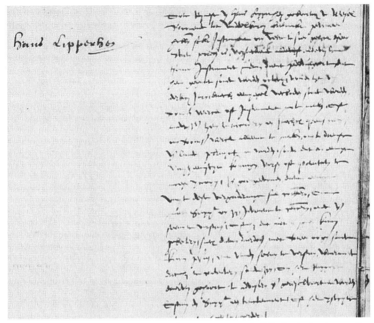

Figure 4. The entry in the minute book of the States General of the Netherlands recording Hans Lipperhey's ill-fated patent application for his telescope, 2 October 1608. (Image courtesy of Algemeen Rijksarchief, via Albert van Helden, 'The invention of the telescope'.)

telescope. As it turned out, he didn't get his patent, but was paid handsomely to make three binocular versions of the telescope, the last of which he delivered on 13 February 1609. That day's entry in the States General's account book recording his final payment is the last we hear of Lipperhey in the historical record – until the sad notice of his burial in Middelburg on 29 September 1619.

So why, in the light of all this, isn't Lipperhey celebrated as the inventor of the telescope? The answer lies in subsequent events, which raise uncomfortable questions of precedence. However, it should be noted (but is frequently ignored) that whatever the truth of his claim to be the inventor of the telescope, Lipperhey can safely be hailed as the first person to make binoculars. That is a task so difficult that over the next two centuries, only a handful of instrument-builders even made the attempt. In fact, it was not until 1823 that the first commercially successful binoculars were produced in the form of opera glasses by Johann Friedrich Voigtländer in Vienna. And the modern binocular, which uses glass prisms to fold up the light path and correctly orientate the image, did not appear until 1894.

COMMON KNOWLEDGE

Hans Lipperhey's moment of glory as the sole inventor of the telescope lasted little more than two weeks. News of his wonderful device spread quickly through the provinces of the Netherlands, and evidently caused consternation in at least two Dutch households when it reached them.

On Friday 17 October, another letter arrived at The Hague, addressed to the States General. This time it was from an instrument-maker in Alkmaar in the northern part of Holland, a man named Jacob Adriaenszoon but more commonly known as Jacob Metius. He was a much more imposing character than the humble Lipperhey. His father, Adriaen, was a former burgomaster of Alkmaar, and his brother (another Adriaen) was a professor of mathematics and astronomy who had studied with none other than the great Tycho Brahe.

It is not clear from the record whether Metius brought the letter himself, but it seems likely that he did. In it, he testified that:

> he, the petitioner, having busied himself for a period of about two years, during the time left over from his principal occupation, with the investigation of some hidden knowledge which may have been attained by certain ancients through the use of glass, came to the discovery that by means of a certain instrument which he, the petitioner, was using for another purpose or intention, the sight of him who was using the same could be stretched out in such a manner that with it things could be seen very clearly which otherwise, because of the distance and remoteness of the places, could not be seen other than entirely obscurely and without recognition and clarity.

To cut a long story short, he had accidentally discovered the telescope. In similarly long-winded style, Metius went on to say that he had heard of the invention made by the spectacle-maker of Middelburg, that his own prototype instrument had been tested against that one, and that he too deserved a patent on the invention because of his own 'ingenuity, great labour and care (through God's blessings).'

Metius' petition was duly noted in the States General's minute book, with a comment that he would be granted modest funding and 'admonished to work further in order to bring his invention to greater perfection, at which time a decision will be made on his patent in the proper manner'. With hindsight, this seems rather generous of the States General. But hardly was the ink dry in their minute book when yet another claim turned up.

Written on 14 October, this was a letter from the same Councillors of Zeeland who had provided Lipperhey's original letter of recommendation. In Middelburg, they said, there were now others who knew the art of seeing far things and places as if nearby. In particular, there was a young man who had demonstrated a similar instrument to Lipperhey's. So what would the Honourable Gentlemen like them to do about him?

If there was any doubt left in the minds of the members of the States General that this invention was already too widely known to be patented, it must have been dispelled altogether by this news.

With those three players assembled on the stage of history, the scene was now set for the true details of the telescope's origin to sink without trace into a morass of conflicting contemporary records. Who first made a telescope? Lipperhey? Metius? Or the 'young man' of Middelburg? And who was this young rascal anyway?

In fact, 'rascal' is probably the most appropriate description. Since 1656, when his association with the first telescope was confirmed by the recollections of several locals who had known him, most scholars have taken him to be Sacharias Janssen, a spectacle-maker who would have been about 20 years old in 1608. But it was Cornelius de Waard, in the early twentieth century, who uncovered most of what we know about him. And it makes pretty interesting reading.

As well as following the family trade of spectacle-making, Sacharias also peddled his wares throughout Europe, and may possibly have been the same individual who was reportedly attempting to sell a telescope with a cracked lens at the Autumn Fair in Frankfurt in September 1608. But this Sacharias Janssen was also frequently on the wrong side of the law, with assault and non-payment of debt among the many items on his criminal record. Most serious were two accusations of forgery, for which he was eventually threatened with the death penalty. It seems that he had produced counterfeit Spanish coins in an admirably patriotic attempt to undermine the Spanish economy, but somehow had forgotten to stop when the Spanish and Dutch eventually signed a truce in 1609. Wisely, Sacharias had disappeared before the sentence could be carried out.

Other records show that the premises of the Janssen family business in Middelburg were just a few doors away from Hans Lipperhey's in the market square. Perhaps ideas had flowed from one to the other. Even more interesting, though, is the testimony of a man who claimed to be Janssen's son, one Johannes Sachariassen. In 1634, this Johannes boasted to a friend that his father, Sacharias, had invented the telescope. He had copied it as early as 1604 from one that belonged to an Italian, an instrument that had apparently carried the inscription 'anno 1[5]90'.

Albert Van Helden has presented a plausible scenario in which this mysterious instrument was one of the weak telescopic aids to vision that Giovanbaptista della Porta might have been describing in his *Natural Magick* of 1589. Middelburg is known to have hosted large numbers of Italian exiles, most of whom were deserters – mercenary soldiers tired of helping the Spanish in their attempt to subdue the United Provinces. Perhaps Janssen had indeed made a copy of an instrument brought from Italy, and had managed to improve it to the stage where it could provide useful magnification.

In any event, these accounts do suggest that Lipperhey might not, after all, have been the original inventor of the telescope, despite having been first off the mark in the historical record. Perhaps it was that proximity to Janssen's shop which gave him some understanding of what his fellow optician was up to. There is even a suggestion in some sources that Lipperhey's own children may have learned the secret of the telescope by holding up two lenses of the right kind, one behind the other – either by accident, or by having been shown.

CONSPIRACY THEORY

As we have seen, there is an enormous amount of roughly contemporary documentation on the origin of the telescope, dating from before 1608 to beyond the middle of the century. Much of it is confused and contradictory, and the problem lies in knowing how much weight to place on each item. In an article such as this, it is only possible to scratch the surface. However, the recent study by M. Barlow Pepin (see 'Further Reading') explores this material in very great detail, and arrives at a rather more subtle interpretation than is given above.

Yes, says Pepin, Janssen did indeed perfect the telescope on the basis of the device he had been shown by an Italian in 1604. Lipperhey's knowledge of how to build such an instrument, however, did not come merely from hanging around outside Janssen's shop doorway. It came, instead, from a much more intriguing source. Pepin cites an extraordinary passage in a book entitled *Telescopium, sive ars perficiendi* by one Girolamo Sirtori, published in 1618, but probably written some six years earlier when the events were still fresh in the author's memory. In it, we read that:

> a man as yet unknown, with the appearance of a Hollander, visited Johann Lippersein [*sic*] at Middelburg in Zeeland. This [Lipperhey] is a man of striking air and appearance, and a maker of spectacles; as no one else in that city: he [the visitor] ordered several lenses made, convex as well as concave. On the appointed day, the stranger returned, demanding the finished work. When he had them to hand, he picked up a pair; specifically a convex and a concave, placing one and then the other before his eye, separating them from one another, little by little as if to reach the focal point; after the manner of checking the spectacle-maker's handiwork. He then paid the artisan and left. The optician, who was not without inkling through all of this, began to do the same thing out of curiosity. He soon solved the problem which nature presented by fixing the spectacle lenses in a tube. As soon as he was finished, he hurried to the Palace of Prince Maurice and presented his invention. The prince already had a telescope, suspected that it might have military value, and of necessity had kept it a secret. But now that he found the concept had become known through chance, he dissembled, rewarding the industry and benevolence of the maker.

Pepin (from whose book the above translation is taken) goes to great lengths to identify the 'unknown man' mentioned in this passage. Remarkably, he finds evidence suggesting that it may have been an undercover emissary of the Spanish commander-in-chief, Marquis Spinola, perhaps looking for the raw material to duplicate an amazing far-seeing instrument that his enemy, Prince Maurice, already had.

This passage throws a different light on the idea that Prince Maurice hadn't seen a telescope until Lipperhey delivered one to him. We are explicitly told that he had one already (or, in an alternative translation of the same passage by Van Helden, *knew* of one already). So were there, in fact, two telescopes? Here again, Pepin cites other evidence, specifically the work of a French diarist of the era, Pierre de l'Estoile. This gentleman was a minor government official with a keen eye for detail in contemporary events. In a diary entry for 30 April 1609, he describes telescopes he had seen on sale in Paris, and adds, 'I have been told that the invention was due to a spectacle-maker of Middelburg in Zeeland, and that last year he presented to Prince Maurice two of them with which things that were three or four miles distant were seen clearly.'

This second mention of two telescopes lends weight to the idea. Of course, it's possible that de l'Estoile was simply misinformed, but what if he wasn't? Taking it at face value, it certainly supports the strange passage in Sirtori's book.

Pepin develops a scenario that accounts for this evidence rather neatly. Suppose the shady Sacharias Janssen had, indeed, spent four years developing the weakly magnifying device shown to him by an Italian, and had managed to make a telescope. Suppose he had presented his invention to Prince Maurice rather earlier in the peace negotiations with Spain, no doubt with an eye on a patent. Now imagine that it was *this* instrument that Maurice gloatingly showed to the Marquis Spinola, not Lipperhey's. That is consistent with the historical documentation but, significantly, it eliminates the need for all the action in the story to be compressed into the last two or three days of September, as in the 'conventional' account related above. This is an aspect of Pepin's theory that he finds particularly appealing.

Pursuing the idea further, what does Spinola now do? He knows the telescope came from Middelburg in Zeeland. Wishing to obtain one for his own forces before he leaves the Netherlands, he therefore instructs his undercover agent to go to Middelburg, hunt out the person who made it, and either buy one or buy the lenses to make one. But there is an unexpected problem. The itinerant Janssen is now on his way to the important Autumn Fair in Frankfurt, some 600 kilometres to the south. So, when the undercover agent looks for a spectacle-maker in Middelburg, whose shop does he find? The passage in Sirtori's *Telescopium, sive ars perficiendi* gives us the answer. And because Prince

Maurice didn't say 'Oh, I've got one of those already' when Lipperhey eventually turned up in The Hague to present his telescope to him, the official record accords priority in the invention to Lipperhey.

Pepin suggests that the reason for Maurice's secrecy is at least partly due to Janssen's shady character, the spectacle-maker much preferring clandestine dealings to anything open and above board. And, indeed, that might also have suited the delicacy of the diplomatic situation. But things came unstuck for Janssen when he arrived back in Middelburg after the two-week trip home from Frankfurt, and found that Lipperhey had somehow pre-empted his claim on the invention. Perhaps Janssen's wish to regain his priority without giving too much away explains why the second letter from the Zeeland Councillors to the States General speaks only of 'a young man', without mentioning any names.

ASTRONOMY'S AWAKENING

Whatever your view of this interpretation of the evidence – unbelievably far-fetched or entirely plausible – I hope you will agree with me that Pepin has performed a service to historians of the telescope by suggesting possibilities that are far from obvious. That, in itself, is a step forward.

For what it's worth, however, my own opinion is that this scenario is unlikely to have happened. I find it hard to believe that Prince Maurice would not have given some hint of the turn of events to the members of the States General, who (unless they were particularly disingenuous in their record-keeping) were completely unaware of the existence of the telescope until Lipperhey turned up. Moreover, the documentary evidence is hardly watertight, being based entirely on second-hand reports.

I suspect that we shall never know for certain who actually invented the telescope unless completely new evidence appears. An answer to the question of why it emerged so suddenly from obscurity – apparently in several places at once – is similarly elusive. But the necessary ingredients were all there: optical technology that had just developed to the stage where lenses of the required quality could be produced, a certain inevitability in the right combination of lenses being discovered once they were available, and the pressure of international crisis to draw the invention out of the hands of its makers and into the waiting grasp of politicians.

There are other snippets of evidence. We know, for example, that a handful of telescopes dating from the first thirty or so years of the seventeenth century and still in existence today used good-quality Venetian glass (intended for mirrors) as the raw material for their lenses. Perhaps it was a shipment of this glass to Holland that triggered the manufacture of the first Dutch telescopes in 1608.

There seems little doubt that several spectacle-makers knew the secret of the telescope in the early 1600s. While Metius's claim to originality appears to be genuine, his device may not have been the first. Alkmaar was relatively remote in northern Holland. On the other hand, Middelburg had a major glass factory of its own, the only one in Zeeland. That small Dutch town seems perhaps the more likely place for the first telescope to have seen the light of day.

As we have seen, it was Galileo who first turned the telescope into an engine of discovery for astronomy. But it would be wrong to imagine that he was the first person to point a telescope towards the sky. In a note written in October 1608, one of the foreign diplomats observing the peace process had said of Lipperhey's first telescope that 'even the stars, which ordinarily are invisible to our sight and our eyes, because of their smallness and the weakness of our sight, can be seen by means of this instrument'.

Someone, therefore, though we have no idea who, had noted the telescope's ability to enhance the eye's sensitivity to faint light very early in the piece, perhaps even during those last few days before Spinola's departure from The Hague at the end of September. Notwithstanding all the questions that still surround the telescope's debut on the world stage, there can be no doubt that this extraordinary month in the autumn of 1608 truly heralded astronomy's awakening.

POSTSCRIPT: SEPTEMBER 2008

In celebration of the four-hundredth birthday of the telescope, the author will lead a European tour of the principal sites of interest in the story, including Tycho Brahe's observatory on the Swedish island of Hven, Padua (where Galileo's first telescopic observations were made) and The Hague. A highlight of the tour will be a visit to the Binnenhof during the last week in September, exactly four centuries after Lipperhey's audience with Prince Maurice. Readers interested in joining the tour will find details at http://www.thriveaustralia.com.au/

FURTHER READING

Galilei, Galileo (1610), *Sidereus Nuncius* (*The Starry Messenger*), trans. Albert Van Helden, Chicago.

Pepin, M. Barlow (2004), *The Emergence of the Telescope: Janssen, Lipperhey and the Unknown Man*, revised edition, T Tauri Productions, Duncanville, Texas.

Ronan, Colin A. (1991), 'The origins of the reflecting telescope', *Jour. Brit. Astron. Assoc.*, vol. 101, no. 6, pp. 335–42. (Text of a BAA Presidential Address. The subject matter is the origin of the telescope, and I understand that the late Dr Ronan subsequently regretted the inclusion of the word 'reflecting' in the title.)

Van Helden, Albert (1977), 'The invention of the telescope', *Trans. Amer. Phil. Soc.*, vol. 67, part 4.

Watson, Fred (2004), *Stargazer: the Life and Times of the Telescope*, Da Capo Press, Cambridge, Mass.

Iapetus, Enceladus and Titan

DAVID M. HARLAND

While observing Saturn on the night of 25 March 1655, Christiaan
Huygens in The Hague discovered that the planet was accompanied by
a satellite, and over the next few weeks he determined that it had
an orbital period of 16 days. On 25 October 1671, Jean-Dominique
Cassini at the Paris Observatory found a second moon. To his surprise,
however, he was unable to see it again until mid December 1672, and
then it vanished until early February 1673. After further observations,
he realized that it had a period of 79 days and was visible only when
near western elongation. He was not able to see it east of Saturn
until he gained access to a more powerful telescope in September 1705.
At its brightest, at tenth magnitude, it was not much inferior to its
companion, but it faded by two magnitudes on the other side of its
orbit. Reasoning by analogy with the Moon, which keeps one hemisphere facing Earth, he speculated that this satellite was the same in this
regard, and that for some mysterious reason its leading hemisphere was
less reflective. On 28 August 1789, while William Herschel in England
was testing his new 48-inch-diameter reflector, he found another
satellite much closer in with a period of about 33 hours. Initially,
the satellites were referred to numerically in order of their discovery,
but in 1850 John Herschel named them Titan, Iapetus and Enceladus,
respectively. Titan is the only member of Saturn's retinue to show a
disc, and in 1908 the Catalan astronomer José Comas-Solá inferred
from what he took to be limb darkening that it must possess a
substantial atmosphere.

The first spacecraft to reach the Saturnian system was Pioneer 11 in
1979, whose imaging system showed Titan's disc to be featureless,
suggesting that its atmosphere was thick with either cloud or haze.
The trajectory of Voyager 1, which flew through the system in 1980,
was selected to provide a close look at Titan. It confirmed that the
moon is enshrouded by an aerosol haze of complex hydrocarbons, and
measured its diameter as 5,140 kilometres. By the time Voyager 2

passed through the system in 1982, we knew that Iapetus does indeed have a large dark patch covering most of its leading hemisphere, which the International Astronomical Union named Cassini Regio, but no detail could be seen within it; and that a large fraction of the surface of Enceladus is a smooth plain that looked as if it had been formed fairly recently, which raised the mystery of how an icy moon barely 500 kilometers in diameter could have undergone cryovolcanism.

On 1 July 2004, the Cassini spacecraft began a four-year tour in orbit of Saturn. This article reports its observations of these three moons and the *in situ* measurements by the Huygens probe that the spacecraft delivered to Titan.

IAPETUS

On 3 July 2004, Cassini imaged Iapetus from a range of 3 million kilometres, and provided our first view of detail on Cassini Regio, the dark area that dominates this moon's leading hemisphere, which appeared featureless in the Voyager imagery of the 1980s. The presence of major impact basins implied the surface dated to an early period of heavy bombardment. When Cassini flew within 1.1 million kilometres on 17 October it revealed a chain of 'white dots' on western Cassini Regio, seemingly individual mountain peaks rising to heights of 10 to 20 kilometres, contiguous with a dark linear feature that ran across the centre of Cassini Regio. On 31 December the spacecraft closed to within 123,400 kilometres and gained imagery at a resolution of 1 kilometre per pixel. The dark linear feature was seen not only to span the width of Cassini Regio but also – because it was visible on the limb – was seen to be a ridge (Figure 1). It was continuous, but in some parts was made up of individual mountains. It simply rose from the adjacent dark terrain without 'foothills'. Further study showed it to run precisely along the equator, and extend on to the bright terrain beyond Cassini Regio. An analysis of the Voyager imagery had revealed Iapetus not to be a precise sphere: although it could be described as a triaxial ellipsoid with dimensions of 1,534 × 1,484 × 1,426 kilometres, its shape was irregular. If the ridge was a compression structure created by the way the moon's interior shrank early on, this would be expected to form along the circumference of the widest diameter (as was the case), after which tidal effects would have first tipped the axis perpendicular

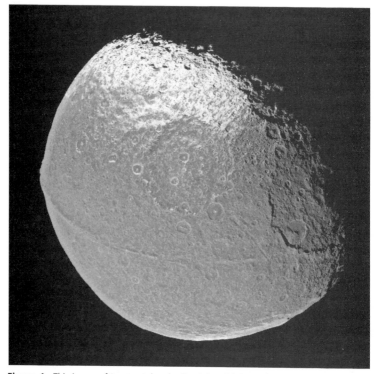

Figure 1. This image of Iapetus taken by Cassini on 31 December 2004 shows the ridge that extends across Cassini Regio. Also visible is a 120-km crater just within the rim of a 600-km impact basin, where a landslide has invaded the floor of the crater and exposed a 15-km-tall scarp. (Image PIA06166 courtesy of NASA, JPL and the Space Science Institute.)

to the orbital plane and then synchronized the rotation. The field of view included the northern polar region. Dark streaks on the bright terrain adjacent to Cassini Regio implied that the dark material had been delivered ballistically from a source centred on the leading hemisphere. But, of course, opinions differed as to whether this material was of endogenic or exogenic origin.

A study by the Arecibo radio telescope (Figure 2), at a wavelength of 12.6 centimetres, of the bright hemisphere in January 2002 and of the dark hemisphere in January 2003 gave the surprising result that the radar could not tell the two hemispheres apart. Although the bright side was known to be primarily water-ice, it appeared much less reflective at this wavelength than the icy satellites of Jupiter. A surface with ammonia mixed in would look like 'clean' ice optically, but would not reflect microwaves so well. The fact that Cassini Regio was indistinguishable to the radar implied that the dark material was merely a thin veneer over the ice. To preclude excavation of the bright substrate, this material must either have been applied very recently, or deposition must be ongoing and at a sufficient rate to cover up exposures. Although the summits of the peaks on western Cassini Regio were bright, they were exceptional. A massive landslide from the 15-kilometre-tall scarp on the rim of a 600-kilometre-diameter basin north of the ridge had spilled across much of the floor of a 120-kilometre crater within the basin and, despite the scale of the event, the exposed scarp was dark. The fact that Cassini Regio is laced with carbon dioxide (very likely a photochemical product trapped in either water-ice, a mineral or a complex organic solid) implied that the dark

Figure 2. The 1,000-ft dish of the Arecibo radio telescope on the island of Puerto Rico is the world's most powerful 'planetary radar'. (Image courtesy of the Arecibo Observatory: National Astronomy and Ionospheric Center, Cornell University and the National Science Foundation.

material had been swept up from space. A far-ultraviolet absorption feature for water-ice was strong for Phoebe (the outer moon suspected by some as being the source of the dark material on Iapetus) and the bright area of Iapetus, but extremely weak for Cassini Regio. Nevertheless, this did not rule out Phoebe as the source of the dark material, since the volatiles could have been liberated during emplacement, concentrating the non-ice material. As Phoebe appears to be a captured object that formed in the frigid outer Solar System, on being trapped in the warmer Saturnian environment it might have undergone a period of outgassing. If the dark material on Iapetus is indeed of exogenic origin, then it was deposited after the ridge had formed, after the moon had adopted its current spin axis, and after its rotation had become synchronized with its orbital period – a timescale that may shed light on when Phoebe was captured.

ENCELADUS

On 15 January 2005, Cassini imaged Enceladus at a range of 367,000 kilometres and showed the leading hemisphere (not viewed by Voyager) to be an extraordinary landscape of swirling curvilinear wrinkles, so establishing that on this moon it is not the smooth terrain that is atypical but the 30 per cent of the surface that is cratered. When the spacecraft passed within 1,264 kilometres on 17 February and imaged the southern part of the trailing hemisphere at a resolution of about 100 metres per pixel, it revealed the smooth terrain to bear faults, fractures, folds and troughs (Figure 3). Tracking by the Deep Space Network suggested the ratio of rock to ice in the interior was greater than thought, increasing the estimated density to 1.6 g/cm^3. The visual and infrared mapping spectrometer established the surface to be pure water-ice. The ultraviolet imaging spectrograph measured the texture of the surface by exploiting the fact that water-ice appears dark at wavelengths shorter than 160 namometres but bright in the range 160–190 nanometres, with the wavelength of this transition depending on the grain size; the results showed coarsely grained ice on the fractures and ridges, which was suggestive of fresh 'snow'. On flying by at 500 kilometres on 9 March, Cassini made a discovery – the moon had a tenuous envelope. During both close fly-bys, the dual-technique magnetometer found that Saturn's magnetic field was 'bent' around

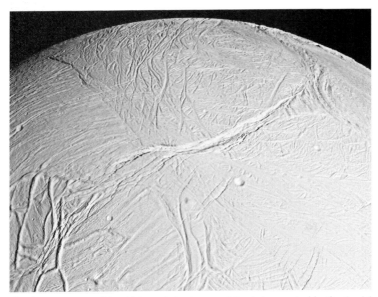

Figure 3. A mosaic of four high-resolution images of Enceladus acquired by the Cassini spacecraft on 17 February 2005, at distances ranging from 26,140 to 17,434 km. The view is about 300 km across and shows a myriad of faults, fractures, folds, troughs and craters, in addition to smoother, apparently resurfaced terrain. (Image PIA06191 courtesy of NASA, JPL and the Space Science Institute.)

the moon by electric currents generated by the interaction of the magnetosphere with neutral atoms of gas. In addition, when neutrals were ionized by plasma, they were 'picked up' by the magnetic field and caused oscillations at frequencies that enabled them to be identified as O^+, OH^+ and H_2O^+ ions – indicating the presence of water vapour. The moon's gravity is so weak that its escape velocity is a mere 212 metres per second. As gas would readily leak away, there would be a net motion away from the moon, which would make the envelope an exosphere rather than an atmosphere. The fact that the envelope persisted indicated that it was being replenished. The source could be outgassing from the interior through fractures in the icy crust, geysers or cryovolcanism. It was decided to lower the next fly-by from 1,000 to 175 kilometres to improve the sensitivity of the magnetospheric and plasma science instruments and directly sample the gaseous envelope.

When Cassini returned to Enceladus on 14 July 2005 the spacecraft penetrated the electrically conducting envelope, which the dual-technique magnetometer revealed to be concentrated at the south pole. The high-rate detector of the dust analyser noted a peak in the number of fine particles when the spacecraft was at an altitude of 460 kilometres, one minute prior to closest approach, which occurred 172 kilometres above latitude 23°S, longitude 325°W. The ion and neutral mass spectrometer measured a large peak in the abundance of water vapour 35 seconds prior to closest approach, just as the trajectory attained its most southerly latitude at an altitude of 270 kilometres. It was inferred that Cassini had passed through the periphery of the cloud. The variation of vapour density with altitude indicated there was a localized source on the surface. In fact, the process that issued water vapour and that which ejected particulates were aspects of the same phenomenon, which was similar to the venting that occurs on a comet.

The 'E' ring extends from the orbit of Mimas out beyond the orbit of Dione, but is concentrated near the orbit of Enceladus; the dust analyser established it to be made up of water-ice grains in the size range 0.3 to 2 micrometres. Terrestrial studies had shown that whereas the material in the 'F' and 'G' rings has a power–law distribution characteristic of débris from impacts, the 'E' ring material is uniform in size.

It had long been speculated that Enceladus was responsible for the 'E' ring, and this was now seen to be the case. But where was the source? The composite infrared spectrometer gave the clue. Enceladus has such a high albedo that it reflects most of the sunlight, making its surface the coldest in the Saturnian system. The temperature at the subsolar point was expected never to exceed 80 K. Even though the south pole was in continual sunlight, the oblique angle of illumination suggested that it ought to be significantly colder, but it was found to be the warmest place on the moon (Figure 4). The optical imagery showed the south polar region to be distinguished by several arcuate features dubbed 'tiger stripes' (Figure 5). Icy boulders up to 100 metres in size litter an area that is notable for lacking the otherwise ubiquitous finely grained frost. In fact, this area contains the largest exposures of coarsely grained ice fractures found anywhere on the moon. Parallel ridges and valleys appear to form a boundary around the south polar terrain that, judging from the absence of impact craters, is extremely young. Although the average temperature across the south polar area was just 85 K, it rose to 145 K in the 'tiger stripes'. When a reanalysis of imagery

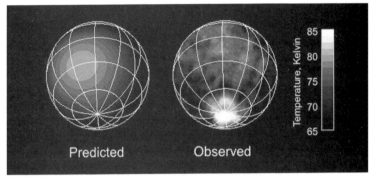

Figure 4. On 14 July 2005 Cassini's composite infrared spectrometer revealed the south pole of Enceladus to be anomalously warm. (Image PIA06432 courtesy of NASA, JPL and GSFC.)

taken on 16 January at a range of 209,000 kilometres showed the moon as a crescent with a glow around its south polar region, it was decided to perform further such observations, and imagery taken on 27 November 2005 showed jets from many sources issuing 500 kilometres into space. The hope had been that Cassini would find a geyser, but this was beyond all expectation! Evidently there was liquid water at shallow depth beneath the south pole, and the 'tiger stripes', running in parallel 40 kilometres apart for a distance of about 140 kilometres, were fractures through which the liquid made its way to the surface to vent into space, with the stream of vapour carrying with it particles of ice and liquid (Figure 6). An analysis of the jets and plumes indicated that most of the particles fell back.

Regarding the source of the heat driving this geyser activity, it has been suggested that Enceladus is squeezed and stretched by tidal force as it travels on its eccentric orbit around Saturn, with the mechanical energy being transformed to heat in the interior. Furthermore, as the orbits of the satellites evolve, resonances must produce periods of enhanced stress. If the ice had ammonia mixed in, this antifreeze would lower the melting point of water-ice by 100°C and reduce its density sufficiently to facilitate solid-state convection. The process of convection is the displacement of heat by the mechanical turnover of material. On an ice world such as Enceladus, buoyancy and pressure differentials can cause low-density material to rise vertically through zones of weakness in a denser overlying layer, forming a structure

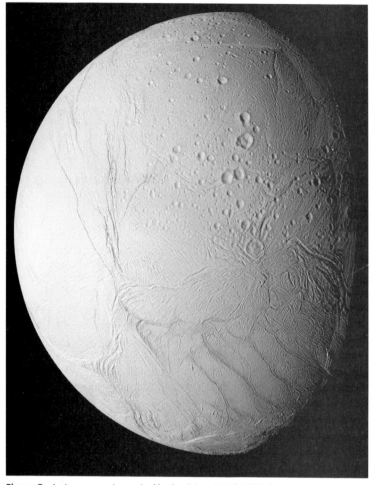

Figure 5. An image mosaic acquired by Cassini on 14 July 2005 showing the 'tiger stripes' in the south polar zone of Enceladus. (Image PIA06254 courtesy of NASA, JPL and the Space Science Institute.)

known as a diapir. As a diapir nears the surface it will give rise to a characteristic tectonism.

It is clear that although Enceladus has had a long history of activity, this is currently limited to the south polar region. Because a rotating body is more stable if its mass is close to its equator, any redistribution

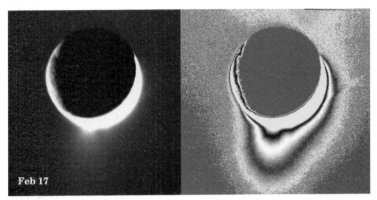

Figure 6. A long-range image of Enceladus taken by Cassini on 17 February 2005 showing a plume venting from its south polar region. On the right is a computer-processed version. (Image PIA07798 courtesy of NASA, JPL and the Space Science Institute.)

of mass within an object will prompt instability with respect to the axis of rotation. The development of a deeply seated 'hot spot' would therefore induce Enceladus to roll over to position this low-density region on its axis. Francis Nimmo of the University of California at Santa Cruz and Robert Pappalardo of the University of Colorado modelled two cases, one with the rising diapir in the icy shell and the other with it in the silicate core. If the diapir is in the icy shell, the shell must be sufficiently thick to maintain significant rigidity. If the diapir is located in the core, the fact that the core would have to be strongly coupled to the overlying ice to cause the moon to roll over meant there could be no global subsurface ocean. If diapiric convection is facilitated by the presence of ammonia in the water-ice, then this too ought to be being vented. Although none was detected, the fact that nitrogen was present in the cloud over the south pole (and indeed in the 'E' ring) indicated that the combination of solar ultraviolet and magnetospheric plasma was rapidly dissociating the ammonia. Observations by the magnetospheric imaging instrument showed that the venting varied significantly over a timescale of days. This explained an earlier observation by the ultraviolet imaging spectrograph. This instrument began to monitor Saturn in December 2003 to study its atmosphere, and in January 2004 it detected the presence of a cloud of atomic oxygen in the 'E' ring. The first hypothesis was that the collision of two yet-to-be-detected moonlets in this vicinity had released a 'puff' of water-ice that then dissociated into its constituent hydrogen and oxygen. It was belatedly realized that the source must have been an outburst from Enceladus.

TITAN

On 2 July 2004, Cassini flew within 339,120 kilometres of Titan and (being south of the plane of the Saturn system) was able to provide a 'first look' at the clouds clustered around the illuminated south pole, and one in the temperate zone at latitude 38°S. The haze scattered light so efficiently that the resolution was degraded, but a variety of linear, circular and curvilinear albedo features were seen in unprecedented detail. When Cassini returned on 26 October with a closest point of approach at an altitude of 1,174 kilometres, the 'detached layers' of haze were situated at a higher level than predicted, and this facilitated direct sampling. The ion and neutral mass spectrometer measured the $^{14}N/^{15}N$ and $^{12}C/^{13}C$ isotopic ratios. The nitrogen ratio indicated that as much as 75 per cent of the original nitrogen in the atmosphere may have leaked to space. As water-ice is an efficient carrier of primordial noble gases, their absence suggested the nitrogen in the atmosphere derived from the volatization of ammonia-ice by the heat of accretion, with the ammonia rapidly being dissociated by solar ultraviolet. This meant that the part of the nebula from which Titan formed was cool enough for ammonia-ice and methane-ice, but too warm for a nitrogen clathrate with trapped primordial noble gases. If the moon has an intrinsic magnetic field, this must be exceedingly weak.

The imagery highlighted a complex interplay of albedo on the surface (Figure 7). There were 'streaks' that were suggestive of the movement of (dark) material across the surface, and the fact that these were preferentially aligned to the prevailing zonal circulation implied wind-blown material. It had been thought that the organic particulates falling out of the haze would be sticky, but a recent study had suggested they would harden during their long descent and, being non-sticky, would pile up on the surface like fine dust. It had also been thought that the surface must be stagnant because the energy of insolation was too weak to drive winds in the lower atmosphere, but then it was realized that gravitational tides imposed by Saturn would create winds

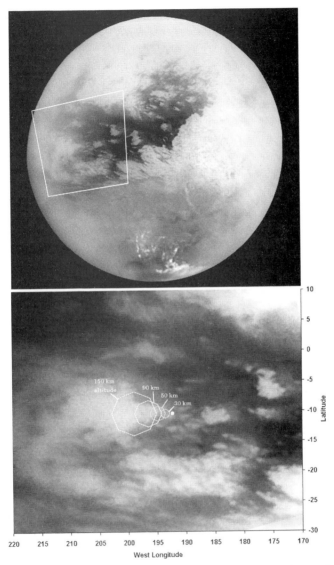

Figure 7. A full-disc mosaic of Titan taken by Cassini's imaging science subsystem during the fly-by of 26 October 2004, and a close-up of the target selected for the Huygens probe with outlines of the areas expected to be imaged at various altitudes. (Image PIA06141 (top) and PIA06173 (bottom) courtesy of NASA, JPL and the Space Science Institute.)

strong enough to blow material about. Imagery from the visual and near-infrared mapping spectrometer showed an infrared-bright circular feature at latitude 8°N and longitude 142°W that was 30 kilometres in diameter and seemed to be elevated, with a pair of elongate features extending to the west. In view of its appearance, it was dubbed 'the snail'. The dome might be a diapir that had broached the icy crust to produce surface flows. Cassini's synthetic-aperture radar imaged a 120-kilometre-wide swath running east–west for a distance of 4,500 kilometres, covering an area equivalent to a mere 1 per cent of the moon's surface at 300 metres per pixel. Statistically, 40 craters with diameters larger than 20 kilometres could have been expected in such an area, but none were visible. Because impacts must have occurred, the absence of craters implied that the surface was active. As in the infrared, there were features in the radar imagery that looked as if they might be of cryovolcanic origin – including one, 180 kilometres in diameter, which bore a similarity to the 'pancake' domes on Venus. The ion and neutral mass spectrometer found argon-40 in the upper atmosphere. This isotope derives mainly from the decay of potassium-40. As an indicator of the extent to which this gas must have leaked out of the core, it supported the case for cryovolcanism. Radar altimetry showed the range of elevation to be confined to 150 metres along a 400-kilometre-long track, and a mere 50 metres on the second half of this line. But since altimetry, radiometry and synthetic-aperture imaging could not be done simultaneously there was no indication of what this area 'looked' like in terms of albedo. One speculation was that if organic particulates were blown into low-lying areas to form level plains, there might be areas that looked like dry lake beds and yet which formed without the involvement of liquid.

Cassini's next fly-by was at an altitude of 1,192 kilometres on 13 December 2004, and it provided a final check of the upper atmosphere for the Huygens team, whose probe was released on 24 December to trace a ballistic arc leading to entry of Titan's atmosphere on 14 January 2005. It had been expected that the probe would emerge from the base of the optically thick haze at an altitude of 70 kilometres, but it did not do so until 45 kilometres and the view of the surface available to the descent imager and spectral radiometer remained murky until 30 kilometres. Sampling measured a constant ratio of methane to nitrogen in the stratosphere and upper troposphere, but at about 20 kilometres this ratio started to increase, and at 8 kilometres the methane reached saturation. At about 7 kilometres the wind speed decreased to a mild 1–2 metres per second and the direction became variable, suggesting that the probe had descended into a convective region in which the local winds were disconnected from the zonal jet stream. During the final phase of the descent, the downward-looking infrared spectrometer took reflectance spectra in order to determine the composition of the surface in the vicinity of the landing point, and at an altitude of 700 metres the probe switched on a 20-watt lamp to 'fill in' the wavelengths lost as sunlight passed through the atmosphere. With the lamp on, the imager's view resembled that of a car shining its headlamps into fog. This suggested there was a drizzle of fine droplets of liquid methane.

As was always the hope, Huygens came down over a boundary between the light and dark areas. The imagery appeared to show a network of dark drainage channels on a bright area leading to a shore-line, with several offshore islands on the dark area. The wind seemed to have carried the probe out over the dark area. The ground-level view showed a solid surface littered with 'rocks'. Since the camera was very close to the ground, the sense of perspective was deceptive: the rocks were not the boulders they appeared; they were actually only a few centimetres in size, the nearest no more than 1 metre away, and they were assuredly not silicate rock but lumps of water-ice (Figure 8). The fact that they were rounded, and sitting exposed on top of darker, finely grained material, suggested they were erosional products washed down the drainage channels on to the plain. The Surface Science Package's data indicated the probe impacted the surface at 4.5 metres per second, with a 15-g deceleration over an interval of some 40 milliseconds. A full analysis concluded that the penetrometer that projected from the base of the probe had struck a pebble and nudged it aside, then readily penetrated a surface that was neither hard like solid ice nor readily compressible like a blanket of fluffy aerosols; it was a 'soft' surface, plausible candidates for which were: (1) a solid granular material with little or no cohesion; (2) a 'mud' of ice grains from impact or fluvial erosion wetted by liquid methane; and (3) a 'tar' of fine-grained ice and photochemical products. The probe had slipped along the surface for several seconds prior to coming to a halt tilted at an angle of 10° with its base dug in about 10 centimetres. The fact that Huygens operated on the surface for over an hour gave a welcome bonus. The measured surface temperature was 93.65 K (±0.25). The lamp for the

Figure 8. A composite view from the descent imager and spectral radiometer of the Huygens probe on the surface of Titan on 14 January 2005, with a computer-processed view of an Apollo astronaut on the Moon to provide a sense of perspective. (Image PIA08115 courtesy of ESA, NASA, JPL and the University of Arizona.)

spectrometer remained illuminated, and would have provided a source of heat. In addition, the inlet of the gas chromatograph mass spectrometer on the base of the probe was held at +90°C, making Huygens by far the warmest object on Titan. There was a significant increase in the methane fraction several minutes after landing, suggesting that heat from the probe was boiling volatiles out of the ground. The lens of the downward-looking imager was embedded, but the repeating views of the oblique and side-looking imagers gave hints that the probe was causing material to splutter across the ground. The implication was that occasional methane rainfall drained from the elevated terrain on to the low-lying ground, where it rapidly soaked into the porous material, which then served as a reservoir for slow evaporation. The volatiles that the gas chromatograph mass spectrometer detected after landing were rich in organics that had not been noted during the descent. Although the signal was dominated by methane, there was ethane and a possibility of benzene and cyanogen (both products of methane and nitrogen chemistry) and carbon dioxide, all of which were indicative of a complex chemistry in the surface material.

On its return on 15 February 2005, Cassini's radar-imaging track showed an 80-kilometre circular feature that was clearly an impact crater surrounded by a blanket of ejecta. However, without direct altimetry it was not possible to know whether it was still a relief feature or had been reduced to a palimpsest. In addition, there was a 450-kilometre-diameter feature that appeared to be a multiple-ringed basin. A radar-bright channel system ran across its south-western 'rim'. Most intriguing, however, were groups of dark, linear features spaced a few kilometres apart that extended for hundreds of kilometres. These 'cat scratches' gave the impression of being dunes of wind-blown material. The composite infrared spectrometer studied circulation in the upper atmosphere. At mid to high northern latitudes the zonal wind inhibited mixing and created an isolated vortex around the pole. Being in continual darkness, the cold stratosphere in this area was sinking, drawing down and concentrating the organics that were manufactured in the outer haze.

During its fly-by on 16 April 2005 Cassini made coordinated observations of a bright arcuate feature at latitude 85°W, longitude 30°S, dubbed 'the smile' due to its shape. The visual and infrared mapping spectrometer showed a bright patch in this vicinity in the 5-micron band, bounded to the south by the arc. Since this wavelength tends to represent thermal emission and this was the brightest point on the moon, it prompted speculation that it represented a 'hot spot' marking a recent impact or cryovolcanic eruption. But when microwave radiometry showed no temperature difference with the adjacent terrain, this ruled out current volcanism. A fairly distant fly-by on 6 June 2005 revealed an oval patch 230 kilometres in length and 70 kilometres in width near the south pole that was darker than anything else in the vicinity and, since there was long-term cloud activity in the south polar region, it was optimistically named Lake Ontario. On the next close fly-by, on 22 August 2005, the radar track showed a pattern of embayments and channels in another area that was suggestive of a shoreline. On 28 October 2005 the radar imaged a large field of dark dunes – the individual structures were 100 metres tall and ran for hundreds of kilometres, with the field stretching 1,000 kilometres along the equatorial zone. It was now realized that the 'cat scratches' seen earlier were smaller examples. Calculations suggested that the variable tidal wind combined with the west-to-east zonal wind to produce surface winds that could readily bounce grains of hydrocarbon haze fallout along the ground in a process called saltation. The result would be a sinuous pattern of longitudinal dunes (Figure 9) aligned with the prevailing wind flow, except where the local wind direction was controlled by elevated terrain. Over time, this process might well trans-

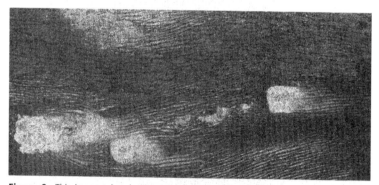

Figure 9. This image taken by Cassini's synthetic-aperture radar on 7 September 2006 shows a region on Titan covered with dark, longitudinal dunes. They are almost certainly made of wind-blown particulate fallout from the hydrocarbon haze. The individual dunes are spaced several kilometres apart, run for hundreds of kilometres, and sweep around the brighter, presumably elevated features. (Image PIA08738 courtesy of NASA and JPL.)

Figure 10. When Cassini's synthetic-aperture radar was finally able to inspect the high northern latitudes of Titan on 22 July 2006 it found unambiguous evidence of lakes of liquid hydrocarbons. (Image PIA09102 courtesy of NASA, JPL and USGS.)

fer material from mid latitudes into the equatorial zone. The presence of dunes also implied an absence of persistent liquids on the surface in the equatorial zone, as liquid would serve as sand traps.

Cassini's search for clear evidence of liquid on the surface of Titan was rewarded on 22 July 2006, when its ground track ran over the northern region that had been in continual darkness since before Cassini's arrival in the system, and the radar imaged dozens of well-defined dark patches up to 1 kilometre in size, some that were tens of kilometres, and one at 100 kilometres (Figures 10 and 11). These were the darkest features yet observed, and dark to radar was usually

Figure 11. On 12 May 2007, the Cassini spacecraft completed its 31st flyby of Saturn's moon Titan. The radar instrument obtained this image showing the coastline and numerous island groups of a portion of a large sea. The liquid, most likely a combination of methane and ethane, appears very dark to the radar instrument. What is striking about this portion of the sea compared to other liquid bodies on Titan is the relative absence of brighter regions within it, suggesting that the depth of the liquid here exceeds tens of metres. (Image PIA09211 courtesy of NASA, JPL.)

either a smooth surface or a radar-absorbing substance – and liquid hydrocarbon would be both. Furthermore, there were channels leading into or out from some patches, with characteristics consistent with their having been created by flowing liquid. On 23 September 2006 fly-by the visual and infrared mapping spectrometer discovered a vast tropospheric cloud occupying the observed range of longitudes (10° to 190°W) and latitudes (51° to 68°N) that appeared to be composed of ethane, apparently the result of the concentration of organic haze in the descending north polar vortex (Figure 12). Ethane raining into lakes of methane would dissolve. If the temperature dipped low enough, ethane would undoubtedly fall as snow, and possibly even form an ice cap. The localization of methane and ethane at the winter pole implied a seasonal cycle in which the volatile hydrocarbons migrated from pole to pole during a local year (lasting 29.5 terrestrial years) and this, in turn, offered an explanation for the current concentration of clouds at the south pole and the absence of liquid on the surface at lower latitudes. If Cassini's mission is able to be extended, it should be possible to observe the onset of the northern summer, with storms forming in the tropics as the volatiles travel south, perhaps temporarily submerging the now inert Huygens probe on the floor of a lake of rainfall run-off.

FURTHER READING

David M. Harland (2007), *Cassini at Saturn: Huygens Results*, Springer–Praxis.

Ralph Lorenz and Jacqueline Mitton (2007), *Titan Unveiled*, Princeton University Press.

Figure 12. On 29 December 2006 Cassini's visible and infrared mapping spectrometer imaged a vast cloud centred over Titan's north (winter) polar region. The hydrocarbon rainfall is almost certainly responsible for the liquid in the lakes in this area. (Image PIA09171 courtesy of NASA, JPL and the University of Arizona.)

Dark Energy and the Accelerating Universe

IAIN NICOLSON

During the 1990s, two independent research teams – the Supernova Cosmology Project and the High-z Supernova Search – both embarked on programmes to detect and study type Ia supernovae in remote (high red shift) galaxies. The results of their endeavours turned our understanding of the Universe on its head.

A type Ia supernova is a spectacular cosmic conflagration that is believed to occur when a white dwarf star drags enough additional matter from a nearby companion to push its mass beyond the

---

Cosmological Red Shift

The red shift of a receding galaxy is a measure of the amount by which lines in its spectrum are displaced from their 'rest wavelengths' (the wavelengths those lines would have if the galaxy were at rest, relative to us). In cosmological terms, red shift is directly related to the amount by which the universe has expanded during the time that it has taken for light to travel from its source to the Earth. Where the symbol z denotes the measured red shift of a particular galaxy, the ratio of the scale of the Universe at the time when light was emitted to its scale when that light was received is given by $1/(1+z)$, so that, for example, light from a galaxy with a measured red shift of 0.5 (which means that the wavelengths of the lines in its spectrum are 50 per cent greater than would be the case if the galaxy were at rest rather than receding from us) set out on its journey across the void when the Universe was $1/(1+0.5) = 1/1.5 = ^2/_3$ of its present size. Similarly, a galaxy at red shift 1 ($z = 1$) is seen as it was when the Universe was half its present size, a galaxy at red shift 2 is seen as it was when the Universe was one-third of its present size, and so on.

maximum that a star of this kind can support. The result is a violent detonation that blows the white dwarf completely to pieces. Supernovae of this particular kind are all remarkably similar to each other and reach closely similar peak brilliancies (about 4 billion times the luminosity of the Sun). Accordingly, they make especially good 'standard candles' for measuring the distances of the galaxies within which they are embedded (the fainter the supernova, the more distant its host galaxy). The aim of the teams' research programmes was to determine the 'expansion history' of the universe – in effect, to measure how its rate of expansion had changed over time – by measuring the apparent brightness and red shifts of remote supernovae (and/or the red shifts of the galaxies within which they were embedded) and comparing their observational data with theoretical model universes to see which gave the best match.

THE ACCELERATING UNIVERSE

Until the late 1990s, most (but not all) cosmologists had assumed that gravity would be slowing the rate of cosmic expansion. If the expansion were decelerating, the Universe would have been expanding faster in the past than it is now, and galaxies would have taken less time to reach their present distances than would have been the case had the universe been expanding at a steady, unchanging rate (the so-called 'coasting' Universe). Consequently, for example, light from a supernova in a galaxy at red shift 0.5 (which exploded when the Universe was two-thirds its present scale) would have taken less time to reach us, and would have travelled a shorter distance, than would have been the case had that light been emitted from a supernova at red shift 0.5 in a coasting Universe. The supernova would be nearer to us, and therefore would appear brighter, than a supernova at the same red shift in a coasting Universe. In a decelerating Universe, distant supernovae should appear fainter than would be the case in a coasting Universe (the more distant the supernova, and the higher its red shift, the greater the discrepancy would be).

In 1998, both teams arrived, independently, at a truly startling conclusion. Rather than being *brighter* than would have been the case in a coasting Universe, remote supernovae were systematically *fainter*, and hence further away. This implied that the expansion of the

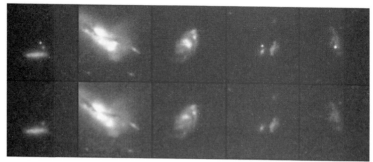

Figure 1. Five distant supernovae and their host galaxies, imaged by the Hubble space telescope. The supernovae can be seen within their host galaxies in the top row of images. The bottom row shows the galaxies before or after the stars exploded. These particular supernovae exploded between 3.5 and 10 billion years ago. (Image courtesy of NASA, ESA and A. Riess (STScI).)

Universe must be *accelerating* rather than decelerating. Subsequently, as more and more supernovae were detected at progressively higher red shifts, and the quality of the data improved, it became more and more apparent that distant supernovae are indeed systematically fainter than would be expected in a coasting or decelerating Universe, and the case for cosmic acceleration became ever stronger.

Because the implications of such a discovery were so profound, cosmologists had to make sure that there was not some other effect, or effects, that could cause distant supernovae to appear fainter than expected, thereby fooling astronomers into thinking that cosmic expansion is accelerating. For example, might the properties and peak luminosities of supernovae in the distant past – billions of years ago – have been subtly different from those of present-day supernovae? If type Ia supernovae had been inherently less luminous in the past, that of itself would cause remote supernovae to appear systematically fainter than expected. Another possibility was that intergalactic space might be permeated by tiny grains of 'dust' that would scatter and absorb light from distant galaxies and supernovae, causing them to appear fainter than they otherwise would do. Ordinary interstellar dust, which is found within galaxies such as our own, attenuates different colours and wavelengths of light by differing amounts, and if intergalactic space were permeated by dust of this kind, its effects would readily be measurable. But if, instead, the space between galaxy clusters contained a tenuous distribution of so-called 'grey dust', which attenuated all wavelengths equally, that would have the effect of making supernovae progressively dimmer at progressively higher red shifts.

In the decade that has elapsed since observational evidence for accelerating expansion first emerged, observers have failed to find any evidence for systematic evolutionary changes in the properties of type Ia supernovae that could significantly undermine their status as good 'standard candles'. Nor has any evidence for the existence of grey dust emerged; indeed, it is difficult to see how dust of this kind could have been formed, in the quantities that would be needed, in the first place.

Arguably the most decisive way to distinguish between genuine acceleration and alternative systematic effects is to measure how the peak brightness of supernovae deviates from what would be expected in a coasting or decelerating Universe at progressively higher red shifts. If – as all the evidence suggests – the Universe began in a hot Big Bang then, for much of its early history, the mean density of matter would have been much greater than it is now; gravity would have had the upper hand, and the expansion would have been decelerating. Beyond a certain particular red shift, which corresponds to the time in cosmic history when early deceleration gave way to later acceleration, the difference in brightness between supernovae in the real Universe and supernovae in a hypothetical coasting Universe should begin to diminish. Indeed, at sufficiently high red shifts supernovae should, in principle, appear to be *brighter* than would be the case in a coasting Universe.

The first strong hint that the anticipated 'turnover' was indeed present came in 2001 when a team headed by Adam Riess, of the Space Telescope Science Institute, worked out the red shift of a supernova (SN1997ff) that had been discovered in Hubble space telescope images taken in 1997, and found it to be 1.7. This was, and remains, the highest-red-shift supernova ever seen. The observational evidence, though not absolutely conclusive, suggested SN1997ff was a type Ia supernova, and its apparent brightness turned out to be markedly brighter (about 50 per cent, though with a considerable margin of error) than would be the case in a coasting Universe, and about 250 per cent brighter than would be expected if grey dust or evolution were affecting its apparent brightness.

By 2004, Riess and his colleagues had discovered sixteen new

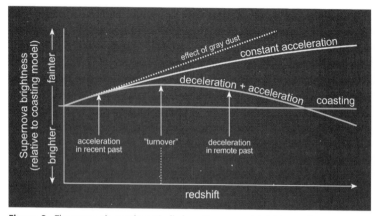

Figure 2. The curves show schematically how the apparent brightness of supernovae at different red shifts would differ from the brightness of supernovae in a coasting Universe (one that expands at a steady rate) if the Universe were continuously accelerating, had switched from early deceleration to recent acceleration, or if grey dust were causing them to appear fainter. (Image reproduced from *Dark Side of the Universe*, by Iain Nicolson, 2007, courtesy of Canopus Books.)

supernovae, six of which had red shifts in excess of 1.25, and were able convincingly to show that all of these remote supernovae were distinctly brighter than would be the case if grey dust or supernova evolution were markedly affecting their brightness. By combining the new results with data on 170 lower-red-shift supernovae, they found compelling influence for early deceleration and later acceleration, and showed that the turnover occurred at a red shift of about 0.46, which corresponds to the epoch when the Universe was about two-thirds of its present scale. These results imply that the switch from deceleration to acceleration must have occurred about 5–6 billion years ago, a conclusion that has been amply confirmed by subsequent observational data.

DARK ENERGY ENTERS THE FRAY

Studies of remote supernovae, the cosmic microwave background (relic radiation from the Big Bang), the evolution of large-scale structure in the Universe as revealed by analyses of the distribution of visible galaxies, gas clouds and dark matter at progressively higher red shifts, together with a wide range of other techniques, have led most cosmologists to the following conclusions about the Universe in which we live: All but a small fraction of the matter that the Universe contains is dark – it emits no detectable amounts of radiation. Ordinary matter (the stuff of which atoms, stars, planets and people are composed, and which is called 'baryonic matter') makes up about one-sixth of the total matter content of the cosmos; the rest appears to be so-called 'cold dark matter', which is thought to consist of relatively slow-moving (hence 'cold') elementary particles that scarcely ever interact with ordinary matter, radiation, or even with themselves, except through the agency of gravity. But matter in all its forms (luminous or dark, baryonic or non-baryonic) comprises less than 30 per cent of the total mass–energy content of the Universe. The remainder (more than 70 per cent) is made up of 'something else' – an extra ingredient that exerts the repulsive influence that, some 5–6 billion years ago, overwhelmed the attractive influence of gravity and propelled the Universe into its current phase of accelerating expansion. The mysterious extra ingredient has come to be known as *dark energy*.

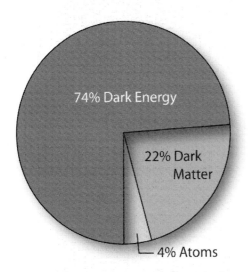

Figure 3. Content of the Universe: the relative proportions of ordinary atomic (baryonic) matter, non-baryonic dark matter, and dark energy as deduced from data obtained by the WMAP spacecraft. (Image courtesy of the NASA/WMAP Science Team.)

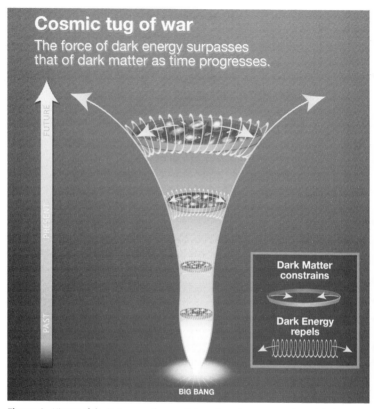

Figure 4. History of the Universe – the cosmic tug of war between gravity and dark energy. (Image courtesy of NASA, ESA and A. Feild (STScI).)

What can this peculiar commodity be? The first candidate that sprang immediately to the minds of theoreticians was the cosmological constant, a quantity that Einstein introduced in 1917 when he was attempting to apply his newly developed general theory of relativity to the Universe as a whole. At that time (a decade before Edwin Hubble had discovered that the galaxies are receding and the Universe is expanding) it was widely believed that the Universe was static – that the galaxies (in today's parlance) were neither approaching nor receding. To prevent galaxies from falling together, Einstein introduced an extra (mathematically legitimate) term into his equations, which allowed space to be curved even in the absence of matter or radiation.

This extra term incorporated a constant, known as the cosmological constant. If the constant were positive (greater than zero), the cosmological term would act as a form of 'cosmic repulsion', a repulsive influence that opposed gravity; a negative value would correspond to an additional attractive influence. By choosing a particular, critical, value of the cosmological constant, Einstein was able to ensure that, at large distances, the effects of gravity and cosmic repulsion would cancel out, so that the Universe would be held in a state of uneasy balance – neither contracting (under the influence of gravity) nor expanding (under the influence of cosmic repulsion).

In the early 1930s, following Hubble's discovery of the recession of the galaxies and what is now known as the Hubble Law, Einstein abandoned the cosmological constant and is said subsequently to have dubbed it 'my greatest blunder' because, had he not introduced it, his equations would have predicted the expansion (or contraction) of the Universe well before observational astronomers discovered this to be so, and would have added yet another triumphant prediction to his prodigious tally.

The discovery of the accelerating expansion of the Universe thrust the cosmological constant back to centre stage. It became the prime suspect for the dark energy component that is driving the acceleration. The modern concept of the cosmological constant, though mathematically equivalent, is different in nature from the constant as envisaged by Einstein. According to quantum mechanical theory, even a pure vacuum (what we think of as 'empty' space) possesses a certain minimum density of energy, called 'vacuum energy', that remains constant at all times – even in a Universe that is expanding. In its modern incarnation the cosmological constant is identified with vacuum energy.

There are, however, two perplexing problems that are associated with the cosmological constant. Firstly, its energy density is about 10^{120} (i.e. 1 followed by 120 zeros) times smaller than elementary quantum calculations suggest it ought to be. This is a *big* discrepancy! The amount of fine-tuning that is required to ensure that the value of the cosmological constant be so small is quite extraordinary. The initial conditions of the Universe somehow had to ensure that the energy density associated with the cosmological constant was utterly microscopic compared with the initial energy densities associated with matter and radiation (both of which would decline rapidly as the

Universe continued to expand). The question of why the cosmological constant is so small and so precisely adjusted is known as the fine-tuning problem. Equally intractable is the so-called 'coincidence problem'. Why are the energy densities of matter and dark energy so closely similar (equal within a factor of three) at this particular time, and why should dark energy have become dominant just a few billion years ago? Had the (constant) vacuum energy density been higher, it would have become dominant long ago, perhaps blasting the Universe apart so rapidly that structures such as galaxies, stars and planets might never have formed. Had it been feebler, its effects would not have become apparent yet, and we would be unaware of the existence of dark energy.

In an attempt to deal with these conundrums, in 1998 a number of theoreticians (notably Paul J. Steinhardt, Rahul Dave and Robert J. Caldwell) began to investigate types of dark energy that could vary with time (and perhaps from place to place); these have come to be known as quintessence. At the time of the Big Bang, the initial energy density of quintessence could have been more closely similar to the initial energy densities of matter and radiation, but thereafter it either declined more slowly than the densities of matter and radiation, or underwent an abrupt change in its rate of decline, so that eventually it became the dominant constituent of the Universe.

By removing the need for the density of dark energy to be fixed at an extraordinarily low value at the time of the Big Bang (as would be the case with the cosmological constant) and instead allowing it to evolve from a wide range of possible initial values, quintessence to a large extent can circumvent the fine-tuning problem, but some degree of fine-tuning is still needed to ensure that dark energy becomes dominant at the 'right' time in the history of the cosmos.

But whereas the cosmological constant and quintessence are the most favoured candidates, many other alternatives have been mooted. A particularly alarming possibility, first suggested in 2003 by Robert R. Caldwell, Marc Kamionkowski and Nevin N. Weinberg, is that, instead of remaining constant (as in the case of the cosmological constant) or declining (quintessence), the energy density and repulsive influence of dark energy may *increase* as the Universe continues to expand. In that case, the repulsive effect of dark energy would become infinite at a finite time in the future. Dark energy of this kind is called 'phantom energy'. With phantom energy in control, clusters of galaxies, then

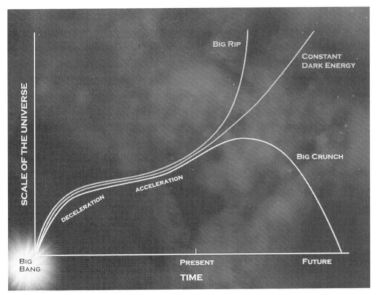

Figure 5. Three possible futures for the dark-energy Universe: eternal accelerating expansion (the Big Chill), Big Rip and Big Crunch. (Image courtesy of NASA/CXC/M.Weiss.)

galaxies themselves, would be torn apart at some time in the not too distant future. Later on, planets would be ripped away from their parent stars, stars and planets themselves would be shredded, molecules severed, atoms pulled apart and elementary particles destroyed in a final, catastrophic, 'Big Rip'.

Another alternative is that dark energy eventually may dwindle to zero (in which case, the evolution of the Universe will once again become dominated by the feeble gravitational influence of matter, and it will revert to expanding at a gently decelerating rate), or it may change sign so as to become negative. If that were to come about, dark energy would become, like gravity, attractive rather than repulsive; with dark energy and gravity 'pulling together', the expansion would come to an end and the Universe thereafter would collapse rather rapidly into a terminal 'Big Crunch'.

A PLETHORA OF THEORIES

But there are other possibilities, too. Perhaps the present-day vacuum is not in its lowest possible energy state. If so, the current phase of acceleration may be taking place because the Universe is undergoing a slow transition from a higher energy state to a lower one, and the acceleration will come to an end once that transition has been completed. There is a parallel here with what happened during the inflationary era – the short-lived, but spectacular, bout of accelerating expansion that, many cosmologists contend, occurred some 10^{-35} seconds after the beginning of time when the Universe made a transition from a higher energy state (called the 'false vacuum') to a lower one (the 'true' vacuum). The end of this transition was marked by the creation of elementary particles and a reversion to decelerating expansion. As with inflation, the end of the current era of acceleration may be marked by the formation of new kinds of particles and structures in the cosmos.

Or perhaps the Universe may undergo a series of alternating bouts of acceleration and deceleration, of which early inflation and the present phase are but two. One suggestion is that dark-energy density tracks, but oscillates above and below, the dominant background mass–energy density (radiation, matter, or whatever); in which case, acceleration occurs when dark energy exceeds the ambient background, and deceleration occurs when dark energy declines below the background. Or it may be that the Universe contains many different quantum fields, each (or some) of which becomes dominant for short periods at different times. In either case, the current phase of acceleration would be temporary and would, eventually, come to an end.

Other theoreticians have raised the possibility that dark matter and dark energy may simply be two sides of the same coin. Models of this kind are often discussed in the context of a 'Chaplygin gas', a type of 'fluid', which is assumed to fill the whole of space and which has the distinctive property that the lower the density, the greater the negative (repulsive) pressure. This allows it to mimic the behaviour of cold dark matter early in the history of the Universe (when the density was high) and to behave like repulsive dark energy later on (when the density is low).

PINNING DOWN THE PROPERTIES OF DARK ENERGY

These are just some of the plethora of current ideas about the possible nature of dark energy. Of these, the front-runners are the cosmological constant and quintessence, with phantom energy snapping at the heels of these two. In order to distinguish between these and other contenders, observational cosmologists are focusing their attention on trying to measure a quantity called the dark energy 'equation of state', which, in essence, is the ratio of the pressure of dark energy to its density; it is denoted by the symbol w. In the case of the cosmological constant, the value of w is precisely -1; for quintessence, w takes values between -1 and $-\frac{1}{3}$; and, for phantom energy, the value of w is less than (i.e. more negative than) -1. In the case of the cosmological constant, the value of w is constant (always equal to -1), but if dark energy is quintessence or phantom energy, the value of w may or may not remain constant.

Clearly, the tussle between the opposing influences of dark energy and gravity will have determined the rate of expansion at different times in cosmic history. Likewise, the repulsive influence of dark energy would to some extent have slowed the rate at which matter fell together to form galaxies, clusters and their precursors, and that should reveal itself in studies of the way luminous and dark matter was distributed, and the degree to which it had clumped together, at different times in the past. Because different types of dark energy affect the rate of cosmic expansion and the growth of structure in different ways, cosmologists hope to be able to pin down the properties of dark energy, and the value of w, through detailed, high-quality measurements of this kind.

Central to cosmologists' efforts to chart out the expansion history of the Universe is the task of measuring the distances of remote galaxies at different red shifts, either with the aid of standard candles (objects of known luminosity, the observed brightness of which depends on their distance), or 'standard rulers' (objects of known physical size, the apparent size of which depends on their distance). While type Ia supernovae remain the pre-eminent standard candle in the astronomer's armoury, a lot of interest has been aroused recently by a potentially very promising standard ruler called baryon acoustic oscillations

(BAO) – fossilized imprints of sound waves that propagated through the early mix of radiation and matter in the primeval fireball, which became 'frozen in' to the tapestry of warmer and cooler patches that cosmologists have detected in the cosmic microwave background, and which then formed subtle large-scale patterns in the distribution of galaxies. Because the expected physical size of these features can be calculated from well-established theory, astronomers can use them as standard rulers, provided that they can actually detect and measure their very subtle imprint in the distribution of matter. This was achieved for the first time in 2005 by teams of astronomers using data from the two largest galaxy distribution surveys so far undertaken – the ongoing Sloan Digital Sky Survey (SDSS) and the Two-degree Field Galaxy Redshift Survey (2dFGRS).

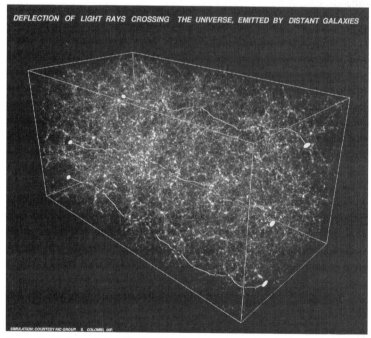

DEFLECTION OF LIGHT RAYS CROSSING THE UNIVERSE, EMITTED BY DISTANT GALAXIES

SIMULATION: COURTESY NIC GROUP. S. COLOMBI, IAP.

Figure 6. Weak gravitational lensing. This simulation shows the distribution of dark matter in a large volume of the Universe, and the deflections experienced by rays of light travelling from left to right through this region. The cumulative effect is to generate small distortions in the apparent shapes of galaxies. (Image courtesy of S. Colombi (IAP)/ CFHT.)

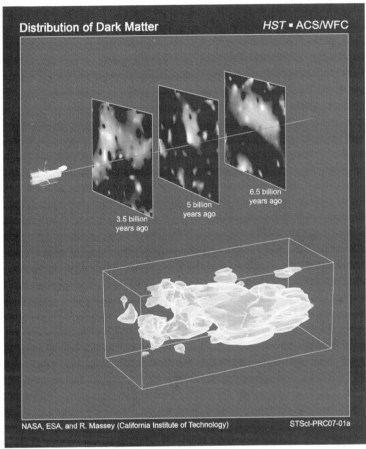

Figure 7. A three-dimensional map of the distribution of dark matter in the Universe based on observations made with the Hubble Space Telescope as part of the Cosmic Evolution Survey. *Top*: Three slices through the evolving distribution of matter. *Bottom*: A three-dimensional map of dark matter made by combining the slices; distance from the Earth increases from left to right. The clumping of dark matter becomes more pronounced from the early Universe (right) to the more recent Universe (left). (Image courtesy of NASA, ESA and R. Massey (California Institute of Technology).)

In order to chart the growth of structure in the Universe, astronomers ideally would like to map out the distribution of matter as a whole (dark matter as well as luminous matter) at different times in cosmic history. The most promising way of attaining this goal is 'weak' gravitational lensing – a technique that measures subtle statistical distortions (called 'cosmic shear') in the shapes of remote galaxies. These distortions are caused by the cumulative effect of the various deflections that rays of light experience as they pass by and through the various clumps of luminous and dark matter that lie between those galaxies and Earth-based observers. Although studies of this kind are still in their infancy, impressive maps of the evolving distribution of dark and luminous matter, measured at a number of different red shift 'slices', have already been obtained by the Cosmic Evolution Survey (COSMOS).

Looking ahead to the next decade, astronomers are developing, or have proposed, a range of ambitious ground-based and space-based projects to tackle the dark-energy problem head on. At ground level, one of the most promising projects is the Large Synoptic Survey Telescope (LSST). With an 8.4-metre primary mirror and 4-metre secondary, feeding light to a 3-billion-pixel digital camera and a range of colour filters, this instrument will be capable of imaging an area of sky fifty times larger than the apparent area of the full Moon once every 10 seconds or so. Its primary goal is to carry out a comprehensive weak-lensing survey of billions of galaxies in order to produce a three-dimensional map of the distribution of dark and luminous matter back to the time when the Universe was about half its present age. It will also have the potential to detect thousands of type Ia supernovae each year. By combining weak-lensing and supernova data, and factoring in precision measurements of the cosmic-matter density obtained by the Wilkinson Microwave Anisotropy Probe (WMAP) and the forthcoming Planck spacecraft (which is due to be launched by the European Space Agency in 2008), the LSST team hope to be able to pin down the value of w to within around 1 per cent or so and its rate of change, if any, to within around 5 per cent.

Prospects for a major space-based project centre on the Joint Dark Energy Mission (JDEM), which is to be funded by NASA and the US Department of Energy. In August 2006, NASA gave the go-ahead for further study and development to three candidate proposals: the Advanced Dark Energy Physics Telescope (ADEPT), the Dark Energy Space Telescope (Destiny), and the Supernova/Acceleration Probe (SNAP). The SNAP proposal is for a 2-metre optical and infrared space telescope dedicated to detecting thousands of type Ia supernovae

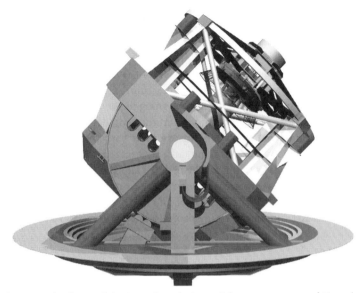

Figure 8. The design of the Large Synoptic Survey Telescope, current as of November 2006. The proposed ground-based 8.4-metre telescope, with its 10 square degree field of view, will take a relentless series of 10-second exposures that will cover the whole available sky every three days. (Image courtesy of LSST Corporation.)

out to red shifts in the region of 1.7 and to conducting a weak-lensing survey covering a thousand square degrees of sky. The Destiny proposal is for a relatively low-cost supernova and weak-lensing mission that would utilize a 1.65-metre space telescope. SNAP and Destiny would each be able to measure the expansion history of the Universe (using supernovae) and the evolution of structure (through weak lensing) to provide independent, complementary constraints on the properties of dark energy. ADEPT would be a near-infrared satellite mission that would measure the locations of 100 million galaxies, in order to detect baryon acoustic oscillations (a 'standard ruler') and would also detect about a thousand type Ia supernovae ('standard candles'). Its aim would be to constrain the properties of dark energy through a double-pronged attack on the expansion history of the universe.

In the meantime, observers are continuing to make great strides. One of the current ongoing projects is the CFHT Legacy Survey, which is using the 3.6-metre Canada–France–Hawaii Telescope to carry out a weak-lensing survey and to search for type Ia supernovae. By late 2005 data from the ongoing supernova part of the project (the Supernova Legacy Survey – SNLS), when combined with baryon acoustic oscillation measurements from the Sloan Digital Sky Survey, was pointing to a value for w that was consistent with the cosmological constant within the limits of observational errors (assuming flat space and a constant value of w, the published figure was -1.023, with errors in the region of 10 per cent or so either way). An analysis of three years of observational data on the cosmic microwave background, obtained by the WMAP spacecraft and published in 2006, also came up with a figure that, within experimental errors, closely tied in with the cosmological constant.

Another major project is ESSENCE (Equation of State: Supernovae trace Cosmic Expansion), a five-year programme initiated in 2002, that uses the 4-metre 'Blanco' telescope at the Cerro Tololo Inter-American Observatory in Chile to identify type Ia supernovae; these are then investigated spectroscopically by larger instruments. In 2007, the ESSENCE team published a paper, based on data from sixty of their growing tally of supernovae, that also implied a value of w consistent with the cosmological constant.

In February 2007, a team headed by Adam Riess published data on twenty-four of the most distant type Ia supernovae known (all with red shifts greater than 1), most of which had been discovered with the Hubble Space Telescope. These data allowed the team to probe the properties of dark energy further back in time than had previously been possible. What they found was that although dark energy did not become dominant until about 5 billion years ago, its repulsive effects were discernible as far back as 9 billion years ago, and its strength in the remote past appeared similar to what it is today, just as would be expected with the cosmological constant. These results appear to rule out models of dark energy that undergo rapid changes in pressure and density. The team also found no evidence that type Ia supernovae have changed in any way over the past 10 billion years, which greatly strengthens their credentials as reliable standard candles.

Most of the current crop of determinations of the dark-energy equation of state have yielded values that are sufficiently close to -1, within their margins of error, to be entirely consistent with the assertion that the cosmological constant (vacuum energy) accounts for the dark-energy component of the universe. It remains to be seen whether or not the huge improvement in observational data that the next decade hopefully will bring will throw up a distinctly different value – a value that will allow cosmologists to come down in favour of something like quintessence or phantom energy. For the moment, at least, the cosmological constant – despite having been rejected and derided by Einstein, its inventor – is holding on to 'pole position' in the dark-energy Grand Prix. As of now, it appears that the Universe may be fated to carry on expanding at an accelerating pace for ever.

The English Copernicans

ALLAN CHAPMAN

When Nicholas Copernicus published his *De Revolutionibus* in 1543, it caused less of a stir than is popularly believed. One reason was that a partial familiarity with the idea of a moving Earth already existed at that time. Not only did Copernicus mention several ancient Greeks who, in various forms, had speculated about a moving Earth, but his own heliocentric ideas seem to have been known by word of mouth well before the book was published. Yet more importantly, Copernicus's arguments for a moving Earth were based on a set of rather abstruse mathematical criteria, while at the same time the heliocentric theory contradicted everyday common-sense experience. For surely, if the Earth were spinning through space, things would fly off and nothing would ever be at rest?

On the other hand, knowledge travelled fast in the sixteenth century, and not long after *De Revolutionibus* had been published in Nuremburg, copies were being purchased in England, as they were in other European countries, for by 1543 a well-organized international book trade was already in existence. And no one was being arrested or burnt at the stake, although Copernicus sometimes got called a fool for holding seemingly absurd views. Evidence suggests, however, that Copernicus's ideas fell on fertile soil in England, and one must ask why. One important factor was the growing prosperity of England at the time. It is true that many people lived in dire poverty, but Tudor and Stuart England had in fact a prosperity that was more widely spread across society in general than probably anywhere else in Europe. Land speculations following King Henry VIII's religious Protestant Reformation and the break-up of the monastic estates after 1533, for instance, had created quite a large class of moderately well-off independent small landowners and businessmen, while at the same time both the monarchy and England's remarkably small aristocracy were hard up by continental European standards. Henry VIII had inherited a very full treasury from his father when he ascended the throne in 1509, but thirty-eight years of heavy spending reduced him to debt at his death. And an English king, unlike his fellow monarchs in continental Europe, could be restrained by Parliament from overtaxing his subjects. Indeed, Parliament, the Merchant Corporation of the City of London, and other great commercial provincial cities such as Norwich, Bristol and York, were all home to a burgeoning class of people who were in business, the law, land speculation and overseas trade: enterprising folk, making money and shrewdly reinvesting it, and often acting as bankers to cap-in-hand aristocrats who needed loans. There was nothing like this powerful commercial middle class in France, Spain or Germany, where society often broke down into more clear-cut divisions of very rich and very poor; the nearest equivalents were Venice, Florence and the great merchant cities of northern Italy, or perhaps Antwerp and Bruges in Belgium. And what did this powerful middle class do with its money? Well, it sent its sons to Oxford and Cambridge Universities and the legal Inns of Court, entered the legal, medical and clerical professions, sat in Parliament, imported, bought and read books, invested in printing and publishing, founded schools and colleges, and gave England the highest overall literacy rate in Europe. And needless to say, these people were interested in all sorts of new ideas, such as geographical exploration, Protestant Christianity, maps, literature, Shakespeare's plays, books of travel – and science. Books on surveying, navigation, astronomy and yes, astrology, abounded. For it was among this new rich and educated middle class that Copernican ideas took root and were openly discussed.

It is not for nothing that our first apparent Copernican – a Welshman – came precisely from this social bracket. A native of Tenby, South Wales, Robert Recorde studied at both Oxford and Cambridge Universities before practising medicine in London, and rising to become physician to King Edward VI. But he also wrote popular and very influential educative books on surveying, arithmetic, geometry, astronomy and science in the English tongue, and was clearly connected with the City's business community. In Recorde's writings, such as *The Castel of Knowledge* (1556), we find not so much an explicit advocacy of Copernicanism as a warning to students not to dismiss it out of hand as an absurdity. For whereas the idea that we might all be flying around the Sun might seem patently ridiculous, when we assumed Copernicanism as a theory it actually made certain planetary calculations much easier to do. Robert Recorde died in prison in 1558, probably of fever, in his forty-seventh year, having been arrested because of his involvement in a lawsuit.

THE IDEAS OF THOMAS DIGGES

How many Latin-literate English and Welsh people – not to mention Scots and Irish, for Scotland was an independent kingdom, with four universities before 1603, while Ireland's Trinity College, Dublin, was founded in 1591 – were reading Copernicus' book in the Elizabethan period we do not know. But when Thomas Digges reissued his deceased father Leonard's *A Prognostication Everlasting* in 1576 he added a Supplement that gives a good indication of what ideas were circulating by that date. For Digges' Supplement, entitled a 'Perfit Description of the Caelestiall Orbes', was not only a plain-English account of the Copernican theory, complete with a printed engraving of the Sun-centred solar system, but also contained an argument for an infinite Universe. Although Copernicus himself had advocated a Sun-centred universe, he had, nonetheless, still worked on the classical assumption that it was bounded by a solid sphere carrying the fixed stars. Thomas Digges, however, suggested that beyond the solar system 'The Orbe of Starres Fixed Infinitely up Extendeth' throughout three-dimensional space, all the way to Heaven. What is more, Digges made the first tentative statement of a cosmological problem to be immortalized 250 years later as 'Olbers' Paradox': if the stars extend to infinity and, geometrically speaking, must fill the entire sky with points of light, then why is the night sky dark?

Many people have wondered how Digges could have come up with this astonishing group of ideas, and it has been surmised that he, and the circle of scientific friends in which he moved, including the famous Elizabethan philosopher Dr John Dee, had some kind of telescope. However, appealing as this idea is, I find it hard to accept. Although we know that the Diggeses, father and son, and Dr Dee were interested in lenses, mirrors and optical puzzles, I know of no one before 1609 who left any record of looking at the heavens with a telescope. And further, I feel certain that had Thomas Digges had access to some sort of telescope in the summer of 1588, when England was in danger of invasion from the Spanish Armada, he would have disclosed the workings of such a potentially invaluable strategic device to his fellow Kentish magistrates. Yet when Digges drew up advice to his magistrate colleagues about coastal defences during the Armada crisis, he spoke only of the usual watchfulness and preparation of signal beacons and stockpiles of munitions, and there were no references to an instrument with which we could see the enemy long before they could see us.

Let us not forget, however, that in 1576 the idea of an infinite Universe was not by any means new, for several medieval scientist-theologians had discussed the idea, dating back at least to the Englishman Thomas Bradwardine in 1328. Indeed, as Bradwardine had argued, why could not an infinitely powerful God have made an infinitely vast Universe if He chose to do so? And far from getting into trouble for these suggestions, Bradwardine became Archbishop of Canterbury. Just as Copernicus himself was acutely aware of the richness of classical and medieval cosmological thought, so too were Digges and his contemporaries.

It is hard to imagine that Thomas Digges was not well acquainted with a brilliant young man who was rising to prominence in the early 1580s: Thomas Harriot. Both men knew Dr Dee and Sir Walter Ralegh; and Ralegh, we should remember, was not just a famous naval hero but also a highly-educated philosopher with a passion for science as it was then understood. Thomas Harriot was an Oxford native and had studied at St Mary's Hall, Oxford, before entering the entourage of his fellow Oxonian, the dazzling Sir Walter.

THOMAS HARRIOT – A CONVINCED COPERNICAN

In 1585/6, at the age of 25, Harriot spent a year in that part of the North American east coast that had just been named Virginia. He had sailed out on a pre-colonization survey expedition as what would later have been called the expedition's scientist. Harriot's *A Brief and True Report of the New Found Land of Virginia* (1588) is a classic of exploration literature, for he became fascinated not just with the minerals, plants and animals of Virginia, but also with its native peoples. A pioneer enthnologist, he learned the local 'Algonkian' language, and wrote down the religious beliefs and tribal stories of the Indians. Then he showed them European technical devices: lenses, mirrors, a curious 'perspective', a spring-driven clock, gunpowder and magnets – which probably makes Harriot the first person to teach Western science on the North American continent! On one occasion, after a violent storm had blown in from the sea and almost wrecked the expedition's ship, Harriot recorded that the natives ascribed it to their storm god *Huracan*. And from the native Indians he, Ralegh and numerous other Elizabethans picked up a passion for tobacco.

Added to all of this, Harriot became a convinced Copernican, believing the Earth to be rotating around the Sun in a possibly infinite Universe. By the early seventeenth century, while now enjoying the opulent patronage of the Earl of Northumberland, he seems to have been the leading light in a circle of brilliant young Englishmen who appear to have held a number of beliefs in common. These included figures like Nicholas Hill, Walter Warner and the Revd Nathaniel Torporley: not household names, I confess, but nonetheless significant thinkers in late Elizabethan England. Their shared beliefs included, for instance, an adherence to the Copernican theory, the conviction that some invisible mathematical force, rather than the classical crystalline spheres, kept the planets in their orbits around the Sun, and an interest in the possible atomic nature of matter, in contradiction to Aristotle's elements of earth, water, air and fire. And perhaps taking their cue from Thomas Digges and several medieval theologians and contemporary Europeans such as Giordano Bruno, they speculated about the 'plurality of worlds', or what we might call extraterrestrial life, as well as infinity.

Harriot was also the first Englishman, and perhaps the first person ever, to look at astronomical bodies through one of the new 'Dutch spyglasses', or telescopes, in 1609. Indeed, one reason why I doubt whether Harriot or anyone else ever had a 'Tudor telescope' back in the 1580s is the sheer wonder with which these men greeted their first novel telescopic glimpses of the Moon, Sun and planets in 1609. By this date Harriot was independently well off, and he got his technician to replicate the lenses of his Dutch telescope, thereby making this man, Christopher Tooke, the first Englishman to manufacture telescopes.

On 26 July 1609, Harriot first examined the Moon through one of his early telescopes, and was amazed at the detail he saw. In particular, the lunar 'seas' fascinated him, while Harriot's Welsh friend, Sir William Lower, who had also acquired a telescope, likened them, in words that have rung down the centuries, 'unto the description of coasts, in the dutch bookes of voyages. In the full she appears like a tarte that my cooke made me the last weeke. Here a vaine of bright stuffe, and there of darke. I must confesse I can see none of this without my cylinder,' or telescope.

And while Galileo obtained his first telescope during the summer of 1609, he does not seem to have used it to observe astronomical bodies until later on in that year, so that Harriot and Lower might have been the first to use the new 'perspectives' astronomically. Harriot in addition made independent observations of Jupiter's moons, and also of sunspots; like Galileo he interpreted them within a Copernican context, but unlike Galileo he published nothing on astronomy in his lifetime, and the importance of his work was not realized until some of his discoveries were published in Oxford in 1832, around 211 years after his death.

ACTIVE COPERNICANS AND DR JOHN WILKINS

Early seventeenth-century England seemed to abound with Copernicans as the theory was discussed across the learned world. No doubt it also received some impetus from Dr William Gilbert, Queen Elizabeth I's physician, whose very influential *De Magnete* (1600) founded the scientific study of geomagnetism; though perhaps not a full Copernican, Gilbert argued that it was physically simpler to think that the Earth spun on its axis every twenty-four hours instead of being fixed under a moving sky. There was also that astonishing institution, Gresham College, in Bishopsgate Street, in the City of London – the world's first free-of-charge college of adult higher education, founded in 1597 under Sir Thomas Gresham's will of 1575. Indeed, anyone could walk in off the street to hear lectures delivered by the seven Gresham Professors. The professorships of Astronomy and Geometry in particular were held by a succession of distinguished men, most of whom were active Copernicans, including Henry Briggs, Henry Gellibrand, Samuel Foster, Sir Christopher Wren, and Robert Hooke.

Quite simply, Copernicanism and 'modern' telescopic astronomy were effectively 'on tap' in the English language for Londoners, and lectures were repeated in Latin for the benefit of visiting foreigners. Similarly, the men who came to hold Oxford's Savilian Chairs of Astronomy after 1619 were mostly Copernicans (in spite of their founder Sir Henry Savile's mathematical conservatism), thereby making heliocentric ideas increasingly available to students and academics. Considering England's burgeoning overseas trade, and explorers like Sir Francis Drake and Henry Hudson, one can understand how deeply geography, navigation, astronomy and practical mathematics penetrated into the English imagination. Indeed, it fed into something of a national passion for mathematics, especially of the more practical kind, which extended across society from ingenious craftsmen to university academics. It is impossible, for instance, to gauge the extent of the influence that the Revd William Oughtred exercised over the almost sixty years that he corresponded with, taught and inspired scores of English mathematicians and astronomers down to his death in 1660 – around 1610, he had devised a calculating instrument 'giving the Prosthaphaereses of the Plannets according to the theory of Copernicus'.

Almost certainly many of the astronomers mentioned above must have had an influence on that trio of Copernicans who were active in Lancashire and Yorkshire between 1635 and 1644: Jeremiah Horrocks, William Crabtree and William Gascoigne (who corresponded with Oughtred), not to mention their friends Christopher Townley, Jeremy Shakerley and others. When Horrocks and Crabtree predicted and observed the first recorded transit of Venus in 1639, they took Copernican planetary theory and computation as read.

Indeed, one indication of the prosperity, freedom and intellectual curiosity of this period is the substantial market that clearly existed in England for scientific books and instruments by 1620. Several hundred mathematical and astronomical writers, teachers and instrument-makers are recorded to have practised, mainly in or around London, between 1560 and 1670, and though not all of them were necessarily Copernicans, the openness to and enthusiasm for astronomy in Tudor and Jacobean society are obvious. Furthermore, while Copernicanism was sometimes attacked by conservative scholars such as Alexander Ross, the controversy was conducted entirely in the context of open debate, and no one was arrested, tried or punished for being a Copernican. Indeed, the Church of England had no policies whatsoever regarding favoured or prohibited theories in science anyway. Only treasonable political activities and subversive allegiances to foreign powers – such as those of Guy Fawkes and the Gunpowder Plotters of 1605 – would get one into trouble. In fact, many Copernicans were even clergymen. One outstanding example of a high-profile clerical

Copernican was the Revd Dr John Wilkins, whose *Discourse on a New World in the Moone* (1638, 1640) took Galileo's, Kepler's and other modern astronomers' ideas, and presented them in a plain and engaging form for English readers. In this book, itself a milestone in the wider popularization of astronomy, Wilkins discussed the great telescopic discoveries of the previous thirty years, provided a full-scale treatment of Copernicus's ideas, and speculated as to whether the Moon, with its 'seas' and mountains, might even be inhabited. And like Digges, he saw the stars as extending away infinitely into space.

Then in 1648, when he was 34, Wilkins returned to Oxford from London to become Warden of Wadham College, and began to attract around him an informal 'Clubbe' of scientific friends. They made telescopic observations from the college gardens, and even experimented with flying machines, for Dr Wilkins was the first to discuss a 'Flying Chariot' or space vehicle (powered by springs and wings) in which one might be able to ascend to the Moon. Indeed, the amiable and ingenious Dr Wilkins was fascinated by the potential of mechanical technology, and in 1648 brought out another scientific book, his highly influential *Mathematical Magick*. This work discussed all manner of contraptions, from automatic spits for cooking meat to wind-powered vehicles for travelling at over twenty miles an hour, and thence to flying machines. Although *Mathematical Magick* was not especially astronomical, the ingenious, inventive spirit that runs through it was entirely at one with the ideas of contemporary Copernicanism and, in particular, with Galileo, who was Wilkins' personal hero.

Wilkins had been an active member of a circle of scientific friends that met at Gresham College, London, before becoming Warden of Wadham in Oxford in 1648, and clearly knew all the Gresham College astronomers, such as Sir Paul Neile and Dr Laurence Rooke, so one can understand how he was able to attract people to his new Oxford 'Clubbe'. Of course, this club included medical men and chemists as well as astronomers, though the leading astronomers in its ranks in addition to himself were Dr Seth Ward and Dr John Wallis, who held Oxford's Savilian Professorships of Astronomy and Geometry respectively. And then there were two brilliant young students: Christopher Wren and his friend Robert Hooke.

THE BRILLIANCE OF WREN AND HOOKE

Posterity remembers Wren as the architect of St Paul's Cathedral, but up to the age of almost 40 his fame rested on his astronomical researches and his achievements while occupying the astronomical chairs first at Gresham College and then at Oxford. As a 17-year-old undergraduate in the late 1640s he had undertaken original telescopic observations of the planets and built models in the hope of fathoming out the as yet unexplained 'ansae' ('handles') or rings of Saturn. Wren was also a mathematician of brilliance, and one wonders what he might have gone on to do had not the circumstance of the Great Fire of London in 1666 diverted his energies to architecture.

Robert Hooke no doubt first met Wren when they were both at Oxford, for while Wren was at Wadham and then at All Souls College, Hooke was at Christ Church. Like Wren, Hooke had displayed amazing intellectual prowess not only as a boy on the Isle of Wight, where he was born in 1635, but at Westminster School (where he built flying machines), and at Oxford. It is my suspicion that Dr Wilkins head-hunted, as it were, the young Hooke for his circle, and like Wren, Hooke always acknowledged Wilkins as his great inspirer. We know, from a 1675 note in Hooke's hand, that Warden Wilkins and he had tried out flying machines together at Wadham in the mid 1650s, though alas, they never succeeded in reaching the Moon! Almost certainly, however, Hooke would have looked at the Moon through Wilkins's celebrated giant telescope – said to have been of 80 feet focal length – and no doubt speculated with him about the 'Selenite' beings who just *might* be living on our satellite.

John Wilkins' club met and researched in Oxford between 1648 and 1659, which was the period when Oliver Cromwell and Parliament ruled England without a king, but in 1660 the monarchy was restored and King Charles II ascended his executed father's throne. Similarly, the Church of England was reinstated, and Professor Seth Ward became first Bishop of Exeter, then of Salisbury, while in 1668 Wilkins became Bishop of Chester. At the same time, Wilkins' club was largely relocated back to London at Gresham College, and now received a title and a charter from King Charles, coming to be known as the Royal Society, and its members as Fellows, proudly placing the letters 'FRS' after their names. Once again, Copernicanism was taken as read within their ranks.

In this new Royal Society, the 28-year-old Robert Hooke, FRS, became Curator of Experiments: the first salaried research scientist in Great Britain. In this capacity he undertook a series of brilliant and original researches in half a dozen sciences that ranged from cosmology to microscopy, and seems to have had access to powerful telescopes of 12, 36 and 60 feet focal length, which he used to do the first detailed drawings of individual lunar craters, comets and the planets. From observations and laboratory experiments (including the dropping of pistol balls into tubs of semi-solidified plaster) conducted in October 1664, moreover, Hooke argued that some lunar craters might have been the product of impacts from space, while others appeared volcanic; and like so many contemporary scientists, he was firmly persuaded that the Moon had living creatures upon it. For reasons hard for us to understand today, he even said that the interior of the crater Hipparchus reminded him of the rolling grasslands of Salisbury Plain! His observations of cometary nuclei and tails (conducted at high magnifications for the period, at or around × 125) led him to believe that some sort of corrosive zone surrounded the Sun, causing the approaching comets to glow and melt away in spectacular streams of light and what we would now call *energy*. And when King Charles founded his Royal Observatory in Greenwich Park in 1675, it was Wren who designed the buildings and Hooke the instruments, while the Observatory's first director, or Astronomer Royal, the Revd John Flamsteed, had been a Copernican for as many years as he had been an astronomer, which went back to his teens.

PROOF THAT EARTH MOVED IN SPACE

We must not forget, however, that in spite of the more or less general acceptance of the Copernican theory by 1670, all the arguments in its favour were still drawn from analogy or from simplicity, for there was still no conclusive physical *proof* that the Earth actually moved in space. Of course, everyone recognized that there was one great potential proof, a stellar parallax motion, but no one had yet succeeded in measuring such a parallax. Many had tried, including Hooke and Flamsteed in the 1660s and 1670s, and the Dane Ole Rømer in the 1690s, but the prevailing instrument technology was insufficiently refined to allow such a tiny angle to be reliably measured.

Between the 1660s and 1720s, however, precision technology had undergone great improvement, and in 1725 the Revd Dr James Bradley, the current Savilian Professor of Astronomy at Oxford, began a series of observations at Kew of the star Gamma Draconis, which passed directly overhead in London, with a 25-foot-focal-length telescope. This 'zenith sector', by the greatest precision instrument-maker of the age, George Graham, was set to point to the exact zenith, so as to see if Gamma Draconis displayed a six-monthly parallax caused by the Earth orbiting the Sun. (A zenith star was chosen in order to eliminate any error deriving from atmospheric refraction.)

Bradley failed to detect a parallax, yet what he discovered was a quite separate and unexpected motion of the star. The parallax he hoped to discover would have manifested itself as a tiny displacement of Gamma Draconis between June and December, but what he actually observed was a displacement at a right angle to the expected axis, between March and September. After struggling to make sense of the phenomenon, Bradley realized that while he had not detected a parallax angle (yet another 110 years of precision-engineering progress would be needed before that would be possible), he had come upon an entirely unexpected phenomenon – the aberration of starlight – that could only be adequately explained if one accepted the Earth's motion around the Sun.

So in 1728, when Bradley announced his discovery of the aberration, we had the first physical, measured piece of evidence that the Earth moved through space, and that the Copernican theory was indeed correct.

It is part of the popular mythology of science that Copernican, Galilean, Keplerian and other 'modern' ideas only received proper recognition after a long hard fight against the powers of superstition and ignorance. This is not, however, what the real, surviving historical record actually tells us: in many Continental European countries, especially Protestant ones, Copernican ideas were openly discussed, while in the British Isles they put down strong and enduring roots among both active scientists and the generality of educated people – and no one got into trouble as a consequence of them.

FURTHER READING

Chapman, A. (1990), 'Jeremiah Horrocks and the Transit of Venus', *1991 Yearbook of Astronomy* (ed. Patrick Moore): London, Sidgwick and Jackson.

Johnson, F. R. (1937), *Astronomical Thought in Renaissance England*: Baltimore, Johns Hopkins University Press.

Koyré, Alexander (1957, 1968), *From the Closed World to the Infinite Universe*: Baltimore, Johns Hopkins University Press.

McLean, Antonia (1972), *Humanism and the Rise of Science in Tudor England*: New York, Neale Watson Academic.

Taylor, Eva G. R. (1968), *The Mathematical Practitioners of Tudor and Stuart England 1485–1714*: Cambridge, Cambridge University Press.

Turner, Gerard L'E. (2000), *Elizabethan Instrument Makers: The Origins of the London Trade in Precision Instrument Making*: Oxford, Oxford University Press.

Part III

Miscellaneous

Some Interesting Variable Stars

JOHN ISLES

All variable stars are of potential interest, and hundreds of them can be observed with the slightest optical aid, even with a pair of binoculars. The stars in the list that follows include many that are popular with amateur observers, as well as some less-well-known objects that are nevertheless suitable for study visually. The periods and ranges of many variables are not constant from one cycle to another, and some are completely irregular.

Finder charts are given after the list for those stars marked with an asterisk. These charts are adapted with permission from those issued by the Variable Star Section of the British Astronomical Association. Apart from the eclipsing variables and others in which the light changes are purely a geometrical effect, variable stars can be divided broadly into two classes: the pulsating stars, and the eruptive or cataclysmic variables.

Mira (Omicron Ceti) is the best-known member of the long-period subclass of pulsating red-giant stars. The chart is suitable for use in estimating the magnitude of Mira when it reaches naked-eye brightness – typically from about a month before the predicted date of maximum until two or three months after maximum. Predictions for Mira and other stars of its class follow the section of finder charts.

The semi-regular variables are less predictable, and generally have smaller ranges. V Canum Venaticorum is one of the more reliable ones, with steady oscillations in a six-month cycle. Z Ursae Majoris, easily found with binoculars near Delta, has a large range, and often shows double maxima owing to the presence of multiple periodicities in its light changes. The chart for Z is also suitable for observing another semi-regular star, RY Ursae Majoris. These semi-regular stars are mostly red giants or supergiants.

The RV Tauri stars are of earlier spectral class than the semi-regulars, and in a full cycle of variation they often show deep minima and double maxima that are separated by a secondary minimum. U Monocerotis is one of the brightest RV Tauri stars.

Among eruptive variable stars is the carbon-rich supergiant R Coronae Borealis. Its unpredictable eruptions cause it not to brighten, but to fade. This happens when one of the sooty clouds that the star throws out from time to time happens to come in our direction and blots out most of the star's light from our view. Much of the time R Coronae is bright enough to be seen in binoculars, and the chart can be used to estimate its magnitude. During the deepest minima, however, the star needs a telescope of 25-centimetre or larger aperture to be detected.

CH Cygni is a symbiotic star – that is, a close binary comprising a red giant and a hot dwarf star that interact physically, giving rise to outbursts. The system also shows semi-regular oscillations, and sudden fades and rises that may be connected with eclipses.

Observers can follow the changes of these variable stars by using the comparison stars whose magnitudes are given below each chart. Observations of variable stars by amateurs are of scientific value, provided they are collected and made available for analysis. This is done by several organizations, including the British Astronomical Association (see the list of astronomical societies in this volume), the American Association of Variable Star Observers (25 Birch Street, Cambridge, Mass. 02138), and the Royal Astronomical Society of New Zealand (PO Box 3181, Wellington).

Star	RA		Declination		Range	Type	Period	Spectrum
	h	m	°	'			(days)	
R Andromedae	00	24.0	+38	35	5.8–14.9	Mira	409	S
W Andromedae	02	17.6	+44	18	6.7–14.6	Mira	396	S
U Antliae	10	35.2	−39	34	5–6	Irregular	—	C
Theta Apodis	14	05.3	−76	48	5–7	Semi-regular	119	M
R Aquarii	23	43.8	−15	17	5.8–12.4	Symbiotic	387	M+Pec
T Aquarii	20	49.9	−05	09	7.2–14.2	Mira	202	M
R Aquilae	19	06.4	+08	14	5.5–12.0	Mira	284	M
V Aquilae	19	04.4	−05	41	6.6–8.4	Semi-regular	353	C
Eta Aquilae	19	52.5	+01	00	3.5–4.4	Cepheid	7.2	F–G
U Arae	17	53.6	−51	41	7.7–14.1	Mira	225	M
R Arietis	02	16.1	+25	03	7.4–13.7	Mira	187	M
U Arietis	03	11.0	+14	48	7.2–15.2	Mira	371	M
R Aurigae	05	17.3	+53	35	6.7–13.9	Mira	458	M
Epsilon Aurigae	05	02.0	+43	49	2.9–3.8	Algol	9892	F+B
R Boötis	14	37.2	+26	44	6.2–13.1	Mira	223	M

Star	RA		Declination		Range	Type	Period	Spectrum
	h	m	°	'			(days)	
X Camelopardalis	04	45.7	+75	06	7.4–14.2	Mira	144	K–M
R Cancri	08	16.6	+11	44	6.1–11.8	Mira	362	M
X Cancri	08	55.4	+17	14	5.6–7.5	Semi-regular	195?	C
R Canis Majoris	07	19.5	−16	24	5.7–6.3	Algol	1.1	F
VY Canis Majoris	07	23.0	−25	46	6.5–9.6	Unique	—	M
S Canis Minoris	07	32.7	+08	19	6.6–13.2	Mira	333	M
R Canum Ven.	13	49.0	+39	33	6.5–12.9	Mira	329	M
*V Canum Ven.	13	19.5	+45	32	6.5–8.6	Semi-regular	192	M
R Carinae	09	32.2	−62	47	3.9–10.5	Mira	309	M
S Carinae	10	09.4	−61	33	4.5–9.9	Mira	149	K–M
l Carinae	09	45.2	−62	30	3.3–4.2	Cepheid	35.5	F–K
Eta Carinae	10	45.1	−59	41	−0.8–7.9	Irregular	—	Pec
R Cassiopeiae	23	58.4	+51	24	4.7–13.5	Mira	430	M
S Cassiopeiae	01	19.7	+72	37	7.9–16.1	Mira	612	S
W Cassiopeiae	00	54.9	+58	34	7.8–12.5	Mira	406	C
Gamma Cas.	00	56.7	+60	43	1.6–3.0	Gamma Cas.	—	B
Rho Cassiopeiae	23	54.4	+57	30	4.1–6.2	Semi-regular	—	F–K
R Centauri	14	16.6	−59	55	5.3–11.8	Mira	546	M
S Centauri	12	24.6	−49	26	7–8	Semi-regular	65	C
T Centauri	13	41.8	−33	36	5.5–9.0	Semi-regular	90	K–M
S Cephei	21	35.2	+78	37	7.4–12.9	Mira	487	C
T Cephei	21	09.5	+68	29	5.2–11.3	Mira	388	M
Delta Cephei	22	29.2	+58	25	3.5–4.4	Cepheid	5.4	F–G
Mu Cephei	21	43.5	+58	47	3.4–5.1	Semi-regular	730	M
U Ceti	02	33.7	−13	09	6.8–13.4	Mira	235	M
W Ceti	00	02.1	−14	41	7.1–14.8	Mira	351	S
*Omicron Ceti	02	19.3	−02	59	2.0–10.1	Mira	332	M
R Chamaeleontis	08	21.8	−76	21	7.5–14.2	Mira	335	M
T Columbae	05	19.3	−33	42	6.6–12.7	Mira	226	M
R Comae Ber.	12	04.3	+18	47	7.1–14.6	Mira	363	M
*R Coronae Bor.	15	48.6	+28	09	5.7–14.8	R Coronae Bor.	—	C
S Coronae Bor.	15	21.4	+31	22	5.8–14.1	Mira	360	M
T Coronae Bor.	15	59.6	+25	55	2.0–10.8	Recurrent nova	—	M+Pec
V Coronae Bor.	15	49.5	+39	34	6.9–12.6	Mira	358	C
W Coronae Bor.	16	15.4	+37	48	7.8–14.3	Mira	238	M
R Corvi	12	19.6	−19	15	6.7–14.4	Mira	317	M
R Crucis	12	23.6	−61	38	6.4–7.2	Cepheid	5.8	F–G
R Cygni	19	36.8	+50	12	6.1–14.4	Mira	426	S
U Cygni	20	19.6	+47	54	5.9–12.1	Mira	463	C
W Cygni	21	36.0	+45	22	5.0–7.6	Semi-regular	131	M

Star	RA		Declination		Range	Type	Period	Spectrum
	h	m	°	′			(days)	
RT Cygni	19	43.6	+48	47	6.0–13.1	Mira	190	M
SS Cygni	21	42.7	+43	35	7.7–12.4	Dwarf nova	50±	K+Pec
*CH Cygni	19	24.5	+50	14	5.6–9.0	Symbiotic	—	M+B
Chi Cygni	19	50.6	+32	55	3.3–14.2	Mira	408	S
R Delphini	20	14.9	+09	05	7.6–13.8	Mira	285	M
U Delphini	20	45.5	+18	05	5.6–7.5	Semi-regular	110?	M
EU Delphini	20	37.9	+18	16	5.8–6.9	Semi-regular	60	M
Beta Doradûs	05	33.6	−62	29	3.5–4.1	Cepheid	9.8	F–G
R Draconis	16	32.7	+66	45	6.7–13.2	Mira	246	M
T Eridani	03	55.2	−24	02	7.2–13.2	Mira	252	M
R Fornacis	02	29.3	−26	06	7.5–13.0	Mira	389	C
R Geminorum	07	07.4	+22	42	6.0–14.0	Mira	370	S
U Geminorum	07	55.1	+22	00	8.2–14.9	Dwarf nova	105±	Pec+M
Zeta Geminorum	07	04.1	+20	34	3.6–4.2	Cepheid	10.2	F–G
Eta Geminorum	06	14.9	+22	30	3.2–3.9	Semi-regular	233	M
S Gruis	22	26.1	−48	26	6.0–15.0	Mira	402	M
S Herculis	16	51.9	+14	56	6.4–13.8	Mira	307	M
U Herculis	16	25.8	+18	54	6.4–13.4	Mira	406	M
Alpha Herculis	17	14.6	+14	23	2.7–4.0	Semi-regular	—	M
68, u Herculis	17	17.3	+33	06	4.7–5.4	Algol	2.1	B+B
R Horologii	02	53.9	−49	53	4.7–14.3	Mira	408	M
U Horologii	03	52.8	−45	50	6–14	Mira	348	M
R Hydrae	13	29.7	−23	17	3.5–10.9	Mira	389	M
U Hydrae	10	37.6	−13	23	4.3–6.5	Semi-regular	450?	C
VW Hydri	04	09.1	−71	18	8.4–14.4	Dwarf nova	27±	Pec
R Leonis	09	47.6	+11	26	4.4–11.3	Mira	310	M
R Leonis Minoris	09	45.6	+34	31	6.3–13.2	Mira	372	M
R Leporis	04	59.6	−14	48	5.5–11.7	Mira	427	C
Y Librae	15	11.7	−06	01	7.6–14.7	Mira	276	M
RS Librae	15	24.3	−22	55	7.0–13.0	Mira	218	M
Delta Librae	15	01.0	−08	31	4.9–5.9	Algol	2.3	A
R Lyncis	07	01.3	+55	20	7.2–14.3	Mira	379	S
R Lyrae	18	55.3	+43	57	3.9–5.0	Semi-regular	46?	M
RR Lyrae	19	25.5	+42	47	7.1–8.1	RR Lyrae	0.6	A–F
Beta Lyrae	18	50.1	+33	22	3.3–4.4	Eclipsing	12.9	B
U Microscopii	20	29.2	−40	25	7.0–14.4	Mira	334	M
*U Monocerotis	07	30.8	−09	47	5.9–7.8	RV Tauri	91	F–K
V Monocerotis	06	22.7	−02	12	6.0–13.9	Mira	340	M
R Normae	15	36.0	−49	30	6.5–13.9	Mira	508	M
T Normae	15	44.1	−54	59	6.2–13.6	Mira	241	M

Star	RA		Declination		Range	Type	Period	Spectrum
	h	m	°	′			(days)	
R Octantis	05	26.1	−86	23	6.3−13.2	Mira	405	M
S Octantis	18	08.7	−86	48	7.2−14.0	Mira	259	M
V Ophiuchi	16	26.7	−12	26	7.3−11.6	Mira	297	C
X Ophiuchi	18	38.3	+08	50	5.9−9.2	Mira	329	M
RS Ophiuchi	17	50.2	−06	43	4.3−12.5	Recurrent nova	—	OB+M
U Orionis	05	55.8	+20	10	4.8−13.0	Mira	368	M
W Orionis	05	05.4	+01	11	5.9−7.7	Semi-regular	212	C
Alpha Orionis	05	55.2	+07	24	0.0−1.3	Semi-regular	2335	M
S Pavonis	19	55.2	−59	12	6.6−10.4	Semi-regular	381	M
Kappa Pavonis	18	56.9	−67	14	3.9−4.8	W Virginis	9.1	G
R Pegasi	23	06.8	+10	33	6.9−13.8	Mira	378	M
X Persei	03	55.4	+31	03	6.0−7.0	Gamma Cas.	—	O9.5
Beta Persei	03	08.2	+40	57	2.1−3.4	Algol	2.9	B
Zeta Phoenicis	01	08.4	−55	15	3.9−4.4	Algol	1.7	B+B
R Pictoris	04	46.2	−49	15	6.4−10.1	Semi-regular	171	M
RS Puppis	08	13.1	−34	35	6.5−7.7	Cepheid	41.4	F−G
L² Puppis	07	13.5	−44	39	2.6−6.2	Semi-regular	141	M
T Pyxidis	09	04.7	−32	23	6.5−15.3	Recurrent nova	7000±	Pec
U Sagittae	19	18.8	+19	37	6.5−9.3	Algol	3.4	B+G
WZ Sagittae	20	07.6	+17	42	7.0−15.5	Dwarf nova	1900±	A
R Sagittarii	19	16.7	−19	18	6.7−12.8	Mira	270	M
RR Sagittarii	19	55.9	−29	11	5.4−14.0	Mira	336	M
RT Sagittarii	20	17.7	−39	07	6.0−14.1	Mira	306	M
RU Sagittarii	19	58.7	−41	51	6.0−13.8	Mira	240	M
RY Sagittarii	19	16.5	−33	31	5.8−14.0	R Coronae Bor.	—	G
RR Scorpii	16	56.6	−30	35	5.0−12.4	Mira	281	M
RS Scorpii	16	55.6	−45	06	6.2−13.0	Mira	320	M
RT Scorpii	17	03.5	−36	55	7.0−15.2	Mira	449	S
Delta Scorpii	16	00.3	−22	37	1.6−2.3	Irregular	—	B
S Sculptoris	00	15.4	−32	03	5.5−13.6	Mira	363	M
R Scuti	18	47.5	−05	42	4.2−8.6	RV Tauri	146	G−K
R Serpentis	15	50.7	+15	08	5.2−14.4	Mira	356	M
S Serpentis	15	21.7	+14	19	7.0−14.1	Mira	372	M
T Tauri	04	22.0	+19	32	9.3−13.5	T Tauri	—	F−K
SU Tauri	05	49.1	+19	04	9.1−16.9	R Coronae Bor.	—	G
Lambda Tauri	04	00.7	+12	29	3.4−3.9	Algol	4.0	B+A
R Trianguli	02	37.0	+34	16	5.4−12.6	Mira	267	M
R Ursae Majoris	10	44.6	+68	47	6.5−13.7	Mira	302	M
T Ursae Majoris	12	36.4	+59	29	6.6−13.5	Mira	257	M
*Z Ursae Majoris	11	56.5	+57	52	6.2−9.4	Semi-regular	196	M

Star	RA		Declination		Range	Type	Period	Spectrum
	h	m	°	′			(days)	
*RY Ursae Majoris	12	20.5	+61	19	6.7−8.3	Semi-regular	310?	M
U Ursae Minoris	14	17.3	+66	48	7.1−13.0	Mira	331	M
R Virginis	12	38.5	+06	59	6.1−12.1	Mira	146	M
S Virginis	13	33.0	−07	12	6.3−13.2	Mira	375	M
SS Virginis	12	25.3	+00	48	6.0−9.6	Semi-regular	364	C
R Vulpeculae	21	04.4	+23	49	7.0−14.3	Mira	137	M
Z Vulpeculae	19	21.7	+25	34	7.3−8.9	Algol	2.5	B+A

V CANUM VENATICORUM   13h 19.5m +45° 32' (2000)

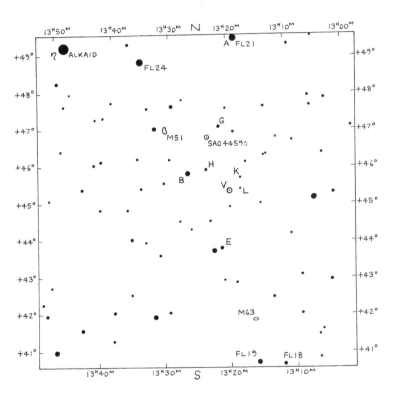

A 5.1   H 7.8
B 5.9   K 8.4
E 6.5   L 8.6
G 7.1

o (MIRA) CETI   02h 19.3m −02° 59′ (2000)

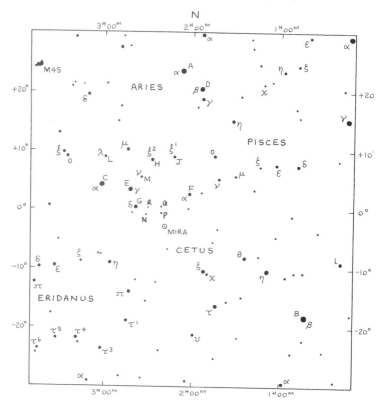

A	2.2	J	4.4
B	2.4	L	4.9
C	2.7	M	5.1
D	3.0	N	5.4
E	3.6	P	5.5
F	3.8	Q	5.7
G	4.1	R	6.1
H	4.3		

R CORONAE BOREALIS   15h 48.6m +28° 09' (2000)

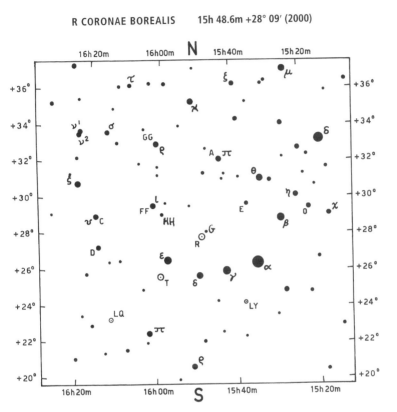

FF 5.0   C 5.8
GG 5.4   D 6.2
A 5.6   E 6.5
HH 7.1
G 7.4

CH CYGNI   19h 24.5m +50° 14′ (2000)

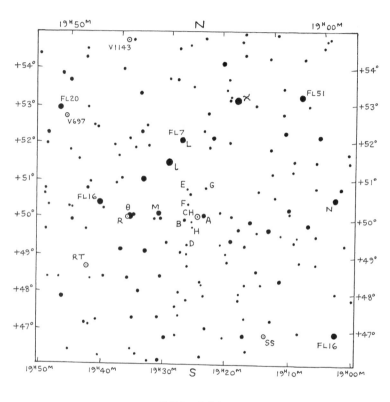

N 5.4	D 8.0
M 5.5	E 8.1
L 5.8	F 8.5
A 6.5	G 8.5
B 7.4	H 9.2

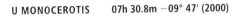

U MONOCEROTIS   **07h 30.8m −09° 47' (2000)**

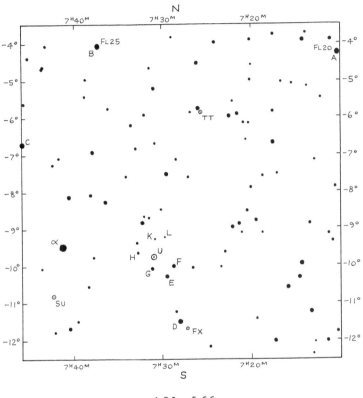

A 5.0	F 6.6
B 5.2	G 7.0
C 5.7	H 7.5
D 5.9	K 7.8
E 6.0	L 8.0

RY URSAE MAJORIS   12h 20.5m +61° 19′ (2000)
Z URSAE MAJORIS   11h 56.5m +57° 52′ (2000)

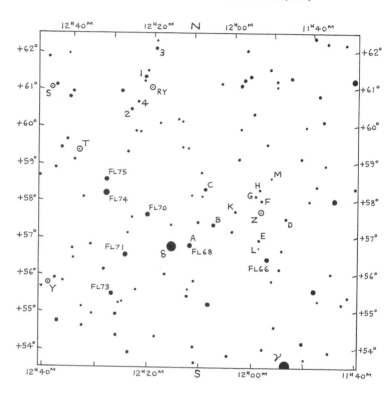

A 6.5	F 8.6	M 9.1
B 7.2	G 8.7	1 6.9
C 7.6	H 8.8	2 7.4
D 8.0	K 8.9	3 7.7
E 8.3	L 9.0	4 7.8

Mira Stars: Maxima, 2008

JOHN ISLES

Below are the predicted dates of maxima for Mira stars that reach magnitude 7.5 or brighter at an average maximum. Individual maxima can in some cases be brighter or fainter than average by a magnitude or more, and all dates are only approximate. The positions, extreme ranges and mean periods of these stars can be found in the preceding list of interesting variable stars.

Star	Mean Magnitude at Maximum	Dates of Maxima
R Andromedae	6.9	27 Jun
W Andromedae	7.4	8 Jun
R Aquarii	6.5	17 Dec
R Aquilae	6.1	21 Mar, 30 Dec
R Boötis	7.2	3 May, 12 Dec
R Cancri	6.8	17 Sep
S Canis Minoris	7.5	29 Feb
R Carinae	4.6	13 May
S Carinae	5.7	12 Mar, 8 Aug
R Cassiopeiae	7.0	20 Dec
R Centauri	5.8	13 Jun
T Cephei	6.0	30 Dec
U Ceti	7.5	12 Apr, 3 Dec
Omicron Ceti	3.4	3 Feb, 30 Dec
T Columbae	7.5	5 Jul
S Coronae Borealis	7.3	25 Sep
V Coronae Borealis	7.5	25 Feb
R Corvi	7.5	20 Mar
R Cygni	7.5	21 Nov
U Cygni	7.2	17 Nov
RT Cygni	7.3	15 Jan, 23 Jul

Star	Mean Magnitude at Maximum	Dates of Maxima
Chi Cygni	5.2	3 Nov
R Geminorum	7.1	21 Dec
U Herculis	7.5	11 Oct
R Horologii	6.0	27 Dec
R Hydrae	4.5	3 Nov
R Leonis	5.8	1 Jan, 5 Nov
R Leonis Minoris	7.1	29 Dec
R Leporis	6.8	18 Oct
RS Librae	7.5	5 May, 9 Dec
V Monocerotis	7.0	3 Jul
R Normae	7.2	3 Dec
T Normae	7.4	9 Apr, 6 Dec
V Ophiuchi	7.5	3 Jun
X Ophiuchi	6.8	10 Jan, 3 Dec
U Orionis	6.3	1 Feb
R Sagittarii	7.3	19 Jun
RR Sagittarii	6.8	2 Feb
RT Sagittarii	7.0	29 Aug
RU Sagittarii	7.2	29 Jun
RR Scorpii	5.9	14 Jun
RS Scorpii	7.0	10 May
S Sculptoris	6.7	22 Dec
R Serpentis	6.9	19 Oct
R Trianguli	6.2	11 Mar, 3 Dec
R Ursae Majoris	7.5	9 Jun
R Virginis	6.9	21 May, 14 Oct
S Virginis	7.0	31 Jan

Some Interesting Double Stars

BOB ARGYLE

The positions, angles and separations given below correspond to epoch 2008.0.

No.	RA		Declin- ation		Star	Magni- tudes	Separa- tion	PA	Cata- logue	Comments
	h	m	°	′			arcsec	°		
1	00	31.5	−62	58	β Tuc	4.4, 4.8	27.1	169	LCL 119	Both again difficult doubles.
2	00	49.1	+57	49	η Cas	3.4, 7.5	13.1	321	Σ60	Easy. Creamy, bluish. P = 480 years.
3	00	55.0	+23	38	36 And	6.0, 6.4	1.0	321	Σ73	P = 168 years. Both yellow. Slowly opening.
4	01	13.7	+07	35	ζ Psc	5.6, 6.5	23.1	63	Σ100	Yellow, reddish-white.
5	01	39.8	−56	12	p Eri	5.8, 5.8	11.6	189	Δ5	Period = 483 years.
6	01	53.5	+19	18	γ Ari	4.8, 4.8	7.5	1	Σ180	Very easy. Both white.
7	02	02.0	+02	46	α Psc	4.2, 5.1	1.8	266	Σ202	Binary, period = 933 years.
8	02	03.9	+42	20	γ And	2.3, 5.0	9.6	63	Σ205	Yellow, blue. Relatively fixed.
					γ2 And	5.1, 6.3	0.3	102	OΣ38	BC. Needs 30 cm. Closing.
9	02	29.1	+67	24	ι Cas AB	4.9, 6.9	2.6	230	Σ262	AB is long-period binary. P = 620 years.
					ι Cas AC	4.9, 8.4	7.2	118		
10	02	33.8	−28	14	ω For	5.0, 7.7	10.8	245	HJ 3506	Common proper motion.

No.	RA		Declin-ation		Star	Magni-tudes	Separa-tion	PA	Cata-logue	Comments
	h	m	°	′			arcsec	°		
11	02	43.3	+03	14	γ Cet	3.5, 7.3	2.3	298	Σ299	Not too easy.
12	02	58.3	−40	18	θ Eri	3.4, 4.5	8.3	90	PZ 2	Both white.
13	02	59.2	+21	20	ε Ari	5.2, 5.5	1.4	208	Σ333	Binary. Little recent motion. Both white.
14	03	00.9	+52	21	Σ331 Per	5.3, 6.7	12.0	85	−	Fixed.
15	03	12.1	−28	59	α For	4.0, 7.0	5.1	300	HJ 3555	P = 269 years. B variable?
16	03	48.6	−37	37	f Eri	4.8, 5.3	8.2	215	Δ16	Pale yellow. Fixed.
17	03	54.3	−02	57	32 Eri	4.8, 6.1	6.9	348	Σ470	Fixed.
18	04	32.0	+53	55	1 Cam	5.7, 6.8	10.3	308	Σ550	Fixed.
19	04	50.9	−53	28	ι Pic	5.6, 6.4	12.4	58	Δ18	Good object for small apertures. Fixed.
20	05	13.2	−12	56	κ Lep	4.5, 7.4	2.0	357	Σ661	Visible in 7.5 cm. Slowly closing.
21	05	14.5	−08	12	β Ori	0.1, 6.8	9.5	204	Σ668	Companion once thought to be close double.
22	05	21.8	−24	46	41 Lep	5.4, 6.6	3.4	93	HJ 3752	Deep yellow pair in a rich field.
23	05	24.5	−02	24	η Ori	3.8, 4.8	1.7	78	DA 5	Slow-moving binary.
24	05	35.1	+09	56	λ Ori	3.6, 5.5	4.3	44	Σ738	Fixed.
25	05	35.3	−05	23	θ Ori AB	6.7, 7.9	8.6	32	Σ748	Trapezium in M42.
					θ Ori CD	5.1, 6.7	13.4	61		
26	05	38.7	−02	36	σ Ori AC	4.0, 10.3	11.4	238	Σ762	Quintuple. A is a close double.
					σ Ori ED	6.5, 7.5	30.1	231		
27	05	40.7	−01	57	ζ Ori	1.9, 4.0	2.6	166	Σ774	Can be split in 7.5 cm. Long-period binary.
28	06	14.9	+22	30	η Gem	var, 6.5	1.6	255	β1008	Well seen with 20 cm. Primary orange.

No.	RA		Declin-ation		Star	Magni-tudes	Separa-tion	PA	Cata-logue	Comments
	h	m	°	′			arcsec	°		
29	06	46.2	+59	27	12 Lyn AB	5.4, 6.0	1.7	70	Σ948	AB is binary, P = 706 years.
					12 Lyn AC	5.4, 7.3	8.7	309		
30	07	08.7	−70	30	γ Vol	3.9, 5.8	14.1	298	Δ42	Very slow binary.
31	07	16.6	−23	19	h3945 CMa	4.8, 6.8	26.8	51	−	Contrasting colours.
32	07	20.1	+21	59	δ Gem	3.5, 8.2	5.6	227	Σ1066	Not too easy. Yellow, pale blue.
33	07	34.6	+31	53	α Gem	1.9, 2.9	4.5	58	Σ1110	Widening. Easy with 7.5 cm.
34	07	38.8	−26	48	κ Pup	4.5, 4.7	9.8	318	H III 27	Both white.
35	08	12.2	+17	39	ζ Cnc AB	5.6, 6.0	1.0	46	Σ1196	Period (AB) = 60 years. Near apastron.
					ζ Cnc AB-C	5.0, 6.2	5.9	70	Σ1196	Period (AB-C) = 1,150 years.
36	08	44.7	−54	43	δ Vel	2.1, 5.1	0.7	319	I 10	Difficult close pair. Period = 142 years.
37	08	46.8	+06	25	ε Hya	3.3, 6.8	2.9	304	Σ1273	PA slowly increasing. A is a very close pair.
38	09	18.8	+36	48	38 Lyn	3.9, 6.6	2.6	226	Σ1334	Almost fixed.
39	09	47.1	−65	04	μ Car	3.1, 6.1	5.0	129	RMK 11	Fixed. Fine in small telescopes.
40	10	20.0	+19	50	γ Leo	2.2, 3.5	4.4	126	Σ1424	Binary, period = 619 years. Both orange.
41	10	32.0	−45	04	s Vel	6.2, 6.5	13.5	218	PZ 3	Fixed.
42	10	46.8	−49	26	μ Vel	2.7, 6.4	2.6	55	R 155	P = 138 years. Near widest separation.
43	10	55.6	+24	45	54 Leo	4.5, 6.3	6.6	111	Σ1487	Slowly widening. Pale yellow and white.

No.	RA		Declin-ation		Star	Magni-tudes	Separa-tion	PA	Cata-logue	Comments
	h	m	°	′			arcsec	°		
44	11	18.2	+31	32	ξ UMa	4.3, 4.8	1.6	226	Σ1523	Binary, 60 years. Needs 7.5 cm.
45	11	21.0	−54	29	π Cen	4.3, 5.0	0.2	172	I 879	Binary, 38.7 years. Very close. Needs 40 cm.
46	11	23.9	+10	32	ι Leo	4.0, 6.7	1.9	102	Σ1536	Binary, period = 186 years.
47	11	32.3	−29	16	N Hya	5.8, 5.9	9.4	210	H III 96	Fixed.
48	12	14.0	−45	43	D Cen	5.6, 6.8	2.8	243	RMK 14	Orange and white. Closing.
49	12	26.6	−63	06	α Cru	1.4, 1.9	4.0	114	Δ252	Third star in a low-power field.
50	12	41.5	−48	58	γ Cen	2.9, 2.9	0.5	334	HJ 4539	Period = 84 years. Closing. Both yellow.
51	12	41.7	−01	27	γ Vir	3.5, 3.5	0.9	41	Σ1670	Periastron in 2005. Now widening quickly.
52	12	46.3	−68	06	β Mus	3.7, 4.0	1.3	48	R 207	Both white. Closing slowly. P = 383 years.
53	12	54.6	−57	11	μ Cru	4.3, 5.3	34.9	17	Δ126	Fixed. Both white.
54	12	56.0	+38	19	α CVn	2.9, 5.5	19.3	229	Σ1692	Easy. Yellow, bluish.
55	13	22.6	−60	59	J Cen	4.6, 6.5	60.0	343	Δ133	Fixed. A is a close pair.
56	13	24.0	+54	56	ζ UMa	2.3, 4.0	14.4	152	Σ1744	Very easy. Naked-eye pair with Alcor.
57	13	51.8	−33	00	3 Cen	4.5, 6.0	7.7	102	H III 101	Both white. Closing slowly.
58	14	39.6	−60	50	α Cen	0.0, 1.2	8.3	237	RHD 1	Finest pair in the sky. P = 80 years. Closing.
59	14	41.1	+13	44	ζ Boo	4.5, 4.6	0.6	296	Σ1865	Both white. Closing – highly inclined orbit.

No.	RA		Declin-ation		Star	Magni-tudes	Separa-tion	PA	Cata-logue	Comments
	h	m	°	′			arcsec	°		
60	14	45.0	+27	04	ε Boo	2.5, 4.9	2.9	344	Σ1877	Yellow, blue. Fine pair.
61	14	46.0	−25	27	54 Hya	5.1, 7.1	8.3	122	H III 97	Closing slowly.
62	14	49.3	−14	09	μ Lib	5.8, 6.7	1.8	6	β106	Becoming wider. Fine in 7.5 cm.
63	14	51.4	+19	06	ξ Boo	4.7, 7.0	6.2	310	Σ1888	Fine contrast. Easy.
64	15	03.8	+47	39	44 Boo	5.3, 6.2	1.8	58	Σ1909	Period = 206 years. Beginning to close.
65	15	05.1	−47	03	π Lup	4.6, 4.7	1.7	64	HJ 4728	Widening.
66	15	18.5	−47	53	μ Lup AB	5.1, 5.2	1.0	320	HJ 4753	AB closing. Underobserved.
					μ Lup AC	4.4, 7.2	22.7	127	Δ180	AC almost fixed.
67	15	23.4	−59	19	γ Cir	5.1, 5.5	0.8	349	HJ 4757	Closing. Needs 20 cm. Long-period binary.
68	15	32.0	+32	17	η CrB	5.6, 5.9	0.5	147	Σ1937	Both yellow. P = 41 yrs. Still widening.
69	15	34.8	+10	33	δ Ser	4.2, 5.2	4.0	173	Σ1954	Long-period binary.
70	15	35.1	−41	10	γ Lup	3.5, 3.6	0.8	277	HJ 4786	Binary. Period = 190 years. Needs 20 cm.
71	15	56.9	−33	58	ξ Lup	5.3, 5.8	10.2	49	PZ 4	Fixed.
72	16	14.7	+33	52	σ CrB	5.6, 6.6	7.2	237	Σ2032	Long-period binary. Both white.
73	16	29.4	−26	26	α Sco	1.2, 5.4	2.7	277	GNT 1	Red, green. Difficult from mid-northern latitudes.
74	16	30.9	+01	59	λ Oph	4.2, 5.2	1.5	35	Σ2055	P = 129 years. Fairly difficult in small apertures.

No.	RA		Declin-ation		Star	Magni-tudes	Separa-tion	PA	Cata-logue	Comments
	h	m	°	′			arcsec	°		
75	16	41.3	+31	36	ζ Her	2.9, 5.5	1.1	196	Σ2084	Period = 34 years. Now widening. Needs 20 cm.
76	17	05.3	+54	28	μ Dra	5.7, 5.7	2.3	8	Σ2130	Period = 672 years.
77	17	14.6	+14	24	α Her	var, 5.4	4.6	103	Σ2140	Red, green. Long-period binary.
78	17	15.3	−26	35	36 Oph	5.1, 5.1	4.9	143	SHJ 243	Period = 471 years.
79	17	23.7	+37	08	ρ Her	4.6, 5.6	4.1	319	Σ2161	Slowly widening.
80	18	01.5	+21	36	95 Her	5.0, 5.1	6.5	257	Σ2264	Colours thought variable in C19.
81	18	05.5	+02	30	70 Oph	4.2, 6.0	5.4	134	Σ2272	Opening. Easy in 7.5 cm.
82	18	06.8	−43	25	h5014 CrA	5.7, 5.7	1.7	3	–	Period = 450 years. Needs 10 cm.
83	18	35.9	+16	58	OΣ358 Her	6.8, 7.0	1.5	150	–	Period = 380 years.
84	18	44.3	+39	40	ε¹ Lyr	5.0, 6.1	2.4	348	Σ2382	Quadruple system with ε². Both pairs
85	18	44.3	+39	40	ε² Lyr	5.2, 5.5	2.4	79	Σ2383	visible in 7.5 cm.
86	18	56.2	+04	12	θ Ser	4.5, 5.4	22.4	104	Σ2417	Fixed. Very easy.
87	19	06.4	−37	04	γ CrA	4.8, 5.1	1.3	23	HJ 5084	Beautiful pair. Period = 122 years.
88	19	30.7	+27	58	β Cyg AB	3.1, 5.1	34.3	54	Σ I 43	Glorious. Yellow, blue-greenish.
					β Cyg Aa	3.1, 5.2	0.2	92	MCA 55	Aa. Period = 97 years. Closing.
89	19	45.0	+45	08	δ Cyg	2.9, 6.3	2.7	221	Σ2579	Slowly widening. Period = 780 years.

No.	RA		Declin-ation		Star	Magni-tudes	Separa-tion	PA	Cata-logue	Comments
	h	m	°	′			arcsec	°		
90	19	48.2	+70	16	ε Dra	3.8, 7.4	3.2	19	Σ2603	Slow binary.
91	20	46.7	+16	07	γ Del	4.5, 5.5	9.1	265	Σ2727	Easy. Yellowish. Long-period binary.
92	20	47.4	+36	29	λ Cyg	4.8, 6.1	0.9	10	OΣ413	Difficult binary in small apertures.
93	20	59.1	+04	18	ε Equ AB	6.0, 6.3	0.6	284	Σ2737	Fine triple. AB is closing.
					ε Equ AC	6.0, 7.1	10.3	66		
94	21	06.9	+38	45	61 Cyg	5.2, 6.0	31.2	151	Σ2758	Nearby binary. Both orange. Period = 659 years.
95	21	19.9	−53	27	θ Ind	4.5, 7.0	7.0	271	HJ 5258	Pale yellow and reddish. Long-period binary.
96	21	44.1	+28	45	μ Cyg	4.8, 6.1	1.7	315	Σ2822	Period = 789 years.
97	22	03.8	+64	37	ξ Cep	4.4, 6.5	8.3	274	Σ2863	White and blue. Long-period binary.
98	22	26.6	−16	45	53 Aqr	6.4, 6.6	1.4	31	SHJ 345	Long-period binary; periastron in 2023.
99	22	28.8	−00	01	ζ Aqr	4.3, 4.5	2.2	176	Σ2909	Period = 587 years. Slowly widening.
100	23	59.4	+33	43	Σ3050 And	6.6, 6.6	2.1	334	–	Period = 350 years.

Some Interesting Nebulae, Clusters and Galaxies

Object	RA		Declina-tion		Remarks
	h	m	°	′	
M31 Andromedae	00	40.7	+41	05	Andromeda Galaxy, visible to naked eye.
H VIII 78 Cassiopeiae	00	41.3	+61	36	Fine cluster, between Gamma and Kappa Cassiopeiae.
M33 Trianguli	01	31.8	+30	28	Spiral. Difficult with small apertures.
H VI 33−4 Persei, C14	02	18.3	+56	59	Double cluster; Sword-handle.
△142 Doradus	05	39.1	−69	09	Looped nebula round 30 Doradus. Naked eye. In Large Magellanic Cloud.
M1 Tauri	05	32.3	+22	00	Crab Nebula, near Zeta Tauri.
M42 Orionis	05	33.4	−05	24	Orion Nebula. Contains the famous Trapezium, Theta Orionis.
M35 Geminorum	06	06.5	+24	21	Open cluster near Eta Geminorum.
H VII 2 Monocerotis, C50	06	30.7	+04	53	Open cluster, just visible to naked eye.
M41 Canis Majoris	06	45.5	−20	42	Open cluster, just visible to naked eye.
M47 Puppis	07	34.3	−14	22	Mag. 5.2. Loose cluster.
H IV 64 Puppis	07	39.6	−18	05	Bright planetary in rich neighbourhood.
M46 Puppis	07	39.5	−14	42	Open cluster.
M44 Cancri	08	38	+20	07	Praesepe. Open cluster near Delta Cancri. Visible to naked eye.
M97 Ursae Majoris	11	12.6	+55	13	Owl Nebula, diameter 3′. Planetary.
Kappa Crucis, C94	12	50.7	−60	05	'Jewel Box'; open cluster, with stars of contrasting colours.
M3 Can. Ven.	13	40.6	+28	34	Bright globular.
Omega Centauri, C80	13	23.7	−47	03	Finest of all globulars. Easy with naked eye.
M80 Scorpii	16	14.9	−22	53	Globular, between Antares and Beta Scorpii.
M4 Scorpii	16	21.5	−26	26	Open cluster close to Antares.

Object	RA		Declina-tion		Remarks
	h	m	°	′	
M13 Herculis	16	40	+36	31	Globular. Just visible to naked eye.
M92 Herculis	16	16.1	+43	11	Globular. Between Iota and Eta Herculis.
M6 Scorpii	17	36.8	−32	11	Open cluster; naked eye.
M7 Scorpii	17	50.6	−34	48	Very bright open cluster; naked eye.
M23 Sagittarii	17	54.8	−19	01	Open cluster nearly 50′ in diameter.
H IV 37 Draconis, C6	17	58.6	+66	38	Bright planetary.
M8 Sagittarii	18	01.4	−24	23	Lagoon Nebula. Gaseous. Just visible with naked eye.
NGC 6572 Ophiuchi	18	10.9	+06	50	Bright planetary, between Beta Ophiuchi and Zeta Aquilae.
M17 Sagittarii	18	18.8	−16	12	Omega Nebula. Gaseous. Large and bright.
M11 Scuti	18	49.0	−06	19	Wild Duck. Bright open cluster.
M57 Lyrae	18	52.6	+32	59	Ring Nebula. Brightest of planetaries.
M27 Vulpeculae	19	58.1	+22	37	Dumb-bell Nebula, near Gamma Sagittae.
H IV 1 Aquarii, C55	21	02.1	−11	31	Bright planetary, near Nu Aquarii.
M15 Pegasi	21	28.3	+12	01	Bright globular, near Epsilon Pegasi.
M39 Cygni	21	31.0	+48	17	Open cluster between Deneb and Alpha Lacertae. Well seen with low powers.

(M = Messier number; NGC = New General Catalogue number; C = Caldwell number.)

Our Contributors

Martin Mobberley is one of the UK's most active imagers of comets, planets, asteroids, variable stars, novae and supernovae and served as President of the British Astronomical Association from 1997 to 1999. In 2000 he was awarded the Association's Walter Goodacre Award. He is the author of five astronomy books published by Springer as well as three children's space-exploration books published by Top That Publishing.

Tom Boles manages Coddenham Observatory in Suffolk, England. He runs three robotic telescopes to search for extragalactic supernovae. His tally at the time of writing is 105 supernova discoveries, which makes him the world's most successful individual discoverer of these objects. He is a time-served astronomical-telescope maker and computer engineer. He is now retired, having held director-level positions with four international IT companies. As well as having contributed to several astronomy textbooks he has made numerous radio and television appearances promoting astronomy. He is a past President of the British Astronomical Association and is one of the few amateur astronomers to be admitted to the International Astronomical Union.

Anthony Misch served on the staff of the Mount Wilson Observatory from 1982 to 1987. As a member of the H and K project, he spent more than 350 nights on the 60-inch. Since 1987 he has been a staff astronomer at the University of California's Lick Observatory on Mount Hamilton. **William Sheehan** has studied galactic pioneers E.E. Barnard and W.W. Morgan as a fellow of the John Simon Guggenheim Memorial Foundation, and is currently writing a book on galaxies. He had the great pleasure of using the 60-inch telescope to observe Mars at its favourable opposition of 2005.

Dr David Rothery chairs courses in volcanology and planetary science at the Open University. He has been interested in space since childhood, and made a research career as a geologist by using satellite images to study the Earth's surface. He was a geologist on the ill-fated Beagle 2 project, and is now UK lead scientist on the Mercury Imaging X-ray Spectrometer. He serves on various research council and space agency advisory boards.

Professor Chris Kitchin was formerly Director of the University of Hertfordshire Observatory. He is an astrophysicist with a great eagerness in encouraging a popular interest in astronomy. He is the author of several books, and appears regularly on television.

Professor Fred Watson is Astronomer-in-Charge of the Anglo-Australian Observatory at Coonabarabran in north-western New South Wales, and is well known throughout Australia for his regular broadcasts on ABC radio. He is an Adjunct Professor in the School of Physical and Chemical Sciences of the Queensland University of Technology, and an honorary Associate Professor of Astronomy in the University of Southern Queensland. A regular contributor to the *Yearbook of Astronomy*, his book *Stargazer: the Life and Times of the Telescope* has been published in Australia by Allen & Unwin. In 2006 he was awarded the Australian Government Eureka Prize for Promoting Understanding of Science.

Dr David M. Harland gained his BSc in astronomy in 1977 and a doctorate in computational science. Subsequently, he has taught computer science, worked in industry and managed academic research. In 1995 he 'retired' and has since published many books on space themes.

Iain Nicolson, formerly Principal Lecturer in Astronomy at the University of Hertfordshire, is a writer and lecturer in the fields of astronomy and space science. A Contributing Consultant to the magazine *Astronomy Now*, he has been a frequent contributor to BBC Television's *The Sky at Night*. He is author or co-author of more than twenty books, the most recent of which, *Dark Side of the Universe*, was published in April 2007 by Canopus Publishing.

Dr Allan Chapman, of Wadham College, Oxford, is probably Britain's leading authority on the history of astronomy. He has published many research papers and several books, as well as numerous popular accounts. He is a frequent and welcome contributor to the *Yearbook*.

Astronomical Societies in the British Isles

British Astronomical Association
　　Assistant Secretary: Burlington House, Piccadilly, London W1V 9AG.
　　Meetings: Lecture Hall of Scientific Societies, Civil Service Commission Building,
　　23 Savile Row, London W1. Last Wednesday each month (Oct.–June), 5 p.m. and
　　some Saturday afternoons.

Association for Astronomy Education
　　Secretary: Teresa Grafton, The Association for Astronomy Education, c/o The Royal
　　Astronomical Society, Burlington House, Piccadilly, London W1V 0NL.

Astronomical Society of Edinburgh
　　Secretary: Graham Rule, 105/19 Causewayside, Edinburgh EH9 1QG.
　　Website: www.roe.ac.uk/asewww/; *Email:* asewww@roe.ac.uk
　　Meetings: City Observatory, Calton Hill, Edinburgh. 1st Friday each month, 8 p.m.

Astronomical Society of Glasgow
　　Secretary: Mr David Degan, 5 Hillside Avenue, Alexandria, Dunbartonshire
　　G83 0BB.
　　Website: www.astronomicalsocietyofglasgow.org.uk
　　Meetings: Royal College, University of Strathclyde, Montrose Street, Glasgow.
　　3rd Thursday each month, Sept.–Apr., 7.30 p.m.

Astronomical Society of Haringey
　　Secretary: Jerry Workman, 91 Greenslade Road, Barking, Essex IG11 9XF.
　　Meetings: Palm Court, Alexandra Palace, 3rd Wednesday each month, 8 p.m.

Astronomy Ireland
　　Secretary: Tony Ryan, PO Box 2888, Dublin 1, Eire.
　　Website: www.astronomy.ie; *Email:* info@astronomy.ie
　　Meetings: 2nd Monday of each month. Telescope meetings every clear Saturday.

Federation of Astronomical Societies
　　Secretary: Clive Down, 10 Glan-y-Llyn, North Cornelly, Bridgend, County Borough
　　CF33 4EF.
　　Email: clivedown@btinternet.com

Junior Astronomical Society of Ireland
　　Secretary: K. Nolan, 5 St Patrick's Crescent, Rathcoole, Co. Dublin.
　　Meetings: The Royal Dublin Society, Ballsbridge, Dublin 4. Monthly.

Society for Popular Astronomy
　　Secretary: Guy Fennimore, 36 Fairway, Keyworth, Nottingham NG12 5DU.
　　Website: www.popastro.com; *Email:* SPAstronomy@aol.com
　　Meetings: Last Saturday in Jan., Apr., July, Oct., 2.30 p.m. in London.

Webb Society
　　Treasurer/Membership Secretary: Steve Rayner, 10 Meon Close, Tadley RG26 4HN.

Aberdeen and District Astronomical Society
Secretary: Ian C. Giddings, 95 Brentfield Circle, Ellon, Aberdeenshire AB41 9DB.
Meetings: Robert Gordon's Institute of Technology, St Andrew's Street, Aberdeen.
Fridays, 7.30 p.m.

Abingdon Astronomical Society (was **Fitzharry's Astronomical Society**)
Secretary: Chris Holt, 9 Rutherford Close, Abingdon, Oxon OX14 2AT.
Website: www.abingdonastro.org.uk; *Email:* info@abingdonastro.co.uk
Meetings: All Saints' Methodist Church Hall, Dorchester Crescent, Abingdon, Oxon.
2nd Monday Sept.–June, 8 p.m. and additional beginners' meetings and observing
evenings as advertised.

Altrincham and District Astronomical Society
Secretary: Derek McComiskey, 33 Tottenham Drive, Manchester M23 9WH.
Meetings: Timperley Village Club. 1st Friday Sept.–June, 8 p.m.

Andover Astronomical Society
Secretary: Mrs S. Fisher, Staddlestones, Aughton, Kingston, Marlborough, Wiltshire
SN8 3SA.
Meetings: Grately Village Hall. 3rd Thursday each month, 7.30 p.m.

Astra Astronomy Section
Secretary: c/o Duncan Lunan, Flat 65, Dalraida House, 56 Blythswood Court,
Anderston, Glasgow G2 7PE.
Meetings: Airdrie Arts Centre, Anderson Street, Airdrie. Weekly.

Astrodome Mobile School Planetarium
Contact: Peter J. Golding, 53 City Way, Rochester, Kent ME1 2AX.
Website: www.astrodome.clara.co.uk; *Email:* astrodome@clara.co.uk

Aylesbury Astronomical Society
Secretary: Alan Smith, 182 Marley Fields, Leighton Buzzard, Bedfordshire LU7 8WN.
Meetings: 1st Monday in month at 8 p.m., venue in Aylesbury area. Details from
Secretary.

Bassetlaw Astronomical Society
Secretary: Andrew Patton, 58 Holding, Worksop, Notts S81 0TD.
Meetings: Rhodesia Village Hall, Rhodesia, Worksop, Notts. 2nd and 4th Tuesdays of
month at 7.45 p.m.

Batley & Spenborough Astronomical Society
Secretary: Robert Morton, 22 Links Avenue, Cleckheaton, West Yorks BD19 4EG.
Meetings: Milner K. Ford Observatory, Wilton Park, Batley. Every Thursday, 8 p.m.

Bedford Astronomical Society
Secretary: Mrs L. Harrington, 24 Swallowfield, Wyboston, Bedfordshire MK44 3AE.
Website: www.observer1.freeserve.co.uk/bashome.html
Meetings: Bedford School, Burnaby Rd, Bedford. Last Wednesday each month.

Bingham & Brooks Space Organization
Secretary: N. Bingham, 15 Hickmore's Lane, Lindfield, West Sussex.

Birmingham Astronomical Society
Contact: P. Bolas, 4 Moat Bank, Bretby, Burton-on-Trent DE15 0QJ.
Website: www.birmingham-astronomical.co.uk; *Email:* pbolas@aol.com
Meetings: Room 146, Aston University. Last Tuesday of month. Sept.–June (except
Dec., moved to 1st week in Jan.).

Blackburn Leisure Astronomy Section
Secretary: Mr H. Murphy, 20 Princess Way, Beverley, East Yorkshire HU17 8PD.
Meetings: Blackburn Leisure Welfare. Mondays, 8 p.m.

Blackpool & District Astronomical Society
Secretary: Terry Devon, 30 Victory Road, Blackpool, Lancashire FY1 3JT.
Website: www.blackpoolastronomy.org.uk; *Email:* info@blackpoolastronomy.org.uk
Meetings: St Kentigern's Social Centre, Blackpool. 1st Wednesday of the month,
7.45 p.m.

Bolton Astronomical Society
Secretary: Peter Miskiw, 9 Hedley Street, Bolton, Lancashire BL1 3LE.
Meetings: Ladybridge Community Centre, Bolton. 1st and 3rd Tuesdays Sept.–May,
7.30 p.m.

Border Astronomy Society
Secretary: David Pettitt, 14 Sharp Grove, Carlisle, Cumbria CA2 5QR.
Website: www.members.aol.com/P3pub/page8.html
Email: davidpettitt@supanet.com
Meetings: The Observatory, Trinity School, Carlisle. Alternate Thursdays, 7.30 p.m.,
Sept.–May.

Boston Astronomers
Secretary: Mrs Lorraine Money, 18 College Park, Horncastle, Lincolnshire LN9 6RE.
Meetings: Blackfriars Arts Centre, Boston. 2nd Monday each month, 7.30 p.m.

Bradford Astronomical Society
Contact: Mrs J. Hilary Knaggs, 6 Meadow View, Wyke, Bradford BD12 9LA.
Website: www.bradford-astro.freeserve.co.uk/index.htm
Meetings: Eccleshill Library, Bradford. Alternate Mondays, 7.30 p.m.

Braintree, Halstead & District Astronomical Society
Secretary: Mr J. R. Green, 70 Dorothy Sayers Drive, Witham, Essex CM8 2LU.
Meetings: BT Social Club Hall, Witham Telephone Exchange. 3rd Thursday each
month, 8 p.m.

Breckland Astronomical Society (was **Great Ellingham and District Astronomy Club**)
Contact: Martin Wolton, Willowbeck House, Pulham St Mary, Norfolk IP21 4QS.
Meetings: Great Ellingham Recreation Centre, Watton Road (B1077), Great
Ellingham, 2nd Friday each month, 7.15 p.m.

Bridgend Astronomical Society
Secretary: Clive Down, 10 Glan-y-Llyn, Broadlands, North Cornelly, Bridgend
County CF33 4EF.
Email: clivedown@btinternet.com
Meetings: Bridgend Bowls Centre, Bridgend. 2nd Friday, monthly, 7.30 p.m.

Bridgwater Astronomical Society
Secretary: Mr G. MacKenzie, Watergore Cottage, Watergore, South Petherton,
Somerset TA13 5JQ.
Website: www.ourworld.compuserve.com/hompages/dbown/Bwastro.htm
Meetings: Room D10, Bridgwater College, Bath Road Centre, Bridgwater. 2nd
Wednesday each month, Sept.–June.

Bridport Astronomical Society
Secretary: Mr G.J. Lodder, 3 The Green, Walditch, Bridport, Dorset DT6 4LB.
Meetings: Walditch Village Hall, Bridport. 1st Sunday each month, 7.30 p.m.

Brighton Astronomical and Scientific Society
Secretary: Ms T. Fearn, 38 Woodlands Close, Peacehaven, East Sussex BN10 7SF.
Meetings: St John's Church Hall, Hove. 1st Tuesday each month, 7.30 p.m.

Bristol Astronomical Society
Secretary: Dr John Pickard, 'Fielding', Easter Compton, Bristol BS35 5SJ.
Meetings: Frank Lecture Theatre, University of Bristol Physics Dept., alternate
Fridays in term time, and Westbury Park Methodist Church Rooms, North View,
other Fridays.

Callington Community Astronomy Group
Secretary: Beccy Watson. *Tel:* 07732 945671
Email: Beccyboo@kimwatson99.fsnet.co.uk
Website: www.callington-astro.org.uk
Meetings: Callington Space Centre, Callington Community College, Launceston
Road, Callington, Cornwall PL17 7DR. 1st and 3rd Saturday of each month,
7.30 p.m., Sept.–July.

Cambridge Astronomical Society
Secretary: Brian Lister, 80 Ramsden Square, Cambridge CB4 2BL.
Meetings: Institute of Astronomy, Madingley Road. 3rd Friday each month.

Cardiff Astronomical Society
Secretary: D.W.S. Powell, 1 Tal-y-Bont Road, Ely, Cardiff CF5 5EU.
Meetings: Dept. of Physics and Astronomy, University of Wales, Newport Road,
Cardiff. Alternate Thursdays, 8 p.m.

Castle Point Astronomy Club
Secretary: Andrew Turner, 3 Canewdon Hall Close, Canewdon, Rochford, Essex
SS4 3PY.
Meetings: St Michael's Church Hall, Daws Heath. Wednesdays, 8 p.m.

Chelmsford Astronomers
Secretary: Brendan Clark, 5 Borda Close, Chelmsford, Essex.
Meetings: Once a month.

Chester Astronomical Society
Secretary: Mrs S. Brooks, 39 Halton Road, Great Sutton, South Wirral LL66 2UF.
Meetings: All Saints' Parish Church, Chester. Last Wednesday each month except
Aug. and Dec., 7.30 p.m.

Chester Society of Natural Science, Literature and Art
Secretary: Paul Braid, 'White Wing', 38 Bryn Avenue, Old Colwyn, Colwyn Bay
LL29 8AH.
Email: p.braid@virgin.net
Meetings: Once a month.

Chesterfield Astronomical Society
President: Mr D. Blackburn, 71 Middlecroft Road, Stavely, Chesterfield, Derbyshire
S41 3XG. Tel: 07909 570754.
Website: www.chesterfield-as.org.uk
Meetings: Barnet Observatory, Newbold, each Friday.

Clacton & District Astronomical Society
Secretary: C. L. Haskell, 105 London Road, Clacton-on-Sea, Essex.

Cleethorpes & District Astronomical Society
Secretary: C. Illingworth, 38 Shaw Drive, Grimsby, South Humberside.
Meetings: Beacon Hill Observatory, Cleethorpes. 1st Wednesday each month.

Cleveland & Darlington Astronomical Society
Contact: Dr John McCue, 40 Bradbury Rd., Stockton-on-Tees, Cleveland TS20 1LE.
Meetings: Grindon Parish Hall, Thorpe Thewles, near Stockton-on-Tees. 2nd Friday,
monthly.

Cork Astronomy Club
Secretary: Charles Coughlan, 12 Forest Ridge Crescent, Wilton, Cork, Eire.
Meetings: 1st Monday, Sept.–May (except bank holidays).

Cornwall Astronomical Society
Secretary: J.M. Harvey, 1 Tregunna Close, Porthleven, Cornwall TR13 9LW.
Meetings: Godolphin Club, Wendron Street, Helston, Cornwall. 2nd and 4th Thursday of each month, 7.30 for 8 p.m.

Cotswold Astronomical Society
Secretary: Rod Salisbury, Grove House, Christchurch Road, Cheltenham, Gloucestershire GL50 2PN.
Website: www.members.nbci.com/CotswoldAS
Meetings: Shurdington Church Hall, School Lane, Shurdington, Cheltenham. 2nd Saturday each month, 8 p.m.

Coventry & Warwickshire Astronomical Society
Secretary: Steve Payne, 68 Stonebury Avenue, Eastern Green, Coventry CV5 7FW.
Website: www.cawas.freeserve.co.uk; *Email:* sjp2000@thefarside57.freeserve.co.uk
Meetings: The Earlsdon Church Hall, Albany Road, Earlsdon, Coventry. 2nd Friday, monthly, Sept.–June.

Crawley Astronomical Society
Secretary: Ron Gamer, 1 Pevensey Close, Pound Hill, Crawley, West Sussex RH10 7BL.
Meetings: Ifield Community Centre, Ifield Road, Crawley. 3rd Friday each month, 7.30 p.m.

Crayford Manor House Astronomical Society
Secretary: Roger Pickard, 28 Appletons, Hadlow, Kent TM1 0DT.
Meetings: Manor House Centre, Crayford. Monthly during term time.

Crewkerne and District Astronomical Society (CADAS)
Chairman: Kevin Dodgson, 46 Hermitage Street, Crewkerne, Somerset TA18 8ET.
Email: crewastra@aol.com

Croydon Astronomical Society
Secretary: John Murrell, 17 Dalmeny Road, Carshalton, Surrey.
Meetings: Lecture Theatre, Royal Russell School, Combe Lane, South Croydon. Alternate Fridays, 7.45 p.m.

Derby & District Astronomical Society
Secretary: Ian Bennett, Freers Cottage, Sutton Lane, Etwall.
Web site: www.derby-astro-soc.fsnet/index.html;
Email: bennett.lovatt@btinternet.com
Meetings: Friends Meeting House, Derby. 1st Friday each month, 7.30 p.m.

Doncaster Astronomical Society
Secretary: A. Anson, 15 Cusworth House, St James Street, Doncaster DN1 3AY
Web site: www.donastro.freeserve.co.uk; *Email:* space@donastro.freeserve.co.uk
Meetings: St George's Church House, St George's Church, Church Way, Doncaster. 2nd and 4th Thursday of each month, commencing at 7.30 p.m.

Dumfries Astronomical Society
Secretary: Mr J. Sweeney, 3 Lakeview, Powfoot, Annan DG13 5PG.
Meetings: Gracefield Arts Centre, Edinburgh Road, Dumfries. 3rd Tuesday Aug.–May, 7.30 p.m.

Dundee Astronomical Society
Secretary: G. Young, 37 Polepark Road, Dundee, Tayside DD1 5QT.
Meetings: Mills Observatory, Balgay Park, Dundee. 1st Friday each month, 7.30 p.m.
Sept.–Apr.

Easington and District Astronomical Society
Secretary: T. Bradley, 52 Jameson Road, Hartlepool, Co. Durham.
Meetings: Easington Comprehensive School, Easington Colliery. Every 3rd Thursday
throughout the year, 7.30 p.m.

Eastbourne Astronomical Society
Secretary: Peter Gill, 18 Selwyn House, Selwyn Road, Eastbourne, East Sussex
BN21 2LF.
Meetings: Willingdon Memorial Hall, Church Street, Willingdon. One Saturday per
month, Sept.–July, 7.30 p.m.

East Riding Astronomers
Secretary: Tony Scaife, 15 Beech Road, Elloughton, Brough, North Humberside
HU15 1JX.
Meetings: As arranged.

East Sussex Astronomical Society
Secretary: Marcus Croft, 12 St Mary's Cottages, Ninfield Road, Bexhill-on-Sea, East
Sussex.
Website: www.esas.org.uk
Meetings: St Marys School, Wrestwood Road, Bexhill. 1st Thursday of each month,
8 p.m.

Edinburgh University Astronomical Society
Secretary: c/o Dept. of Astronomy, Royal Observatory, Blackford Hill, Edinburgh.

Ewell Astronomical Society
Secretary: Richard Gledhill, 80 Abinger Avenue, Cheam SM2 7LW.
Website: www.ewell-as.co.uk
Meetings: St Mary's Church Hall, London Road, Ewell. 2nd Friday of each month
except August, 7.45 p.m.

Exeter Astronomical Society
Secretary: Tim Sedgwick, Old Dower House, Half Moon, Newton St Cyres, Exeter,
Devon EX5 5AE.
Meetings: The Meeting Room, Wynards, Magdalen Street, Exeter. 1st Thursday of
month.

Farnham Astronomical Society
Secretary: Laurence Anslow, 'Asterion', 18 Wellington Lane, Farnham, Surrey
GU9 9BA.
Meetings: Central Club, South Street, Farnham. 2nd Thursday each month, 8 p.m.

Foredown Tower Astronomy Group
Secretary: M. Feist, Foredown Tower Camera Obscura, Foredown Road, Portslade,
East Sussex BN41 2EW.
Meetings: At the above address, 3rd Tuesday each month. 7 p.m. (winter), 8 p.m.
(summer).

Greenock Astronomical Society
Secretary: Carl Hempsey, 49 Brisbane Street, Greenock.
Meetings: Greenock Arts Guild, 3 Campbell Street, Greenock.

Grimsby Astronomical Society
Secretary: R. Williams, 14 Richmond Close, Grimsby, South Humberside.
Meetings: Secretary's home. 2nd Thursday each month, 7.30 p.m.
Guernsey: La Société Guernesiasie Astronomy Section
Secretary: Debby Quertier, Lamorna, Route Charles, St Peter Port, Guernsey GY1 1QS.
and Jessica Harris, Keanda, Les Sauvagees, St Sampson's, Guernsey GY2 4XT.
Meetings: Observatory, Rue du Lorier, St Peter's. Tuesdays, 8 p.m.
Guildford Astronomical Society
Secretary: A. Langmaid, 22 West Mount, The Mount, Guildford, Surrey GU2 5HL.
Meetings: Guildford Institute, Ward Street, Guildford. 1st Thursday each month
except Aug., 7.30 p.m.
Gwynedd Astronomical Society
Secretary: Mr Ernie Greenwood, 18 Twrcelyn Street, Llanerchymedd, Anglesey
LL74 8TL.
Meetings: Dept. of Electronic Engineering, Bangor University. 1st Thursday each
month except Aug., 7.30 p.m.
The Hampshire Astronomical Group
Secretary: Geoff Mann, 10 Marie Court, 348 London Road, Waterlooville,
Hampshire PO7 7SR.
Website: www.hantsastro.demon.co.uk; *Email:* Geoff.Mann@hazleton97.fsnet.co.uk
Meetings: 2nd Friday, Clanfield Memorial Hall, all other Fridays Clanfield
Observatory.
Hanney & District Astronomical Society
Secretary: Bob Church, 47 Upthorpe Drive, Wantage, Oxfordshire OX12 7DG.
Meetings: Last Thursday each month, 8 p.m.
Harrogate Astronomical Society
Secretary: Brian Bonser, 114 Main Street, Little Ouseburn TO5 9TG.
Meetings: National Power HQ, Beckwith Knowle, Harrogate. Last Friday each
month.
Hastings and Battle Astronomical Society
Secretary: K.A. Woodcock, 24 Emmanuel Road, Hastings, East Sussex TN34 3LB.
Email: keith@habas.freeserve.co.uk
Meetings: Herstmonceux Science Centre. 2nd Saturday of each month, 7.30 p.m.
Havering Astronomical Society
Secretary: Frances Ridgley, 133 Severn Drive, Upminster, Essex RM14 1PP.
Meetings: Cranham Community Centre, Marlborough Gardens, Upminster, Essex.
3rd Wednesday each month except July and Aug., 7.30 p.m.
Heart of England Astronomical Society
Secretary: John Williams, 100 Stanway Road, Shirley, Solihull B90 3JG.
Website: www.members.aol.com/hoeas/home.html; *Email:* hoeas@aol.com
Meetings: Furnace End Village, over Whitacre, Warwickshire. Last Thursday each
month, except June, July & Aug., 8 p.m.
Hebden Bridge Literary & Scientific Society, Astronomical Section
Secretary: Peter Jackson, 44 Gilstead Lane, Bingley, West Yorkshire BD16 3NP.
Meetings: Hebden Bridge Information Centre. Last Wednesday, Sept.–May.

Herschel Astronomy Society
Secretary: Kevin Bishop, 106 Holmsdale, Crown Wood, Bracknell, Berkshire
RG12 3TB.
Meetings: Eton College. 2nd Friday each month, 7.30 p.m.

Highlands Astronomical Society
Secretary: Richard Green, 11 Drumossie Avenue, Culcabock, Inverness IV2 3SJ.
Meetings: The Spectrum Centre, Inverness. 1st Tuesday each month, 7.30 p.m.

Hinckley & District Astronomical Society
Secretary: Mr S. Albrighton, 4 Walnut Close, The Bridleways, Hartshill, Nuneaton,
Warwickshire CV10 0XH.
Meetings: Burbage Common Visitors Centre, Hinckley. 1st Tuesday Sept.–May,
7.30 p.m.

Horsham Astronomy Group (was **Forest Astronomical Society**)
Secretary: Dan White, 32 Burns Close, Horsham, West Sussex RH12 5PF.
Email: secretary@horshamastronomy.com
Meetings: 1st Wednesday each month.

Howards Astronomy Club
Secretary: H. Ilett, 22 St George's Avenue, Warblington, Havant, Hampshire.
Meetings: To be notified.

Huddersfield Astronomical and Philosophical Society
Secretary: Lisa B. Jeffries, 58 Beaumont Street, Netherton, Huddersfield, West
Yorkshire HD4 7HE.
Email: l.b.jeffries@hud.ac.uk
Meetings: 4a Railway Street, Huddersfield. Every Wednesday and Friday, 7.30 p.m.

Hull and East Riding Astronomical Society
President: Sharon E. Long
Email: charon@charon.karoo.co.uk
Website: http://www.heras.org.uk
Meetings: The Wilberforce Building, Room S25, University of Hull, Cottingham
Road, Hull. 2nd Monday each month, Sept.–May, 7.30–9.30 p.m.

Ilkeston & District Astronomical Society
Secretary: Mark Thomas, 2 Elm Avenue, Sandiacre, Nottingham NG10 5EJ.
Meetings: The Function Room, Erewash Museum, Anchor Row, Ilkeston. 2nd
Tuesday monthly, 7.30 p.m.

Ipswich, Orwell Astronomical Society
Secretary: R. Gooding, 168 Ashcroft Road, Ipswich.
Meetings: Orwell Park Observatory, Nacton, Ipswich. Wednesdays, 8 p.m.

Irish Astronomical Association
President: Terry Moseley, 31 Sunderland Road, Belfast BT6 9LY, Northern Ireland.
Email: terrymosel@aol.com
Meetings: Ashby Building, Stranmillis Road, Belfast. Alternate Wednesdays,
7.30 p.m.

Irish Astronomical Society
Secretary: James O'Connor, PO Box 2547, Dublin 15, Eire.
Meetings: Ely House, 8 Ely Place, Dublin 2. 1st and 3rd Monday each month.

Isle of Man Astronomical Society
Secretary: James Martin, Ballaterson Farm, Peel, Isle of Man IM5 3AB.
Email: ballaterson@manx.net
Meetings: Isle of Man Observatory, Foxdale. 1st Thursday of each month, 8 p.m.

Isle of Wight Astronomical Society
Secretary: J. W. Feakins, 1 Hilltop Cottages, High Street, Freshwater, Isle of Wight.
Meetings: Unitarian Church Hall, Newport, Isle of Wight. Monthly.

Keele Astronomical Society
Secretary: Natalie Webb, Department of Physics, University of Keele, Keele,
Staffordshire ST5 5BG.
Meetings: As arranged during term time.

Kettering and District Astronomical Society
Asst. Secretary: Steve Williams, 120 Brickhill Road, Wellingborough,
Northamptonshire.
Meetings: Quaker Meeting Hall, Northall Street, Kettering, Northamptonshire.
1st Tuesday each month, 7.45 p.m.

King's Lynn Amateur Astronomical Association
Secretary: P. Twynman, 17 Poplar Avenue, RAF Marham, King's Lynn.
Meetings: As arranged.

Lancaster and Morecambe Astronomical Society
Secretary: Mrs E. Robinson, 4 Bedford Place, Lancaster LA1 4EB.
Email: ehelenerob@btinternet.com
Meetings: Church of the Ascension, Torrisholme. 1st Wednesday each month except
July and Aug.

Knowle Astronomical Society
Secretary: Nigel Foster, 21 Speedwell Drive, Balsall Common, Coventry,
West Midlands CV7 7AU.
Meetings: St George & St Theresa's Parish Centre, 337 Station Road, Dorridge,
Solihull, West Midlands B93 8TZ. 1st Monday of each month (+/− 1 week for Bank
Holidays) except August.

Lancaster University Astronomical Society
Secretary: c/o Students' Union, Alexandra Square, University of Lancaster.
Meetings: As arranged.

Laymans Astronomical Society
Secretary: John Evans, 10 Arkwright Walk, The Meadows, Nottingham.
Meetings: The Popular, Bath Street, Ilkeston, Derbyshire. Monthly.

Leeds Astronomical Society
Secretary: Mark A. Simpson, 37 Roper Avenue, Gledhow, Leeds LS8 1LG.
Meetings: Centenary House, North Street. 2nd Wednesday each month, 7.30 p.m.

Leicester Astronomical Society
Secretary: Dr P.J. Scott, 21 Rembridge Close, Leicester LE3 9AP.
Meetings: Judgemeadow Community College, Marydene Drive, Evington, Leicester.
2nd and 4th Tuesdays each month, 7.30 p.m.

Letchworth and District Astronomical Society
Secretary: Eric Hutton, 14 Folly Close, Hitchin, Hertfordshire.
Meetings: As arranged.

Lewes Amateur Astronomers
Secretary: Christa Sutton, 8 Tower Road, Lancing, West Sussex BN15 9HT.
Meetings: The Bakehouse Studio, Lewes. Last Wednesday each month.

Limerick Astronomy Club
Secretary: Tony O'Hanlon, 26 Ballycannon Heights, Meelick, Co. Clare, Eire.
Meetings: Limerick Senior College, Limerick. Monthly (except June and Aug.),
8 p.m.

Lincoln Astronomical Society
Secretary: David Swaey, 'Everglades', 13 Beaufort Close, Lincoln LN2 4SF.
Meetings: The Lecture Hall, off Westcliffe Street, Lincoln. 1st Tuesday each month.

Liverpool Astronomical Society
Secretary: Mr K. Clark, 31 Sandymount Drive, Wallasey, Merseyside L45 0LJ.
Meetings: Lecture Theatre, Liverpool Museum. 3rd Friday each month, 7 p.m.

Norman Lockyer Observatory Society
Secretary: G.E. White, PO Box 9, Sidmouth EX10 0YQ.
Website: www.ex.ac.uk/nlo/; *Email:* g.e.white@ex.ac.uk
Meetings: Norman Lockyer Observatory, Sidmouth. Fridays and 2nd Monday each month, 7.30 p.m.

Loughton Astronomical Society
Secretary: Charles Munton, 14a Manor Road, Wood Green, London N22 4YJ.
Meetings: 1st Theydon Bois Scout Hall, Loughton Lane, Theydon Bois. Weekly.

Lowestoft and Great Yarmouth Regional Astronomers (LYRA) Society
Secretary: Simon Briggs, 28 Sussex Road, Lowestoft, Suffolk.
Meetings: Community Wing, Kirkley High School, Kirkley Run, Lowestoft. 3rd Thursday each month, 7.30 p.m.

Luton Astronomical Society
Secretary: Mr G. Mitchell, Putteridge Bury, University of Luton, Hitchin Road, Luton.
Website: www.lutonastrosoc.org.uk; *Email:* user998491@aol.com
Meetings: Univ. of Luton, Putteridge Bury (except June, July and August), or Someries Junior School, Wigmore Lane, Luton (July and August only), last Thursday each month, 7.30–9.00 p.m.

Lytham St Annes Astronomical Association
Secretary: K.J. Porter, 141 Blackpool Road, Ansdell, Lytham St Anne's, Lancashire.
Meetings: College of Further Education, Clifton Drive South, Lytham St Anne's. 2nd Wednesday monthly Oct.–June.

Macclesfield Astronomical Society
Secretary: Mr John H. Thomson, 27 Woodbourne Road, Sale, Cheshire M33 3SY
Website: www.maccastro.com; *Email:* jhandlc@yahoo.com
Meetings: Jodrell Bank Science Centre, Goostrey, Cheshire. 1st Tuesday of every month, 7 p.m.

Maidenhead Astronomical Society
Secretary: Tim Haymes, Hill Rise, Knowl Hill Common, Knowl Hill, Reading RG10 9YD.
Meetings: Stubbings Church Hall, near Maidenhead. 1st Friday Sept.–June.

Maidstone Astronomical Society
Secretary: Stephen James, 4 The Cherry Orchard, Haddow, Tonbridge, Kent.
Meetings: Nettlestead Village Hall. 1st Tuesday in the month except July and Aug., 7.30 p.m.

Manchester Astronomical Society
Secretary: Mr Kevin J. Kilburn FRAS, Godlee Observatory, UMIST, Sackville Street, Manchester M60 1QD.
Website: www.u-net.com/ph/mas/; *Email:* kkilburn@globalnet.co.uk
Meetings: At the Godlee Observatory. Thursdays, 7 p.m., except below.
Free Public Lectures: Renold Building UMIST, third Thursday Sept.–Mar., 7.30 p.m.

Mansfield and Sutton Astronomical Society
Secretary: Angus Wright, Sherwood Observatory, Coxmoor Road, Sutton-in-Ashfield, Nottinghamshire NG17 5LF.
Meetings: Sherwood Observatory, Coxmoor Road. Last Tuesday each month, 7.30 p.m.

Mexborough and Swinton Astronomical Society
Secretary: Mark R. Benton, 14 Sandalwood Rise, Swinton, Mexborough, South Yorkshire S64 8PN.
Website: www.msas.org.uk; *Email:* mark@masas.f9.co.uk
Meetings: Swinton WMC. Thursdays, 7.30 p.m.

Mid-Kent Astronomical Society
Secretary: Peter Parish, 30 Wooldeys Road, Rainham, Kent ME8 7NU.
Meetings: Bredhurst Village Hall, Hurstwood Road, Bredhurst, Kent. 2nd and last Fridays each month except August, 7.45 p.m.
Website: www.mkas-site.co.uk

Milton Keynes Astronomical Society
Secretary: Mike Leggett, 19 Matilda Gardens, Shenley Church End, Milton Keynes MK5 6HT.
Website: www.mkas.org.uk; *Email:* mike-pat-leggett@shenley9.fsnet.co.uk
Meetings: Rectory Cottage, Bletchley. Alternate Fridays.

Moray Astronomical Society
Secretary: Richard Pearce, 1 Forsyth Street, Hopeman, Elgin, Moray, Scotland.
Meetings: Village Hall Close, Co. Elgin.

Newbury Amateur Astronomical Society (NAAS)
Secretary: Mrs Monica Balstone, 37 Mount Pleasant, Tadley RG26 4BG.
Meetings: United Reformed Church Hall, Cromwell Place, Newbury. 1st Friday of month, Sept.–June.

Newcastle-on-Tyne Astronomical Society
Secretary: C.E. Willits, 24 Acomb Avenue, Seaton Delaval, Tyne and Wear.
Meetings: Zoology Lecture Theatre, Newcastle University. Monthly.

North Aston Space & Astronomical Club
Secretary: W.R. Chadburn, 14 Oakdale Road, North Aston, Sheffield.
Meetings: To be notified.

Northamptonshire Natural History Society (Astronomy Section)
Secretary: R.A. Marriott, 24 Thirlestane Road, Northampton NN4 8HD.
Email: ram@hamal.demon.co.uk
Meetings: Humfrey Rooms, Castilian Terrace, Northampton. 2nd and last Mondays, most months, 7.30 p.m.

Northants Amateur Astronomers
Secretary: Mervyn Lloyd, 76 Havelock Street, Kettering, Northamptonshire.
Meetings: 1st and 3rd Tuesdays each month, 7.30 p.m.

North Devon Astronomical Society
Secretary: P.G. Vickery, 12 Broad Park Crescent, Ilfracombe, Devon EX34 8DX.
Meetings: Methodist Hall, Rhododendron Avenue, Sticklepath, Barnstaple. 1st Wednesday each month, 7.15 p.m.

North Dorset Astronomical Society
Secretary: J.E.M. Coward, The Pharmacy, Stalbridge, Dorset.
Meetings: Charterhay, Stourton, Caundle, Dorset. 2nd Wednesday each month.

North Downs Astronomical Society
Secretary: Martin Akers, 36 Timber Tops, Lordswood, Chatham, Kent ME5 8XQ.
Meetings: Vigo Village Hall. 3rd Thursday each month. 7.30 p.m.

North-East London Astronomical Society
Secretary: Mr B. Beeston, 38 Abbey Road, Bush Hill Park, Enfield EN1 2QN.
Meetings: Wanstead House, The Green, Wanstead. 3rd Sunday each month (except Aug.), 3 p.m.

North Gwent and District Astronomical Society
Secretary: Jonathan Powell, 14 Lancaster Drive, Gilwern, nr Abergavenny, Monmouthshire NP7 0AA.
Meetings: Gilwern Community Centre. 15th of each month, 7.30 p.m.

North Staffordshire Astronomical Society
Secretary: Duncan Richardson, Halmerend Hall Farm, Halmerend, Stoke-on-Trent, Staffordshire ST7 8AW.
Email: dwr@enterprise.net
Meetings: 21st Hartstill Scout Group HQ, Mount Pleasant, Newcastle-under-Lyme ST5 1DR. 1st Tuesday each month (except July and Aug.), 7–9.30 p.m.

Northumberland Astronomical Society
Contact: Dr Adrian Jametta, 1 Lake Road, Hadston, Morpeth, Northumberland NE65 9TF.
Email: adrian@themoon.co.uk
Website: www.nastro.org.uk
Meetings: Hauxley Nature Reserve (near Amble). Last Thursday of every month (except December), 7.30 pm. Additional meetings and observing sessions listed on website.
Tel: 07984 154904

North Western Association of Variable Star Observers
Secretary: Jeremy Bullivant, 2 Beaminster Road, Heaton Mersey, Stockport, Cheshire.
Meetings: Four annually.

Norwich Astronomical Society
Secretary: Dave Balcombe, 52 Folly Road, Wymondham, Norfolk NR18 0QR.
Website: www.norwich.astronomical.society.org.uk
Meetings: Seething Observatory, Toad Lane, Thwaite St Mary, Norfolk. Every Friday, 7.30 p.m.

Nottingham Astronomical Society
Secretary: C. Brennan, 40 Swindon Close, The Vale, Giltbrook, Nottingham NG16 2WD.
Meetings: Djanogly City Technology College, Sherwood Rise (B682). 1st and 3rd Thursdays each month, 7.30 p.m.

Oldham Astronomical Society
Secretary: P.J. Collins, 25 Park Crescent, Chadderton, Oldham.
Meetings: Werneth Park Study Centre, Frederick Street, Oldham. Fortnightly, Friday.

Open University Astronomical Society
Secretary: Dr Andrew Norton, Department of Physics and Astronomy, The Open University, Walton Hall, Milton Keynes MK7 6AA.
Website: www.physics.open.ac.uk/research/astro/a_club.html
Meetings: Open University, Milton Keynes. 1st Tuesday of every month, 7.30 p.m.

Orpington Astronomical Society

Secretary: Dr Ian Carstairs, 38 Brabourne Rise, Beckenham, Kent BR3 2SG.
Meetings: High Elms Nature Centre, High Elms Country Park, High Elms Road, Farnborough, Kent. 4th Thursday each month, Sept.–July, 7.30 p.m.

Papworth Astronomy Club

Contact: Keith Tritton, Magpie Cottage, Fox Street, Great Gransden, Sandy, Bedfordshire SG19 3AA.
Email: kpt2@tutor.open.ac.uk
Meetings: Bradbury Progression Centre, Church Lane, Papworth Everard, nr Huntingdon. 1st Wednesday each month, 7 p.m.

Peterborough Astronomical Society

Secretary: Sheila Thorpe, 6 Cypress Close, Longthorpe, Peterborough.
Meetings: 1st Thursday every month, 7.30 p.m.

Plymouth Astronomical Society

Secretary: Alan G. Penman, 12 St Maurice View, Plympton, Plymouth, Devon PL7 1FQ.
Email: oakmount12@aol.com
Meetings: Glynis Kingham Centre, YMCA Annex, Lockyer Street, Plymouth. 2nd Friday each month, 7.30 p.m.

PONLAF

Secretary: Matthew Hepburn, 6 Court Road, Caterham, Surrey CR3 5RD.
Meetings: Room 5, 6th floor, Tower Block, University of North London. Last Friday each month during term time, 6.30 p.m.

Port Talbot Astronomical Society (formerly **Astronomical Society of Wales**)

Secretary: Mr J. Hawes, 15 Lodge Drive, Baglan, Port Talbot, West Glamorgan SA12 8UD.
Meetings: Port Talbot Arts Centre. 1st Tuesday each month, 7.15 p.m.

Portsmouth Astronomical Society

Secretary: G.B. Bryant, 81 Ringwood Road, Southsea.
Meetings: Monday, fortnightly.

Preston & District Astronomical Society

Secretary: P. Sloane, 77 Ribby Road, Wrea Green, Kirkham, Preston, Lancashire.
Meetings: Moor Park (Jeremiah Horrocks) Observatory, Preston. 2nd Wednesday, last Friday each month, 7.30 p.m.

Reading Astronomical Society

Secretary: Mrs Ruth Sumner, 22 Anson Crescent, Shinfield, Reading RG2 8JT.
Meetings: St Peter's Church Hall, Church Road, Earley. 3rd Friday each month, 7 p.m.

Renfrewshire Astronomical Society

Secretary: Ian Martin, 10 Aitken Road, Hamilton, South Lanarkshire ML3 7YA.
Website: www.renfrewshire-as.co.uk; *Email:* RenfrewAS@aol.com
Meetings: Coats Observatory, Oakshaw Street, Paisley. Fridays, 7.30 p.m.

Rower Astronomical Society

Secretary: Mary Kelly, Knockatore, The Rower, Thomastown, Co. Kilkenny, Eire.

St Helens Amateur Astronomical Society

Secretary: Carl Dingsdale, 125 Canberra Avenue, Thatto Heath, St Helens, Merseyside WA9 5RT.
Meetings: As arranged.

Salford Astronomical Society
Secretary: Mrs Kath Redford, 2 Albermarle Road, Swinton, Manchester M27 5ST.
Meetings: The Observatory, Chaseley Road, Salford. Wednesdays.

Salisbury Astronomical Society
Secretary: Mrs R. Collins, 3 Fairview Road, Salisbury, Wiltshire SP1 1JX.
Meetings: Glebe Hall, Winterbourne Earls, Salisbury. 1st Tuesday each month.

Sandbach Astronomical Society
Secretary: Phil Benson, 8 Gawsworth Drive, Sandbach, Cheshire.
Meetings: Sandbach School, as arranged.

Sawtry & District Astronomical Society
Secretary: Brooke Norton, 2 Newton Road, Sawtry, Huntingdon, Cambridgeshire PE17 5UT.
Meetings: Greenfields Cricket Pavilion, Sawtry Fen. Last Friday each month.

Scarborough & District Astronomical Society
Secretary: Mrs S. Anderson, Basin House Farm, Sawdon, Scarborough, North Yorkshire.
Meetings: Scarborough Public Library. Last Saturday each month, 7–9 p.m.

Scottish Astronomers Group
Secretary: Dr Ken Mackay, Hayford House, Cambusbarron, Stirling FK7 9PR.
Meetings: North of Hadrian's Wall, twice yearly.

Sheffield Astronomical Society
Secretary: Darren Swindels, 102 Sheffield Road, Woodhouse, Sheffield, South Yorkshire S13 7EU.
Website: www.sheffieldastro.org.uk; *Email:* info@sheffieldastro.org.uk
Meetings: Twice monthly at Mayfield Environmental Education Centre, David Lane, Fulwood, Sheffield S10, 7.30–10 p.m.

Shetland Astronomical Society
Secretary: Peter Kelly, The Glebe, Fetlar, Shetland ZE2 9DJ.
Email: theglebe@zetnet.co.uk
Meetings: Fetlar, Fridays, Oct.–Mar.

Shropshire Astronomical Society
Contact: Mr David Woodward, 20 Station Road, Condover, Shrewsbury, Shropshire SY5 7BQ.
Website: http://www.shropshire-astro.com; *Email:* jacquidodds@ntlworld.com
Meetings: Quarterly talks at the Gateway Arts and Education Centre, Chester Street, Shrewsbury and monthly observing meetings at Rodington Village Hall.

Sidmouth and District Astronomical Society
Secretary: M. Grant, Salters Meadow, Sidmouth, Devon.
Meetings: Norman Lockyer Observatory, Salcombe Hill. 1st Monday in each month.

Solent Amateur Astronomers
Secretary: Ken Medway, 443 Burgess Road, Swaythling, Southampton SO16 3BL.
Web site: www.delscope.demon.co.uk;
Email: kenmedway@kenmedway.demon.co.uk
Meetings: Room 8, Oaklands Community School, Fairisle Road, Lordshill, Southampton. 3rd Tuesday each month, 7.30 p.m.

Southampton Astronomical Society
Secretary: John Thompson, 4 Heathfield, Hythe, Southampton SO45 5BJ.
Web site: www.home.clara.net/lmhobbs/sas.html;
Email: John.G.Thompson@Tesco.net
Meetings: Conference Room 3, The Civic Centre, Southampton. 2nd Thursday each month (except Aug.), 7.30 p.m.

South Downs Astronomical Society
Secretary: J. Green, 46 Central Avenue, Bognor Regis, West Sussex PO21 5HH.
Website: www.southdowns.org.uk
Meetings: Chichester High School for Boys. 1st Friday in each month (except Aug.).

South-East Essex Astronomical Society
Secretary: C.P. Jones, 29 Buller Road, Laindon, Essex.
Website: www.seeas.dabsol.co.uk/; *Email:* cpj@cix.co.uk
Meetings: Lecture Theatre, Central Library, Victoria Avenue, Southend-on-Sea. Generally 1st Thursday in month, Sept.–May, 7.30 p.m.

South-East Kent Astronomical Society
Secretary: Andrew McCarthy, 25 St Paul's Way, Sandgate, near Folkestone, Kent CT20 3NT.
Meetings: Monthly.

South Lincolnshire Astronomical & Geophysical Society
Secretary: Ian Farley, 12 West Road, Bourne, Lincolnshire PE10 9PS.
Meetings: Adult Education Study Centre, Pinchbeck. 3rd Wednesday each month, 7.30 p.m.

Southport Astronomical Society
Secretary: Patrick Brannon, Willow Cottage, 90 Jacksmere Lane, Scarisbrick, Ormskirk, Lancashire L40 9RS.
Meetings: Monthly Sept.–May, plus observing sessions.

Southport, Ormskirk and District Astronomical Society
Secretary: J.T. Harrison, 92 Cottage Lane, Ormskirk, Lancashire L39 3NJ.
Meetings: Saturday evenings, monthly, as arranged.

South Shields Astronomical Society
Secretary: c/o South Tyneside College, St George's Avenue, South Shields.
Meetings: Marine and Technical College. Each Thursday, 7.30 p.m.

South Somerset Astronomical Society
Secretary: G. McNelly, 11 Laxton Close, Taunton, Somerset.
Meetings: Victoria Inn, Skittle Alley, East Reach, Taunton, Somerset. Last Saturday each month, 7.30 p.m.

South-West Hertfordshire Astronomical Society
Secretary: Tom Walsh, 'Finches', Coleshill Lane, Winchmore Hill, Amersham, Buckinghamshire HP7 0NP.
Meetings: Rickmansworth. Last Friday each month, Sept.–May.

Stafford and District Astronomical Society
Secretary: Miss L. Hodkinson, 6 Elm Walk, Penkridge, Staffordshire ST19 5NL.
Meetings: Weston Road High School, Stafford. Every 3rd Thursday, Sept.–May, 7.15 p.m.

Stirling Astronomical Society
Secretary: Hamish MacPhee, 10 Causewayhead Road, Stirling FK9 5ER.
Meetings: Smith Museum & Art Gallery, Dumbarton Road, Stirling. 2nd Friday each month, 7.30 p.m.

Stoke-on-Trent Astronomical Society
Secretary: M. Pace, Sundale, Dunnocksfold, Alsager, Stoke-on-Trent.
Meetings: Cartwright House, Broad Street, Hanley. Monthly.

Stratford-upon-Avon Astronomical Society
Secretary: Robin Swinbourne, 18 Old Milverton, Leamington Spa, Warwickshire CV32 6SA.
Meetings: Tiddington Home Guard Club. 4th Tuesday each month, 7.30 p.m.

Sunderland Astronomical Society
Contact: Don Simpson, 78 Stratford Avenue, Grangetown, Sunderland SR2 8RZ.
Meetings: Friends Meeting House, Roker. 1st, 2nd and 3rd Sundays each month.

Sussex Astronomical Society
Secretary: Mrs C.G. Sutton, 75 Vale Road, Portslade, Sussex.
Meetings: English Language Centre, Third Avenue, Hove. Every Wednesday, 7.30–9.30 p.m., Sept.–May.

Swansea Astronomical Society
Secretary: Dr Michael Morales, 238 Heol Dulais, Birch Grove, Swansea SA7 9LH.
Website: www.crysania.co.uk/sas/astro/star
Meetings: Lecture Room C, Science Tower, University of Swansea. 2nd and 4th Thursday each month from Sept.–June, 7 p.m.

Tavistock Astronomical Society
Secretary: Mrs Ellie Coombes, Rosemount, Under Road, Gunnislake, Cornwall PL18 9JL.
Meetings: Science Laboratory, Kelly College, Tavistock. 1st Wednesday each month, 7.30 p.m.

Thames Valley Astronomical Group
Secretary: K.J. Pallet, 82a Tennyson Street, South Lambeth, London SW8 3TH.
Meetings: As arranged.

Thanet Amateur Astronomical Society
Secretary: P.F. Jordan, 85 Crescent Road, Ramsgate.
Meetings: Hilderstone House, Broadstairs, Kent. Monthly.

Torbay Astronomical Society
Secretary: Tim Moffat, 31 Netley Road, Newton Abbot, Devon TQ12 2LL.
Meetings: Torquay Boys' Grammar School, 1st Thursday in month; and Town Hall, Torquay, 3rd Thursday in month, Oct.–May, 7.30 p.m.

Tullamore Astronomical Society
Secretary: Tom Walsh, 25 Harbour Walk, Tullamore, Co. Offaly, Eire.
Website: www.iol.ie/seanmck/tas.htm; *Email:* tcwalsh25@yahoo.co.uk
Meetings: Order of Malta Lecture Hall, Tanyard, Tullamore, Co. Offaly, Eire. Mondays at 8 p.m., every fortnight.

Tyrone Astronomical Society
Secretary: John Ryan, 105 Coolnafranky Park, Cookstown, Co. Tyrone, Northern Ireland.
Meetings: Contact Secretary.

Usk Astronomical Society
Secretary: Bob Wright, 'Llwyn Celyn', 75 Woodland Road, Croesyceiliog, Cwmbran NP44 2OX.
Meetings: Usk Community Education Centre, Maryport Street, Usk. Every Thursday during school term, 7 p.m.

Vectis Astronomical Society
>   *Secretary:* Rosemary Pears, 1 Rockmount Cottages, Undercliff Drive, St Lawrence, Ventnor, Isle of Wight PO38 1XG.
>   *Website:* www.wightskies.fsnet.co.uk/main.html;
>   *Email:* may@tatemma.freeserve.co.uk
>   *Meetings:* Lord Louis Library Meeting Room, Newport. 4th Friday each month except Dec., 7.30 p.m.

Vigo Astronomical Society
>   *Secretary:* Robert Wilson, 43 Admers Wood, Vigo Village, Meopham, Kent DA13 0SP.
>   *Meetings:* Vigo Village Hall. As arranged.

Walsall Astronomical Society
>   *Secretary:* Bob Cleverley, 40 Mayfield Road, Sutton Coldfield B74 3PZ.
>   *Meetings:* Freetrade Inn, Wood Lane, Pelsall North Common. Every Thursday.

Wellingborough District Astronomical Society
>   *Secretary:* S.M. Williams, 120 Brickhill Road, Wellingborough, Northamptonshire.
>   *Meetings:* Gloucester Hall, Church Street, Wellingborough. 2nd Wednesday each month, 7.30 p.m.

Wessex Astronomical Society
>   *Secretary:* Leslie Fry, 14 Hanhum Road, Corfe Mullen, Dorset.
>   *Meetings:* Allendale Centre, Wimborne, Dorset. 1st Tuesday of each month.

West Cornwall Astronomical Society
>   *Secretary:* Dr R. Waddling, The Pines, Pennance Road, Falmouth, Cornwall TR11 4ED.
>   *Meetings:* Helston Football Club, 3rd Thursday each month, and St Michall's Hotel, 1st Wednesday each month, 7.30 p.m.

West of London Astronomical Society
>   *Secretary:* Duncan Radbourne, 28 Tavistock Road, Edgware, Middlesex HA8 6DA.
>   *Website:* www.wocas.org.uk
>   *Meetings:* Monthly, alternately in Uxbridge and North Harrow. 2nd Monday in month, except Aug.

West Midlands Astronomical Association
>   *Secretary:* Miss S. Bundy, 93 Greenridge Road, Handsworth Wood, Birmingham.
>   *Meetings:* Dr Johnson House, Bull Street, Birmingham. As arranged.

West Yorkshire Astronomical Society
>   *Secretary:* Pete Lunn, 21 Crawford Drive, Wakefield, West Yorkshire.
>   *Meetings:* Rosse Observatory, Carleton Community Centre, Carleton Road, Pontefract. Each Tuesday, 7.15 p.m.

Whitby and District Astronomical Society
>   *Secretary:* Rosemary Bowman, The Cottage, Larpool Drive, Whitby, North Yorkshire YO22 4ND.
>   *Meetings:* Whitby Mission, Seafarers' Centre, Haggersgate, Whitby. 1st Tuesday of the month, 7.30 p.m.

Whittington Astronomical Society
>   *Secretary:* Peter Williamson, The Observatory, Top Street, Whittington, Shropshire.
>   *Meetings:* The Observatory. Every month.

Wiltshire Astronomical Society
  Secretary: Simon Barnes, 25 Woodcombe, Melksham, Wiltshire SN12 6HA.
  Meetings: St Andrew's Church Hall, Church Lane, off Forest Road, Melksham,
  Wiltshire.
Wolverhampton Astronomical Society
  Secretary: Mr M. Bryce, Iona, 16 Yellowhammer Court, Kidderminster,
  Worcestershire DY10 4RR.
  Website: www.wolvas.org.uk; *Email:* michaelbryce@wolvas.org.uk
  Meetings: Beckminster Methodist Church Hall, Birches Barn Road, Wolverhampton.
  Alternate Mondays, Sept.–Apr., extra dates in summer, 7.30 p.m.
Worcester Astronomical Society
  Secretary: Mr S. Bateman, 12 Bozward Street, Worcester WR2 5DE.
  Meetings: Room 117, Worcester College of Higher Education, Henwick Grove,
  Worcester. 2nd Thursday each month, 8 p.m.
Worthing Astronomical Society
  Contact: G. Boots, 101 Ardingly Drive, Worthing, West Sussex BN12 4TW.
  Website: www.worthingastro.freeserve.co.uk;
  Email: gboots@observatory99.freeserve.co.uk
  Meetings: Heene Church Rooms, Heene Road, Worthing. 1st Wednesday each
  month (except Aug.), 7.30 p.m.
Wycombe Astronomical Society
  Secretary: Mr P. Treherne, 34 Honeysuckle Road, Widmer End, High Wycombe,
  Buckinghamshire HP15 6BW.
  Meetings: Woodrow High House, Amersham. 3rd Wednesday each month, 7.45 p.m.
The York Astronomical Society
  Contact: Hazel Collett, Public Relations Officer
  Tel: 07944 751277
  Website: www.yorkastro.freeserve.co.uk; *Email:* info@yorkastro.co.uk
  Meetings: The Knavesmire Room, York Priory Street Centre, Priory Street, York.
  1st and 3rd Friday of each month (except Aug.), 8 p.m.

Any society wishing to be included in this list of local societies or to
update details, including any website addresses, is invited to write to
the Editor (c/o Pan Macmillan, 20 New Wharf Road, London N1 9RR),
so that the relevant information may be included in the next edition of
the *Yearbook*.

The William Herschel Society maintains the museum established at 19 New King Street, Bath BA1 2BL – the only surviving Herschel House. It also undertakes activities of various kinds. New members would be welcome; those interested are asked to contact the Membership Secretary at the museum.

The South Downs Planetarium (Kingsham Farm, Kingsham Road, Chichester, West Sussex PO19 8RP) is now fully operational. For further information, visit www.southdowns.org.uk/sdpt or telephone (01243) 774400